Sound

A TEXT BOOK

BY

ARTHUR TABER JONES

Professor of Physics, Smith College

NEW YORK

D. VAN NOSTRAND COMPANY, Inc.

250 FOURTH AVENUE

1937

Copyright, 1937
By
D. VAN NOSTRAND COMPANY, Inc.

PRINTED IN U. S. A.

PRESS OF
BRAUNWORTH & CO., INC.
BUILDERS OF BOOKS
BRIDGEPORT, CONN.

PREFACE

THIS book is primarily for college students who have had an introductory course in physics. It is also designed for students who have had no previous training in physics but are interested in the scientific background of speech or music. Introductory courses in physics usually treat the topic of sound rather briefly, and the knowledge of physics that is assumed in this book is little more than an understanding of such basic terms as *force, mass, energy,* and some beginnings of a feeling for the methods of thought that are employed in physics. I believe that students who have had no training whatever in physics will be able to read the book with profit, and I hope with pleasure. The book contains very little mathematics, in fact, little more than arithmetic and very simple algebra.

It does not follow that the entire book is easy to read. One important function of a college is to aid students in developing the ability to reason correctly and to stimulate an enjoyment of intellectual activity. This particular end is not attained by unduly simple reading; it is to be attained by showing the student how people before him have reasoned, and providing him an incentive to reason for himself. This may well involve an approach which is somewhat historical. In connection with some given problem the student learns what hypotheses have been advanced, and how these hypotheses have been sustained or abandoned or modified. There are then presented to him problems on which he can test his own powers. Thus he learns various facts, and he learns, also, something of the difficulties involved in reaching reliable conclusions. A growing appreciation of these difficulties should be accompanied by a maturing judgment, and by an increasingly tolerant attitude toward beliefs which differ from those at which he has himself arrived.

To achieve this end, certain of the material in this book is presented from a somewhat historical point of view. But if this approach were employed for all topics it would be necessary to exclude a considerable amount of the material now in the book, or else to increase both the size of the book and the time required to read it. Consequently much of the book is organized in a more conventional manner. I have tried to strike a happy mean between the two extremes.

There is always danger that the material in a textbook may be stated as if it were final. I have tried to be cautious in this regard. I believe, moreover, that it is desirable to include some discussion of subjects which are not yet well understood. It is well for the student to know that some problems are not yet solved. This book includes a small amount of material of this type.

I have emphasized ideas which seem to me fundamental to the understanding of acoustic problems. I have not included any work on ultrasonics, I have not assumed any acquaintance with electric circuits, and I have touched only very casually on modern electric equipment for investigating acoustic phenomena. These restrictions have made it possible to carry various problems considerably farther than is customary in textbooks.

The questions that occur at frequent intervals throughout the text are designed to stimulate thought. Many of the footnotes are admittedly beyond the range of student reading, but it is hoped that their presence will help to develop a respect for scientific accuracy and some appreciation of the vast amount of labor that has been devoted to certain problems. No laboratory experiments are described, and no attention is paid to manipulative technique, but the text itself and the references to original papers may suggest many a laboratory project.

Although I have exercised considerable care in the preparation of the manuscript and in the reading of the proof, it would be most remarkable if there are not errors that have escaped my watchfulness. I shall be grateful to readers who call to my attention any errors that they may find.

I wish to express my most hearty thanks to the many persons and organizations that have generously contributed in various ways to the production of this book. The following firms and institutions have kindly given permission for the reproduction of quotations or figures from their publications: American Academy of Arts and Sciences, American Architect and Architecture, American Philosophical Society, D. Appleton-Century Company, Architectural Quarterly of Harvard University, Edward Arnold and Company, Bataafsch Genootschap der Proefondervindelijke Wijsbegeerte, Bill Brothers, Dodd Mead and Company, Encyclopaedia Britannica, Harvard University Press Henry Holt and Company, Alfred A. Knopf, Longmans, Green and Company, The Macmillan Company, Musical Opinion, Nature, Newton and Company, The Oxford University Press, The Physical Society (London), Charles Scribner's Sons, Julius Springer, Taylor and Francis, Fried. Vieweg und Sohn.

Many individuals who have given permission for the use of quotations or figures from their works are named in connection with the quotations or figures in question. I wish especially to express my thanks to Professor Dayton C. Miller, who sent me a number of his original photographs, to Professor E. N. da C. Andrade, who sent me photographs for two figures, and to Professor Samuel R. Williams, who drew the curve for Fig. 13 on a machine designed at Amherst College by Assistant Professor Theodore Soller.

My thanks are also due to my colleagues Associate Professors James F. Koehler and Nora M. Mohler, who read parts of the manuscript, to my daughter Esther E. Jones, who read the entire galley proof and page proof, and to the Van Nostrand Company, who have given me permission to copy from another of their publications, and who have been most courteous and most ready to meet my desires while the book has been going through the press.

ARTHUR TABER JONES.

NORTHAMPTON, MASSACHUSETTS,
    May 19, 1937.

CONTENTS

CHAPTER I

PRELIMINARY IDEAS

CHAPTER II

THE PRODUCTION OF VARIOUS NOISES

CHAPTER III

VIBRATORY MOTION

CHAPTER IV

SIMPLE TONES AND COMBINATIONS OF TONES

CONTENTS

CHAPTER V

MUSICAL SCALES

CHAPTER VI

TRANSMISSION OF SOUND

CHAPTER VII

FREE VIBRATION

CONTENTS

ix

CONTENTS

CHAPTER IX

HEARING

CHAPTER X

MUSICAL INSTRUMENTS

CHAPTER XI

Speech and Song

CHAPTER XII

Technical Applications

CONTENTS

APPENDIXES

CHAPTER ONE

PRELIMINARY IDEAS

1. **Introduction.**—Interest in the subject of sound goes back through many centuries. The developing art of music was followed in time by a desire to understand music as well as to produce it, and it seems likely that this desire was closely related to the beginnings of the study of sound. Although these beginnings go back at least to Pythagoras in the sixth century B.C., it was not until the seventeenth century A.D.—about the time of Bach and Handel—that the modern scientific study of sound really began, with investigations by Galileo Galilei (1564-1642) and Father Marin Mersenne (1588-1648).

During the next two centuries much was learned, but by the end of the nineteenth century it seemed that the fundamental problems in sound had largely been solved, and interest shifted to other fields. During the World War sound was employed in new ways, and since that time there has been a revival of interest in the subject. Meantime the telephone industry had been developing and the phonograph had been invented. It was not many years until the broadcasting of radio programs and the development of motion pictures with sound brought new problems. Radio tubes and the electric circuits associated with them opened up new methods of study, and interest in the subject is again flourishing.

In 1928 the ACOUSTICAL SOCIETY OF AMERICA was formed, and inside of half a dozen years its membership

1

had grown to nearly seven hundred and fifty—including a hundred in other countries. In 1929 the publication of the JOURNAL OF THE ACOUSTICAL SOCIETY began, in 1932 LES PRESSES UNIVERSITAIRES DE FRANCE began to publish the REVUE D'ACOUSTIQUE, and in 1936 there appeared the first numbers of a German journal, the AKUSTISCHE ZEIT-SCHRIFT. The number of published papers on sound has also been growing rapidly. During the quarter century ending about 1935 the number per year has quadrupled, and the subject is again experiencing a lively and healthy growth.[1]

Persons who set out to read this book will do so with differing backgrounds. Some will find that most of the material in this first chapter is familiar to them. Others will find that they are acquainted with parts of it. Those who have taken an introductory course in physics ought to be well prepared to read the book. But the knowledge of physics that is assumed is really rather small. It consists principally of a scientific way of looking at problems, and of an understanding of a small number of technical terms like *force, work, pressure, energy.*

As we enter upon our subject it may be well to stop for

[1] The statement about the quadrupling in number of published papers on sound is based on the number summarized in SCIENCE ABSTRACTS. SCIENCE ABSTRACTS appears monthly, and contains brief summaries of articles which add to our knowledge of physics and electrical engineering. The publication of this journal began in 1898, and in that year there were abstracts of 940 articles on physics. This included only 14 articles on sound. The volumes for the five years 1905-1909 contain a total of 10,842 abstracts on physics, and of these 160 are on sound. The volumes for the five years 1930-1934 contain a total of 24,654 abstracts on physics, and of these 642 are on sound.

Thus during these twenty-five years the rate of publication in physics has more than doubled, and the rate of publication in sound has quadrupled. To put the matter in another way, during this quarter century contributions to the knowledge of physics, as a whole, have grown from an average of about 6 a day to nearly 14 a day, and during the same time contributions to the knowledge of sound have grown from less than 3 in a month to a number approaching 11 in a month.

a moment to compare the ear and the eye. Hearing and seeing are probably the two means by which we obtain the largest part of our information about the world around us. In both cases we believe that something happens outside of us, and that information about the happening is brought to us by waves of some sort. But the differences in the waves themselves and in the means by which they are received are great. The possibilities open to the ear and to the eye have been contrasted by Helmholtz in the following words.

"It is seldom possible to survey a large surface of water from a high point of sight, without perceiving a great multitude of different systems of waves mutually overtopping and crossing each other. This is best seen on the surface of the sea, viewed from a lofty cliff, when there is a lull after a stiff breeze. We first see the great waves, advancing in far-stretching ranks from the blue distance, here and there more clearly marked out by their white foaming crests, and following one another at regular intervals towards the shore. From the shore they rebound, in different directions according to its sinuosities, and cut obliquely across the advancing waves. A passing steamboat forms its own wedge-shaped wake of waves, or a bird, darting on a fish, excites a small circular system. The eye of the spectator is easily able to pursue each one of these different trains of waves, great and small, wide and narrow, straight and curved, and observe how each passes over the surface, as undisturbedly as if the water over which it flits were not agitated at the same time by other motions and other forces. I must own that whenever I attentively observe this spectacle it awakens in me a peculiar kind of intellectual pleasure, because it bares to the bodily eye, what the mind's eye grasps only by the help of a long series of complicated conclusions for the waves of the invisible atmospheric ocean. . . .

"The eye has a great advantage over the ear in being able to survey a large extent of surface at the same moment. Hence the eye readily sees whether the individual waves of water are rectilinear or curved, and whether they have the same centre of curvature, and in what direction they are advancing. . . . But the ear is much more unfavourably situated in relation to a system of waves of sound, than the eye for a system of waves of water. The ear is affected only by the motion of that mass of air which happens to be in the immediate neighborhood of its tympanum within the aural passage. . . . The ear is therefore in nearly the same condition as the eye would be if it looked at one point of the surface of the water, through a long narrow tube, which would permit of seeing its rising and falling, and were then required to undertake an analysis of the compound waves. . . .

"If, then, notwithstanding these difficulties, the ear is capable of distinguishing musical tones arising from different sources—and it really shows a marvellous readiness in so doing—it must employ means and possess properties altogether different from those employed or possessed by the eye." [2]

[2] Hermann Ludwig Ferdinand von Helmholtz, *Die Lehre von den Tonempfindungen*, translated into English by Alexander J. Ellis under the title *Sensations of Tone*, Longmans, Green & Co., ed. 4 (1912), pp. 26, 28, 29.

The following statement about Helmholtz is quoted from Florian Cajori's *History of Physics*, Macmillan, ed. 2 (1929), p. 221:

"Hermann von Helmholtz (1821-1894) was born at Potsdam, studied medicine in Berlin, became assistant at the charity hospital there, then military surgeon in Potsdam (1843-1847), teacher of anatomy at Berlin, of physiology at Königsberg, later at Bonn and Heidelberg (1858-1871). In 1871 he accepted the chair of physics at the University of Berlin. He possessed an intellect of extraordinary breadth and depth. He was of the first rank as a physiologist, as a physicist, and as a mathematician. Many years ago W. K. Clifford, in his article 'Seeing and Thinking,' spoke of him as follows: 'In the first place he began by studying physiology, dissecting the eye and the ear, and finding out how they acted, and what was their precise constitution;

In whatever way the ear may accomplish what it does, the problem of hearing is in part a problem of psychology as well as physics. And when we begin to inquire further about the action of the ear we are led into questions of anatomy and physiology. In the words just quoted from Helmholtz he speaks of a "peculiar kind of intellectual pleasure." In the study of the phenomena of sound we deal with several types of pleasure: There is the simple sensuous pleasure of hearing beautiful sounds; there is the pleasure we take in musical sounds which are combined in certain ways to form chords; there is the pleasure of gaining some understanding of the phenomena of sound. Obviously any study of sound which is at all complete must involve some problems from the field of aesthetics. In fact, the study of the one subject of sound may lead into many fields.

2. **The Transmission of Sound.**—We are aware that some sounds are produced in connection with vibrations. We can see the blurred outline of a cello string, we may feel the tremor of the building when a large organ pipe is played, and by touching a finger to a bell that has been struck we may realize the vibration that is going on. In fact, sounds are not only associated with vibrations, but almost every sound is produced either by a vibration or by a sudden movement of some sort.

When two men are several hundred feet apart and one of them strikes a blow, the other can see the action before

but he found that it was impossible to study the proper action of the eye and ear without studying also the nature of light and sound, which led him to the study of physics. He had already become one of the most accomplished physiologists of this century when he commenced the study of physics, and he is now one of the greatest physicists of this century. He then found it was impossible to study physics without knowing mathematics; and accordingly he took to studying mathematics and he is now one of the most accomplished mathematicians of this century.' "

he hears it. This fact must have been noticed ages ago, and a natural conclusion is that sound travels more slowly than light. Some of the questions that arise in the study of sound have to do with the speed at which it travels. How fast does sound travel? As it goes is the speed steady, or does the sound go faster and faster, or perhaps slower and slower? Do all sounds go at the same speed? Do sounds travel in other substances than air, and if so do they go faster or slower than in air, or at the same rate?

The first determinations of the speed of sound appear to have been made by Marin Mersenne (1588-1648) and Pierre Gassendi (1592-1655). Mersenne was a Franciscan friar, and has been called "the Father of Acoustics." His *Harmonie Universelle,* published in Paris in 1636, was the first extended treatise on sound and its relation to music. Gassendi was a famous philosopher and versatile savant. For the last ten years of his life he was professor of mathematics at the Collége Royal in Paris. Both Mersenne and Gassendi determined the speed of sound by finding the time which elapsed between the flash from a distant gun and the arrival of the sound.[3] Light travels so quickly that no appreciable error is made by assuming that it takes no time at all, so that the interval in question is the time required by sound to travel the given distance.

Another early determination of the speed of sound was made by the ACCADEMIA DEL CIMENTO. The Accademia del Cimento (Academy of Experiment) was founded in

[3] Mersenne also determined the speed by finding the time in which an echo came from a reflecting surface. He suggested, perhaps not entirely seriously, that if it were possible to make an echo respond many times, with the last response louder than the first, or to make it give back something different from the original sound—for instance, he suggested, to reply in Spanish when the original words were in French, or to reply at a different pitch, say an octave higher or lower—it might be possible to develop a new science of sounds, which we might, if we wished, call *echometry.*

Florence fifteen years after the death of Galileo. Although there were only nine members, and the Academy survived for only a decade, it carried out a series of important experiments. Its determination of the speed of sound was made by the method already employed by Mersenne and by Gassendi, but with improvements which led to a more trustworthy result.

Any effects that temperature or wind might have on the speed of sound were not yet known. Mersenne supposed that winds would have an effect by speeding up the sound when it traveled with the wind, and slowing it down when it traveled against the wind, but he did not regard his experiments as sufficiently accurate to show whether this was the case or not. In fact, in none of these first experiments was there found any effect of wind.

We now know that wind does have an effect. But it is not surprising that it was not detected by these early experimenters, for even a gale usually blows only some fifty miles an hour, and sound travels at fifteen times that speed.

The first experimenter who found that wind does affect the speed of sound was William Derham,[4] rector of the church at Upminster, some dozen miles east from London. During the years 1704 to 1706 he carried out a very careful series of observations of the time that elapsed from the firing of a gun until the sound arrived, and he did this at distances which varied from a mile to a dozen miles. Near the beginning of the paper in which he reports this study he lists nineteen questions that he set himself to answer. The questions dealt with such problems as these: Whether sound arrives from a gun in the same time when the gun points away from the observer as when it points toward him; whether the sound arrives in the same time when the barometer is rising as when it is falling; whether

4 William Derham (1657-1735), Phil. Trans. 26, 2 (1708).

loud sounds and faint ones travel at the same rate; whether sound travels by the shortest path; whether it covers the same space in the same time on the tops of mountains and in valleys; whether the sounds from all sources—guns, bells, heavy hammer blows—have the same speed; whether the speed is the same by night and by day, in winter and in summer, in England, France, Italy, Germany, and other countries.

In the course of his study Derham was able to find answers to many of his questions. One of the questions was whether wind affects the speed of sound, and he found definitely that sounds travel faster with the wind and more slowly against the wind.

We have long known that it is air through which the waves of sound usually travel. But the definite establishing of many of our scientific ideas has been a slow process. This very familiar idea that air is the medium in which sound usually travels is one that in the latter part of the seventeenth century and the early part of the eighteenth was not so generally accepted as it is today. To us it seems that the effect of a wind in aiding or opposing the spread of sound is one evidence that the medium which conveys the sound is the air. But to Derham, who first detected this effect, it seemed that the great difference in the speeds of sound and wind showed that sound must be carried by some medium much more ethereal than that in which the winds blow.

Half a century before the effect of wind on the speed of sound was known the famous "bell in vacuum" experiment was carried out. In 1643 Evangelista Torricelli (1608-1647), the most eminent of Galileo's pupils, invented the barometer. To make a simple barometer a glass tube of sufficient length, and closed at one end, is filled with mercury, the open end covered with a thumb, the tube turned upside down and the lower end dipped below the surface in a trough of mercury. When the thumb is removed the top of the mercury in the tube drops to a level some 75 cm. above that in the trough. The space above the mercury is a moderately good vacuum, and is often called a "torricellian vacuum."

If the space at the top of the tube is large enough it may contain a bell, and if the bell rings while it is not surrounded by air no sound will be heard unless sound is conveyed by something different from air. Soon after the invention of the barometer this experiment was tried by several experimenters, but the results were not conclusive.

After the air pump was invented it became possible to carry out the experiment in a way that was more convincing. The air pump was invented by Otto von Guericke (1602-1686). The first form of his pump was devised about 1650, and apparently without any knowledge of Torricelli's barometer. One of the experiments that Guericke tried with his pump was to hang inside of the receiver a clockwork so arranged that it caused a bell to strike at frequent intervals for about half an hour. As the air was pumped out the sound from the bell became fainter and fainter, and when the air was allowed to enter again the sound was restored. Curiously enough Guericke did not regard this experiment as showing that sound is conveyed by means of air: If it were, he asks, how is it that a sound can reach our ears when the air is at rest? [5]

Not far from the same time Robert Boyle [6] tried a similar experiment, making use of "a watch with a good alarum." He says, "We took a Watch, whose Case we

---

[5] Otto von Guericke's *Neue Magdeburgische Versuche über den Leeren Raum* (1672); translated from Latin into German and printed as vol. 59 of Ostwald's *Klassiker der exakten Wissenschaften*. See pp. 46 and 112 in the latter volume.

[6] Robert Boyle (1627-1691), *New Experiments Physico-Mechanical Touching the Spring of the Air and its Effects*, ed. 2 (1662), p. 106; *The Philosophical Works of the Honourable Robert Boyle, Esq.*, vol. 2 (1725), p. 509.

open'd, that the contain'd Air might have free egress into that of the Receiver. And this Watch was suspended in the cavity of the Vessel onely by a Pack-thred, as the unlikeliest thing to convey a sound to the top of the Receiver." The result of the experiment was the same as that of Guericke—the sound decreased as the air was pumped out, and increased again when the air was again admitted. Boyle says that the result of this experiment "seems to prove, that whether or no the Air be the onely, it is at least, the principal medium of Sounds."

It is now well known that the air thins out rapidly as we ascend from the ground, and that at a height of a few hundred miles practically no air remains. Since sound does travel as waves in air, but does not travel, as light does, through a vacuum, it follows that any signals from the earth to Mars can never be sent by means of sound, and that any explosions or other terrific outbursts on the sun can never send waves of sound to persons on the earth.

Since the time of Mersenne and Gassendi and the other early experimenters many determinations of the speed of sound have been made, and we now know that all ordinary sounds travel at nearly the same speed in air, that sounds may travel in many other substances beside air, that the speed is different in different substances, and that the speed in air or any other substance depends somewhat on a number of different factors. The higher the temperature the faster sound travels. A very loud sound also travels somewhat faster than an ordinary sound. Sound travels faster with the wind than against it. In water sound travels more than four times as fast as in the air. In a stratified geological formation it may travel along the strata half again as fast as across the strata. In a tube sound travels slightly more slowly than in the open. For ordinary pitches the speed is almost the same whether the pitch is high or low— that is, for ordinary pitches the speed is very nearly independent of pitch. The same is true with regard to the pressure to which the air is subject, and with regard to its moisture content—the speed depends hardly at all on the pressure or on the humidity.

In air at 0° C. sound travels at about 331.5 meters per second, or about 1087.5 feet per second. It is convenient to remember that for each centigrade degree that the temperature rises the speed increases by about 0.6 meter per second or 2 feet per second. At ordinary room temperature the speed of sound is not far from 345 meters per second or 1130 feet per second.

3. **Characteristics of Musical Sounds.**—A "noise" is sometimes defined as any sound that is not wanted. According to this definition there are times when a musical sound may become a noise. Nevertheless, a musical sound is often characterized by a steadiness, a smoothness, and a pleasing quality that we do not usually associate with noises. The distinction between noises and musical sounds, it is true, is not sharp—as may be illustrated by dropping upon a table suitably chosen pieces of wood. Any one piece of wood falling alone upon the table gives rise to a noise. But if four of them have been cut to proper sizes the dropping upon the table of one after another is at once recognized as giving the tones of a musical chord.

A musical sound is usually regarded as characterized by three properties: Its **pitch**, its **loudness**, and its **quality**. The steadiness of a sustained musical sound suggests that the vibration which gives rise to it is equally steady. Something swings back and forth and back and forth, and does this at a regularly recurring rate, each vibration being like the preceding one. We say that such a motion is *periodic,* and the *period* of the motion is the time in which the body goes through one *cycle*—that is, the time in which it makes a single one of the back and forth vibrations. The *frequency* of the motion is the number of cycles made in one second—or, if the motion does not last that long, the number that would be made in one second if the motion did continue.[7] Thus if a piano string swings from one end of its path to the other and back again 200 times in a second, its period is $\frac{1}{200}$ second and its frequency is 200 cycles per second.[8]

The **pitch** of a tone is related to the frequency of the vibration, and this relationship was known at least as early as Galileo. He found that the greater the frequency the higher is the pitch.[9] Thus if vibrations occur at the rate of 200 in a second we hear a certain pitch. If they occur at 300 in a second we hear a higher pitch. It has been customary to say that pitch is determined by frequency, so that for a certain frequency we hear always the same pitch. Although this statement is nearly true it is now known [10] that there are cases where an increase in loudness, without any change in frequency, changes the pitch that is heard.

A well known piece of apparatus by which to show that

---

[7] The words "period" and "frequency" have been used, and are still occasionally used, with a slightly different meaning. *Period* has sometimes meant the time that elapses while a particle makes an "oscillation" —from one end of its path to the other. That is, it sometimes means half of what we now usually call the period. The *frequency* is then the number of oscillations made in a second, and so is twice as great as we now usually regard it. In order to distinguish the two meanings use is occasionally made of such expressions as *period of simple oscillation* or *period of simple vibration, period of double vibration* or *period of complete vibration, frequency of simple oscillation, frequency of double vibration.*

[8] It has been suggested that a frequency of one cycle per second be called a *Hertz*—in honor of the German physicist, Heinrich Rudolf Hertz (1857-1894), who made the first experimental study of radio waves. This name has been adopted by a number of authors, especially in Germany. In English-speaking countries the unit most used when dealing with sound is the *cycle per second,* although it is not uncommon to omit the last two words—and speak of so many *cycles.* When no unit is mentioned it is understood that the frequency is measured in cycles per second.

[9] Galileo Galilei, *Two New Sciences,* translated into English by Henry Crew and Alfonso de Salvio, p. 101.

[10] Harvey Fletcher, of the Bell Telephone Laboratories, Journ. Acoust. Soc. 6, 59 (1934).

pitch ordinarily rises with the frequency is Seebeck's siren.[11] A circular disk has an axle passing perpendicularly through its center, and the disk is so mounted that it spins on this axle. A circle, concentric with the circumference, is drawn on the disk, and on this circle are cut through the disk a series of equally spaced holes. If a nozzle is brought near to the circle of holes, and wind from the nozzle is blown through while the disk spins, the series of puffs of air that come through the holes gives rise to a more or less musical tone. The faster the disk spins the more frequently do the puffs come through and the higher is the pitch of the tone.

It has been known for a long time that the **loudness** of a sound is related to the work done in producing the sound— and consequently, for a given pitch, to the extent of the vibration that occurs. Speaking loudly requires more effort than speaking quietly. When a piano is struck vigorously the strings swing farther and the sound is louder than when the keys are pressed gently. When a violin bow is pressed hard and drawn quickly the vibration is greater in extent and the tone is louder than when the bowing is light.

An understanding of **quality** requires an appreciation of the fact that most musical tones are not simple, but consist of other tones. In some cases a number of the component tones can be heard without the use of any equip-

[11] Ludwig Friedrich Wilhelm August Seebeck (1805-1849), Professor of Physics in the University at Leipzig, Pogg. An. 53, 417 (1841). The use of a series of puffs of air to give rise to a tone was employed some forty years earlier by John Robison [Encycl. Brit. ed. 3, vol. 2 of supplement (1801), art. Temperament of the Musical Scale]. When the puffs came at a certain rate Robison says that "the sound *g in alt* was most smoothly uttered, equal in sweetness to a clear female voice." When they came at another rate he says "the sound was more mellow than any man's voice at the same pitch."

Seebeck's siren was a modification of a siren that was devised as early as 1819 by Baron Charles Cagniard de la Tour (1777-1859).

The name "siren" was given by Cagniard de la Tour because he found that his instrument would sing when under water.

ment, especially after attention has been directed to them and a little practice has been gained. The pitch that we associate with a compound tone is usually that of the component which has the lowest frequency, and this lowest frequency component is then called the *fundamental* tone. The other components are called *overtones*. Sometimes the overtones are called *harmonics,* although this term really ought to be restricted to cases in which the overtones have frequencies 2, 3, 4, 5, etc. times that of the fundamental. Very often the term *partial tone,* or simply *partial,* is used to include the fundamental and the overtones, and sometimes the expression *upper partial* is used with the same meaning as "overtone."

The numbering of the partials and overtones is sometimes a bit confusing. Suppose that the fundamental makes 100 vibrations in a second, and that there are two overtones which make respectively 200 and 300 vibrations per second. The fundamental is the *first partial.* The 200-cycle tone is the *first overtone,* but it is also the *second partial.* Similarly the 300-cycle tone is the *second overtone,* and it is also the *third partial.* This confusion would be avoided if we stopped speaking about overtones and spoke always of partial tones. But both terms are in use, and we shall find it convenient to employ sometimes one and sometimes the other.

We shall have more to say about quality in Chapter Nine, but for the present we may simply mention that the cause of differences in quality is now known to depend in large part on the frequencies and intensities of the various component tones, and that this relationship was not well understood until long after there was knowledge of the general relationships between pitch and frequency and between loudness and energy of vibration.

4. **Names for Pitches.**—Most of the persons who read this book are probably familiar with the piano key-

board, shown in part in Fig. 1. The white and black lever ends on which the fingers press are usually spoken of as *keys*. However, because the word "key" is also in general use with an entirely different meaning, these lever ends are also sometimes called *digitals*.

The digitals occur in groups of twelve—seven white digitals and five black ones—and this grouping is repeated a number of times on the keyboard. The change of pitch from the beginning of one group of twelve digitals to the beginning of the next is said to be an *octave*. In this country and in England the pitches given by the white digitals are indicated by the letters shown in Fig. 1. The black digital between *c* and *d* gives the pitch *c♯* (*c* sharp) or *d♭* (*d* flat), that between *d* and *e* gives *d♯* or *e♭*, and

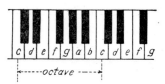

Fig. 1.—Part of Piano Keyboard.

so on. One tone is said to be *sharper* than another when it is of higher pitch, and *flatter* when it is of lower pitch.

In Germany the same letters are used except that *b* stands for our *b♭*, that our *b* is called *h,* and that *cis, fis,* etc. are often used instead of *c♯, f♯,* etc., and *des, es,* etc. instead of *d♭, e♭,* etc.

In France the pitches corresponding to *c, d, e, f, g, a, b* are called *ut, ré, mi, fa, sol, la, si,* and sharps and flats are often indicated by such expressions as *ut dièse* for *c♯* and *si bémol* for *b♭*. The first six of these French names are the first syllables in successive half lines in the following hymn to St. John. This hymn was probably written about the year 770, and the music given here may not be an entirely accurate representation of the way in which it was sung. The introduction of the six syllables to represent the pitches on which they fall in this hymn is credited to a Benedictine monk by the name of Guido of Arezzo, who lived in the eleventh century. The *si* was added later. It will be seen that it is formed from the first letters of the words "Sancte Ioannes." In Italy, as in France, the syllables *re, mi, fa, sol, la,* and *si* are in use, but the *ut* has been replaced by the first syllable of the word *"do*minus"—a syllable which it is easier to sing.

Ut que-ant lax- is re-so-na- re fi-bris Mi — ra ges-to-rum

fa-mu-li tu- o-rum, Sol- ve pol-lu-ti la-bi-i re- a- tum

Sanc- te Io-an-nes.

The names already given extend through only one octave. In each succeeding octave they are repeated, so that some notation is needed to indicate in which octave a given tone occurs. Unfortunately a number of notations for this purpose are in use. Four of them are shown in Table One. The notation employed by Helmholtz is often used. That in the last line of the table has certain advantages but has not been generally adopted. In this book we shall use the notation in the third line.

Table One—Notation for Different Octaves

The symbols in any one column indicate the same pitch. In any one line they indicate successive octaves.

Helmholtz			$C_{,,}$	$C_{,}$	C	c	c'	c''	c'''	c^{IV}	c^{V}
French						ut_1	ut_2	ut_3	ut_4	ut_5	ut_6	ut_7
Frequently used						c_1	c_2	c_3	c_4	c_5	c_6	c_7
Recently proposed [12]			c_4	c_5	c_6	c_7	c_8	c_9	c_{10}	c_{11}	c_{12}

[12] Report of Committee on Acoustic Standardization, Journ. Acoust. Soc. 2, 318 (1931).

Throughout any one octave the subscript—or other similar symbol—is the same as that for the c at which the octave may be regarded as starting. Thus in the notation employed in this book we have c_3, then d_3, then e_3, and so on until we come to c_4, d_4, e_4, and so on.

The pitch indicated in the table by c' or ut_3 or c_3 or c_8 is that of "middle c"—near the middle of the piano keyboard. The reason for calling this pitch c_3 is that when this is done the lowest note on the keyboard of an organ is c_1. This does not mean that no note below c_1 can be played on an organ. On most organs means are provided by which it is possible to play notes that are an octave or two lower.

In work in physics the frequency of middle c is often taken as 256 cycles per second. For musical purposes the a above middle c is often taken as having a frequency of 435 or 440, and middle c of 258.7 or 261.6.

5. Musical Intervals.—Let us start at any point on the piano keyboard and number the white digitals. If we start at a c, d is the second white digital, e the third, and so on. In musical terminology the *interval* from c to d is said to be a *second*, that from c to e a *third*, etc. Instead of using the term an *eighth* we usually say that one pitch is an *octave* above another.

The names of intervals are frequently qualified in some way. Thus the interval ce is called a *major third*, $ce♭$ a *minor third*, cf a *perfect fourth*, cg a *perfect fifth*, ca a *major sixth*, $ca♭$ a *minor sixth*. Students of music are already familiar with these names. Here we simply add that fa and gb are also major thirds, whereas eg and ac are minor thirds.

Two other terms for which we shall have occasional use are "step" and "half step." A *half step* is the interval from the pitch given by any digital on the piano to the next one. Thus it is a half step from c_3 to $c♯_3$, or from e_3 to f_3. A *whole step* is the interval from the pitch given by any digital to the second following. Thus it is a whole step from c_3 to d_3, or from e_3 to $f\sharp_3$. The terms *tone* and *semitone* are often used to mean the same as "step" and "half step," but since the word "tone" has also an entirely different meaning we shall in this book use the terms "step" and "half step."

In Chapters Four and Five we shall consider how various intervals are related to frequency. Probably the simplest guess would be that an interval is determined by the difference in frequency of vibration. Thus if a 200-cycle tone is an octave above a 100-cycle tone we might guess that a 300-cycle tone would be an octave above a 200-cycle tone. Unfortunately the relationship proves not to be so simple. It is true that a 200-cycle tone is an octave above a 100-cycle tone, but a tone which is an octave above the 200-cycle tone is a 400-cycle tone. The octave of any tone has a frequency twice that of the given tone. Intervals are not determined by difference in frequency of vibration. **Intervals are determined by ratios of frequencies.**

6. Musical Keys.—If we play on the piano a simple melody that involves only the white digitals we are very likely to find it satisfying for the music to end on c. The music is probably "in the key of c". It would be entirely possible to play the same melody with every tone one step, say, higher than before. This of course would be likely to involve the use of some of the black digitals. But the melody would be recognized as the same one that was played before, and unless it was played immediately after it had been heard in the key of c many persons would not know that any change had been made. In the second case it was played "in the key of d." This note to which all others bear certain definite relationships, and which is an especially satisfying note on which to end, is called the *keynote*.

It is only very short and simple pieces of music that are entirely in a single key. In most cases the music begins in one key, shifts temporarily into some other key, or perhaps passes into a number of keys one after another, and ends in the key in which it started. The conducting of the music from one key to another in a manner that is smooth and not too abrupt is known as *modulation*.

In medieval music there were a number of different "modes"—from which term we get our word "modulation" —and two of these have survived as our "major mode" and "minor mode." If a melody can be played on the white digitals of a piano, perhaps making fairly frequent use of *g*, and perhaps ending on *c* preceded by *d* or *b*, it is very likely to be in the key of *c major*. If it uses principally the white digitals, but makes frequent use of *a* and *e*, with perhaps an occasional *g♯*, and perhaps ends on *a* preceded by *b* or *g♯*, the music is probably in *a minor*.

In fact if we start at *c* and run up an octave or two on the white digitals of a piano we are playing the *scale of c major*. In this scale we notice that the successive intervals in an octave are two whole steps, then a half step, then three whole steps, and then another half step. Whenever the intervals in a scale follow each other in this order the scale is major. Any note whatever may be chosen for keynote, but *c* is the only major key in which the scale can be played on a piano without the use of any of the black digitals.

If we start on *a* and run up an octave or two, again using only the white digitals, we are playing one form of the *scale of a minor*. In this scale we notice that the successive intervals in an octave are one whole step, then a half step, two whole steps, another half step, and then two more whole steps. Whenever the intervals in a scale follow each other in this order the scale is minor. A minor scale, like a major scale, may have any note we choose for its keynote.

If we play up or down a number of notes in any major

or minor scale we are said to be proceeding *diatonically.*
A diatonic scale is thus distinguished from a *chromatic scale,*
in which all the black and white digitals are used.

7. **Tonic Sol-Fa.**—Before closing this preliminary
chapter we turn briefly to the "movable do" that is used in
the "tonic sol-fa method" of teaching singing. Probably
most of those who read this book are already familiar with
the elements of the method.

We have seen that the notes *c, d, e, f, g, a,* and *b* are
sometimes called *do, re, mi, fa, sol, la,* and *si.* In the tonic
sol-fa method these same syllables are used—with *si* replaced by *ti*—but are not restricted to the above pitches.
When the key is major *do* always stands for the keynote,
no matter what its pitch may be. Since it is the relationship
of the various notes to the keynote that is maintained when
we pass from one key to another it is simpler to become
familiar with these few relationships than to sing by keeping
in mind all the whole system of keys with the various sharps
and flats that occur in them.

CHAPTER TWO

THE PRODUCTION OF VARIOUS NOISES

8. Pulses of Compression and Rarefaction.—We have all heard footsteps, thunder, the crumpling of paper, the pattering of rain, the babbling of a brook, and many other familiar noises. How are these sounds produced? Do we feel fairly sure that the explanations we give are correct? How can we test our explanations?

Let us begin with an exploding firecracker. During the explosion there is a chemical process which changes a mass of powder into gas. If this gas is not to take up more room than the powder from which it was formed it must be held in by a considerable pressure. If the gas is to be under pressure it must itself exert a pressure on the wall of the firecracker, and if the wall is not strong enough to withstand the pressure it bursts. As the gas rushes out it pushes away the air ahead of it. That air is compressed, moves forward a little, and compresses the air just ahead of it. That in turn moves forward slightly and compresses the air ahead of it. Thus the gas produced by the explosion travels outward only a short distance, whereas the compression which the gas starts travels outward through layer after layer of air for a considerable distance.

Now air has inertia. It follows that a layer of air which is moving forward will not stop until something pushes backward on it. When a compression is spreading out in all directions the inertia of each layer of air causes it to swing so far that it actually leaves behind it a region in which the air expands and becomes rarefied. Then with a compression in front of it and a rarefaction behind it the layer of air is brought to rest and may even be started to moving backward.

Fig. 2 is a curve obtained by an instrument which can record very rapid changes in the pressure of the air. It will be seen that when the wave arrived the pressure rose rapidly and then fell off until it was less than before the

FIG. 2.—Change in Pressure during a Sound [From Geiger and Scheel, *Handbuch der Physik,* Springer, vol. 8 (1927), p. 635.] The sound came from an explosion of 1000 kg. of powder at a distance of 1 km.

wave came—thus showing that there really was first a compression and then a rarefaction.

It seems fair to conclude that the wave from the firecracker consists of a pulse of compression followed by a pulse of rarefaction—and perhaps of further compressions and rarefactions. Except close to the firecracker there is no streaming of the air as a whole. During the passing of a compression the air moves forward, during the passing of a rarefaction it actually moves backward, and after the passing of both the compression and the rarefaction it may again be at rest. The distance that the air travels in its forward and backward movement is very minute, but the distance to which the compression and rarefaction travel may be great. It is when this double pulse of compression and rarefaction reaches our ears that we hear the explosion.

One other matter should be emphasized. If there is to be a sound it is found that the compression or rarefaction must be produced quickly. A very small change in pressure is sufficient to be heard as a sound if it occurs quickly enough. It is well known that the pressure of the air on top of a mountain is less than it is in a valley. The decrease in pressure caused by moving upward for a short distance is very small, but the ear is so extremely sensitive that the head would need to be moved up and down only a fraction of an inch for the difference in pressure to produce a sound if the head could be moved rapidly enough.

Sounds are produced whenever the motion of a body proceeds with sudden jerks that set up sufficient compressions and rarefactions in the surrounding air. It is probably in this way that the sound is produced when a stick is broken, or when a wood fire crackles, or when paper is crumpled.

Noises which are not desired may be made less annoying if means can be found for making the compressions and rarefactions less intense or less sudden. In the silencers used on guns and large gas engines and in the mufflers on automobiles the exhaust gases are caused to enter the external air gradually instead of suddenly.

Question 1. What stops the backward movement of the air in a rarefaction?

Question 2. The blowing of a soap bubble pushes air outward as the bubble grows. Why does it not produce a sound?

Question 3. When a soap bubble bursts why is the report so faint?

Question 4. There is often a report when an incandescent lamp is broken. How is the sound probably produced?

Question 5. How is the sound produced when a piece of paper is torn?

Question 6. How is the crunching sound produced when you walk on very cold snow?

Question 7. How is the sound produced when drops of water get into a hot frying pan with grease?

Question 8. If a drop of oil is placed between a flat glass plate and a fairly flat lens, a crackling sound may often be heard when the lens is rocked. How is this sound produced?

9. Thunder.—It is now generally believed that lightning and thunder are the light and sound produced by enormous electric sparks. The question how an electric spark produces a sound cannot be answered fully without more understanding of the nature of an electric spark than is assumed in this book. We can, however, give a partial answer.

An electric discharge heats the air through which it passes, and so produces a sudden increase in its pressure. This increase causes a pulse of compression to move outward from the path of the spark, the compression is followed, as in the case of the firecracker, by a rarefaction, and these perhaps by further compressions and rarefactions.

Now the report of an electric spark in a laboratory is sharp and crisp, whereas a peal of thunder usually lasts for some time. Moreover, the thunder often rumbles along, occasionally growing louder, and only gradually fading away. Why is there this difference?

When lightning flashes between a cloud and the earth the length of its path may be in the neighborhood of a mile, and when the flash is from cloud to cloud the length may be several miles. A single electric discharge is usually over in a very small fraction of a second, and light travels so rapidly that we see all parts of the flash at practically the instant of the discharge. But sound travels so much more slowly that the noise from different parts of the path is likely to reach us at different times. So the thunder may last for several seconds instead of coming as a single sharp clap.

The rumbling of the thunder is probably not due to any single cause. No doubt a part of it is sometimes due to reflection from buildings, hills, or possibly even from clouds. But it is probable that the importance of reflection is often overestimated, for the rumbling is much the same over the ocean, on a prairie, and among the mountains. If a second or third discharge comes before the sound from the first has died out there will of course be variations in the loud-

ness of the sound. It often happens that several discharges
follow each other inside of a fraction of a second, and in
such cases there may be all sorts of irregular reinforcement
and interference between the various compressions and rarefactions. Another cause for the rumbling appears to be
the shape of the path followed by the discharge. The path
is usually not straight. If it had the shape shown in Fig. 3
an observer at O would hear first a
sound from all parts that lie between
A and B, then successively from the
parts between B and C, then simulta-
neously from all parts between C and
D, and so on. That is, he would hear
a loud sound, followed by a fainter
one, then a loud sound, and again a
fainter one. Succession of discharges and crookedness of
path may be important causes of rumbling. Another cause
will be considered in Art. 46.

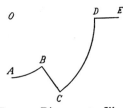

FIG. 3.—Diagram to Illus-
trate Rumbling of Thunder.

Question 9. What objection is there to explaining thunder by
the bumping of clouds against each other?

Question 10. During a flash of lightning the point of the path
that is nearest to an observer is a quarter of a mile from him, and the
farthest point of the path is a mile and a half away. For how long
a time does the thunder last? Assume that it is not prolonged by
reflection.

Question 11. How can we form some estimate of the distance
to the nearest point of a lightning discharge?

10. Sounds from Guns.—When a gun is fired, more
than one sound is often heard. The explosion of the powder produces sound in somewhat the same manner that we
have already considered in connection with a firecracker.
But when an observer is at a distance from a gun he often
hears a sharp report or "crack" before the sound from the
explosion reaches him. The crack is not produced by the
bullet hitting a target or other hard surface, for it may be

heard when the bullet buries itself in soft earth. It appears
to be produced by the bullet while flying, and it is produced
only by projectiles that travel faster than sound.

The nose of a bullet pushes away the air ahead of it,
and thus tends to set up a compression. If the bullet is
traveling more slowly than sound the compression is small,
because any incipient compression spreads out faster than
the bullet follows. But if the bullet travels faster than
sound a considerable compression does develop, and from
this compressed region in front of the bullet the air streams
off at the sides, producing there a compression which travels
off with the appropriate speed of sound. It is when this
compression reaches an observer that he hears the crack
from the bullet.

To understand the shape of this compressed region consider Fig. 4. The bullet is traveling toward the left. At

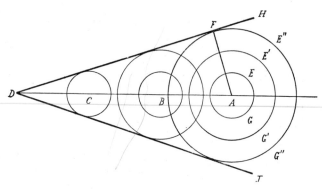

FIG. 4.—The Producing of a Bow Wave.

a certain instant its nose is at A, and at the ends of successive thousandths of a second it is at B, C, D. While the
bullet travels from A to D the compression from A travels
a shorter distance AF, and if this compression were to
spread uniformly in all directions its position at the ends
of successive thousandths of a second would be indicated

by the circles *EG, E'G', E"G"*. Similarly, while the bullet travels from any other point *B* to *D* the compression from *B* would spread as indicated by the circles around *B*. When the bullet is at *D* the compressions from the various points of the path have reached the positions shown by the outermost circles. Since compressions start not only from the points *A, B, C,* and *D,* but also from many intermediate points, the resultant compression is represented by the lines *DH* and *DJ*. Thus when the bullet moves in a straight line with a speed greater than that of sound it produces a nearly conical "bow wave" *HDJ*.

Question 12. Aside from the difference in loudness, do you see any way in which the sound waves produced by the explosion of powder in a gun may differ from those produced by the explosion of powder in a firecracker?

Question 13. If the construction used in Fig. 4 is employed for a bullet that travels more slowly than sound what is the shape found for the bow wave?

The angular opening of the bow wave depends on the relation between the speed of the bullet and that of sound. In Fig. 5 *HDJ* represents the bow wave, *AD* represents the distance that the bullet has traveled in some short time, and *AF*—drawn perpendicular to *DH*—represents the distance that the sound has traveled in the same time. If we

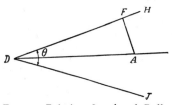

FIG. 5.—Relative Speeds of Bullet and Sound.

knew the angular opening θ at the vertex of the bow wave we could lay off lines *DH* and *DJ* on a sheet of paper, choose any point *A* on the bisector of the angle θ, and measure *AD* and *AF*. Then if *AD* turned out to be twice as long as *AF* we should know that the bullet was traveling twice as fast as sound. If we knew the speed of sound we could in this way find the speed of the bullet.

Question 14. Is the angular opening of the bow wave greater when the bullet travels at 1500 ft./sec. or at 2000 ft./sec.?

Question 15. What is the shape of the bow wave if the bullet is slowing down? If it is speeding up?

Question 16. Hiram Maxim tells of shooting down a railroad track past a row of equally spaced telegraph poles. The rifle was equipped with a silencer which deadened the noise from the explosion, and the railroad ran along an open meadow. He heard a rapid succession of cracks which came to him after reflection from the telegraph poles. If the speed of the bullet was in the neighborhood of 2000 ft./sec. and the speed of sound about 1000 ft./sec., how rapidly would the cracks be heard to follow each other?

Question 17. Mr. Maxim also tells of going up onto a knoll away from trees and other reflecting objects and shooting straight up into the air. The rifle was equipped with a silencer. What do you suppose he heard?

Question 18. In what way should you expect the sound from a bow wave to differ for different speeds or sizes or shapes of the projectile?

It is possible to find the angular opening of a bow wave —and incidentally to show that the bow wave really exists —by taking a photograph. These photographs are made possible by the fact that a beam of light bends when it enters the compressed air of a bow wave.

Fig. 6 is a copy of such a photograph. It will be seen that in addition to the bow wave there is, nearly parallel to it, a well marked stern wave. There is also a confused wake behind the bullet, and sometimes, as in this case there is a train of waves that form more or less circular arcs inside of the stern wave. Immediately behind the bullet there must be a region of decreased pressure into which the surrounding air flows rapidly, and it has been suggested that this leads to the formation of eddies which constitute the wake, and that the stern wave may in reality be a bow wave from the head of this wake.

From the photograph it will also be seen that the outline of the bow wave is not exactly straight. If the speed of either the bullet or the sound wave were changing as it traveled, that change might account for a curving of the waves. Now it is known that a very marked compression travels somewhat faster than an ordinary compression. It is also known that air is warmed by a quick compression, and that sound travels faster in warmer air. For both of these

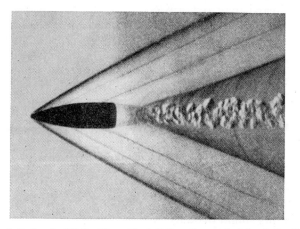

FIG. 6.—A Bullet in Flight [from Carl Julius Cranz, *Lehrbuch der Ballistik*, Springer (1926)].

reasons the bow wave must travel faster at first before it has spread far from the nose of the bullet.

Question 19. Is the curve in the bow wave in a direction which could be accounted for by a decrease in the speed of the wave as it travels?

Question 20. If the bow wave were strictly conical might the position from which the photograph is taken make it appear to be curved?

Question 21. Dayton C. Miller [Physical Review 15, 230 (1920)] has found that when the crack passes an observer there may be a sudden compression, followed by a rarefaction, and this in turn by a second compression. In the case of a 14-inch shell, passing the observer at a distance of about 700 ft., and flying at about

2600 ft./sec., the total time occupied by the passing of the compression-rarefaction-compression was about 0.02 sec. As they traveled through the air how far apart were the two compressions? Does it seem likely that the second compression was that from the stern wave?

Meteorites sometimes explode. But they often travel much faster than sound, and it has been suggested that the report heard may not always come from an explosion—it may sometimes be caused by the passing of a bow wave set up by the meteorite. It has also been suggested[13] that the sound produced when a whip is cracked may be due to a bow wave, the tip of the lash finally traveling faster than sound.

11. **Sounds from Impact.**—Noises are often produced when one body strikes another. As a particular case consider two ivory balls suspended by threads so that they rest in contact with each other. If one ball is drawn aside and then released it swings against the other and sets it swinging, and at the instant of collision there is an abrupt sound. How is this sound produced?

Several hypotheses suggest themselves. It may be that the collision sets up waves of compression and rarefaction that run back and forth through the balls and so set up waves in the air. It may be that the air is squeezed out from between the balls so suddenly as to start a compression in the neighboring air. It may be that the air following a swinging ball has its motion stopped so suddenly as to produce a compression. Is any of these hypotheses correct? May it be that the sound is produced in more than one of these ways, and perhaps in other ways?

Consider first the hypothesis that the sound is produced by means of waves that run back and forth through the

[13] Scientific American **112.** 308 (1915); **113,** 231 (1915). Other suggestions as to the cause of the sound when a whip is cracked are given in Scientific American **113,** 43 and 79 (1915).

balls. The collision cannot be absolutely instantaneous. From the instant when the balls first touch they begin to press on each other and to bend each other slightly out of shape. This distortion calls into play forces which tend to restore the balls to their original shape, and so to drive them apart. The time during which the balls are in contact is very brief, but it may nevertheless prove to be large enough to be important.

A certain time is also required for a wave to run from one side of a ball to the other and back again. Suppose it should turn out that a wave runs back and forth a considerable number of times while the balls are still in contact. This would mean that the pressure which sets up a compression in the ball would last throughout the time of that compression and the next rarefaction and the next compression and the next rarefaction, and so on. That is, the pressure would interfere greatly with the very waves that it was producing. Hardly any part of the energy of the blow would go to setting up waves in the balls, and we might suspect that any waves which really were set up would be so extremely minute as not to produce any audible sound.

Suppose, on the other hand, that the balls are in contact for a time which is smaller than that required for a wave to run back and forth through a ball. Then the blow might well be sufficiently sudden to set up appreciable waves.

The time during which two balls are in contact when one strikes the other can be determined experimentally. For brass balls 3 cm. in diameter it is of the order of 0.0001 sec. to 0.0002 sec. For a brass ball of this size it is possible to calculate that a wave would run back and forth through the ball about nine times in 0.0001 sec., and that the fraction of the energy turned into vibration is only about one seven-millionth of the energy of the approaching ball.

Moreover, if waves run back and forth in the ball nine

times in 0.0001 sec., the pitch of any sound that they might produce would have a frequency of about 90,000 vibrations in each second, which is a pitch so high that we could not hear it.

Since the waves would run back and forth through the balls a number of times before the contact is over, and since the amount of energy in these waves would be so extremely minute, and especially since the pitch would be too high to be audible, we are safe—at least in the case of brass balls 3 cm. in diameter—in concluding that our first hypothesis need not be considered further.

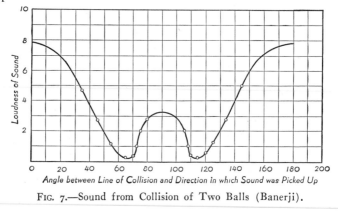

Fig. 7.—Sound from Collision of Two Balls (Banerji).

A test of the second and third hypotheses has been carried out by Banerji.[14] It was thought that the sound from the blow might be louder in some directions than in others. If the compression is caused by the sudden squeezing of air from between the balls, the sound should be loudest across the path of the ball; and if the compression is caused by the sudden stopping of air behind the ball, the sound should be loudest back of the ball.

Banerji measured the loudness of the sound in different directions from the colliding balls. The results are rather surprising. They are shown in Fig. 7. It will be seen that

[14] Sudhansukumar Banerji, Phil. Mag. 32, 96 (1916).

the curve is higher at 0° than at 90°, showing that the compression produced behind the ball when it stops is more important than that produced by the air squeezed out from between the balls. The experiment was tried with balls of ivory, marble, aluminum, and wood, and the curves were in all cases similar to that in Fig. 7.

Question 22. If we were to attempt to check the curve in Fig. 7 by ear would it be better to work indoors or out?

Question 23. Why does the curve in Fig. 7 rise to the same level at 0° and at 180°?

Question 24. The curve in Fig. 7 shows that the sound is very faint at angles of about 67° and 113°. What explanations can you suggest?

Question 25. How is the sound from the clapping of hands probably produced?

Question 26. How is the sound from horses' hoofs on a road probably produced?

Question 27. How is the sound from the pattering of rain on a roof probably produced?

12. Sounds from Liquid Drops and Bubbles.—Sounds like the roar of a cataract and the thunder of surf are not well understood. In a paper published in 1848 Magnus[15] referred briefly to the sound produced when a slender stream of water runs into water and carries down air bubbles,[16] and shortly afterward Tyndall[17] suggested that

---

[15] Heinrich Gustav Magnus (1802-1870), translated in Phil. Mag. 1, 1 (1851). Magnus was Professor of Physics in the University in Berlin.

[16] "When a jet strikes a tranquil surface placed at some distance from the orifice, but before it has attained its maximum contraction, a considerable concavity is sometimes formed round the jet without the entrance of any air. As soon, however, as the least motion is imparted to the surface, the air is observed to enter immediately. Let the surface, for instance, be put in motion by permitting water-drops to fall upon it from a height of a few inches, and at a small distance from the jet. The drops would of themselves carry no air downwards; but as soon as they meet the surface a peculiar sound is heard proceeding from the point where the jet strikes the fluid, and at the same moment air-bubbles are formed and carried downwards."

[17] John Tyndall (1820-1893), Phil. Mag. 1, 105 (1851). Tyndall was a

the sound is probably caused by the bursting of these bubbles. "To the same cause," Tyndall says, "the rippling of streams and the sound of breakers appear to be almost exclusively due."

About seventy years later Raman and Dey [18] pointed out that a drop of water falling into water makes no sound when it falls for only a short distance, and A. T. Jones [19] found that sounds are produced for certain heights of fall and not for others. If the height of fall is gradually increased there is no sound until the drops fall several centimeters. Then almost every drop makes a sharp click that can be heard to a distance of several meters, and then, as the height of fall continues to increase, there follow one or more regions in which the drops enter the water silently, separated by regions in which they click. If the height of fall is further increased there is a region from about 12 cm. to 50 cm. in which the drops usually enter silently,[20] but when the height of fall becomes still greater there is a gentle pat from each drop, and as the height of fall becomes still greater the pat grows stronger.

When a drop clicks it is sometimes accompanied by the formation of a small bubble, but it often clicks when no bubble is visible, and bubbles are often formed when no click is heard. Neither the click when a drop falls a short distance, nor the pat when it falls a greater distance, seems to be caused by the bursting of a bubble.

clear and brilliant lecturer and writer. He was Professor of Natural Philosophy at the Royal Institution in London.

[18] C. V. Raman and Ashutosh Dey, Phil. Mag. **39**, 145 (1920). Sir Chandrasekhar Venkataram Raman is at the Indian Institute of Science at Bangalore, India. He was awarded the 1930 Nobel prize in physics.

[19] Arthur Taber Jones, Science **52**, 295 (1920).

[20] When a smooth solid sphere falls into water from a height which is not too great it also enters silently. If the sphere is rough, or if the height is greater, there is a splash accompanied by sound. See footnote 18; A. Mallock, Roy. Soc. London, Proc. **95A**, 138 (1918); A. L. Narayan, Phil. Mag. **42**, 773 (1921); and pp. 73-74 in A. M. Worthington's beautiful *Study of Splashes* (1908).

It is even possible that the bursting of a bubble does not usually produce any appreciable sound. If air is blown slowly through a glass tube that ends some 15 cm. below the surface of water it will be noticed that there is a gentle report each time that a bubble tears itself loose from the end of the tube, and that the bursting of the bubble when it reaches the surface is often entirely inaudible. If the bubbles follow each other rapidly enough there may be two or more bubbles on the surface at the same time, and if these bubbles unite to form a larger bubble there is a shimmering sound at the instant when they join. If the bursting itself gives rise to any sound it is—in this case at any rate—an extremely faint one.

How these various sounds are produced we do not yet know, but it may well be that they have something to do with the roar of a cataract and the thunder of surf. The whole matter deserves further study.

CHAPTER THREE

VIBRATORY MOTION

13. Simple Harmonic Motion.—The sounds that we considered in Chapter Two are not particularly musical, and in that respect they differ from many of the sounds that we shall discuss. A musical sound is produced by some sort of a vibration, and when we deal with vibrations a number of terms are in such constant use that it is desirable to become familiar with them as soon as possible. In Chapter One we have already introduced the terms "periodic," "period," and "frequency."

Most vibratory motions are decidedly complicated. The type of vibration that is usually regarded as simplest is called "simple harmonic motion," and is represented very closely by the motion of a pendulum bob. To reach a more accurate conception of simple harmonic motion let us suppose that the bob of a pendulum is swinging in a horizontal circle instead of back and forth in a vertical plane, and suppose that the setting sun casts a shadow of the bob on a vertical wall. Sometimes the bob moves toward the wall and sometimes away from it, sometimes it moves parallel to the wall, but the shadow moves back and forth on the wall in a straight line. The motion of the shadow is a good representation of simple harmonic motion. The motion of the bob is a uniform circular motion and the sunlight projects this motion onto the wall. Simple harmonic motion is often defined with the aid of a "reference particle" (P in Fig. 8), which is conceived to move with uniform speed in the circumference of a circle. If any straight line is drawn in the plane of the circle, then the projection of the reference particle upon the straight line moves with *simple harmonic motion* (Fig. 8).

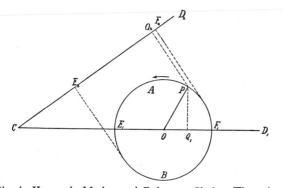

FIG. 8.—Simple Harmonic Motion and Reference Circle. The reference particle P moves with uniform speed around the reference circle PAB. CD_1 and CD_2 are any straight lines drawn in the plane of the circle. Q_1 and Q_2 are the projections of P on these lines. The motion of P around the circle causes Q_1 to move back and forth along a straight line between E_1 and F_1, and Q_2 to move back and forth along a straight line between E_2 and F_2. Q_1 has simple harmonic motion, and Q_2 has simple harmonic motion.

Question 28. If the wall in the illustration just given is vertical but not perpendicular to the direction in which the light comes from the setting sun, should you expect the shadow to describe a simple harmonic motion?

Question 29. Can you imagine any kind of vibration that seems to you simpler than simple harmonic motion?

When a particle has simple harmonic motion—or any other vibratory motion—its *displacement* is its distance from the middle point of its path—or natural position of equilibrium—usually regarded as positive when on one side of the equilibrium position and negative when on the other. Thus in Fig. 9 if O is the equilibrium position of a particle which is vibrating between A and B, its displacement when at C may be + 10 mm., when at D may be + 15 mm., and when at E may be — 15 mm. The *amplitude* of a simple harmonic motion usually means the largest value of the displacement, and is almost always taken as positive. In Fig. 9 the amplitude is the distance OB or OA.

The *phase* of a simple harmonic motion has to do with the instantaneous position of the particle in its vibration, and is often expressed in terms of the angle which has been described by the reference point P in Fig. 8. The word

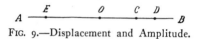

FIG. 9.—Displacement and Amplitude.

is most often used when we deal with two simple harmonic motions and are concerned with their "difference in phase." Thus if two particles have simple harmonic motions along the line CD_1 in Fig. 8, and if the angle Q_1OP is the same for both, we say that the two particles are "in phase with each other" or "in the same phase." If the angle Q_1OP for one particle is 180° larger than for the other we say that the particles are "in opposite phases" or that they "differ in phase by 180°." Differences in phase are also sometimes expressed in fractions of a period. One particle may be a quarter of a period ahead of another, or one may be a sixth of a period behind another.

Question 30. Two particles Q_1 and Q_1' vibrate with simple harmonic motion along the same line CD_1 (Fig. 8). The particles have the same period, but the amplitude of Q_1' is twice that of Q_1. Is it possible to make any simple statement that tells how the displacements of the particles compare when their phases are the same? when the phases are opposite? when one is a quarter of a period ahead of the other?

14. Curves to Represent Vibrations.—It is often helpful to represent the manner in which some quantity changes by means of a graph. For the displacement in a simple harmonic motion the graph has the simple wavy form shown in Fig. 10. At the points A, E, I the particle has its greatest displacement upward, at C, G it has its greatest displacement downward, and at *B, D, F, H* it is at the middle of its path.

Since the graph in Fig. 10 shows the displacement at different times it is often called a *displacement-time* curve.

Question 31. How could you make use of a reference circle to draw the displacement-time curve for a simple harmonic motion?

The slope of the displacement-time curve shows how the particle is moving. Where the curve slopes upward toward the right the particle is moving upward, where it slopes downward toward the right the particle is moving downward, where the slope is most rapid the particle is

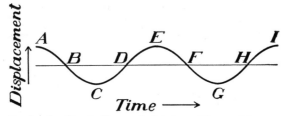

FIG. 10.—Graph of a Simple Harmonic Motion. The particle moves up and down with simple harmonic motion. Imagine that the particle carries a pencil which presses against a piece of paper. If the paper moves steadily to the left the pencil draws the graph.

moving most rapidly, and where the curve is horizontal the particle is not moving. In Fig. 10 we see that the particle moves most rapidly when it is at the middle of its path, and that near the ends of the path the motion is very slow.

When we know how the speed of the particle changes as time goes on we can draw a graph of the speed. This speed-time curve is highest where the upward speed is greatest, lowest where the downward speed is greatest, and crosses the axis at the instants when the speed vanishes.

Question 31a. When a particle moves with simple harmonic motion how does the appearance of the speed-time curve compare with that of the displacement-time curve?

Question 32. The magnitude of an acceleration is given by the rate at which the speed increases. Thus from a graph of speed it is possible to get a graph of acceleration in the same manner in which the graph of speed is obtained from the graph of displacement. In the case of a simple harmonic motion how does the acceleration-time curve compare with the displacement-time curve?

The answers to questions 31a and 32 have been found by making use of graphs for displacement, speed, and acceleration. The answer to question 32 is of interest because it is closely related to a second way in which simple harmonic motion is sometimes defined.[21]

15. Simultaneous Vibratory Motions.—Such curves as we have just been considering are especially helpful when we deal with more complicated motions. Consider first the result obtained by combining two simple harmonic motions which lie along the same line. If an experimenter moves a piece of chalk up and down with simple harmonic motion and at the same time walks steadily past a blackboard, he draws on the blackboard the displacement-time curve for simple harmonic motion. If the blackboard were moving up and down with simple harmonic motion, and the experimenter held the chalk at rest while he walked steadily, he would draw the displacement-time curve for the motion of the blackboard. If both chalk and blackboard move up and down with simple harmonic motions, the graph that is drawn represents the resultant of the two motions. When more than two simple harmonic motions are combined the resultant curves may be exceedingly complicated. Even with only two the curve takes forms which depend on the relative frequencies, amplitudes, and initial phases of the components.

The general method of finding the resultant of two vibratory motions is shown in Fig. 11. More may be com-

[21] Simple harmonic motion is sometimes defined as a motion in which the acceleration and displacement are proportional to each other, and are opposite in phase.

bined in a similar way. If this is done with much accuracy it requires considerable time. In some simple cases rather rough drawings suffice to give an idea of the result, and for cases which are not too complicated machines have been invented that draw the resultant quickly and with surprising accuracy.

Questions 33, 34, and 35 are to be answered with the aid of rough drawings.

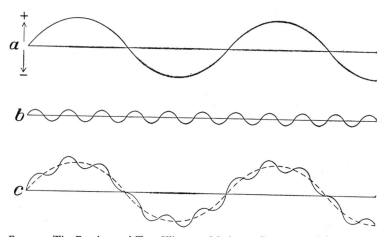

FIG. 11.—The Resultant of Two Vibratory Motions. Curves *a* and *b* represent the displacements in two simple harmonic motions. The resultant curve *c* is found by adding the displacements algebraically. Thus when *a* and *b* are both positive *c* is higher than either; when *a* and *b* are both negative *c* is lower than either; and when one is positive and the other negative *c* lies above or below the axis according to which component is numerically the larger. In the third graph the curve *a* has been copied as a dotted line, and it will be seen that the resultant curve may be found by simply superposing one of the component curves on the other.

Question 33. If two simple harmonic motions have the same frequency and equal amplitudes how does the resultant depend on the relation between their phases?

Question 34. If the amplitudes of two simple harmonic motions are equal and the frequencies are nearly the same what is the appearance of the resulting displacement-time curve?

Fig. 12.—Curves Produced by Two Simple Harmonic Motions in Perpendicular Directions [From Edwin H. Barton, *Text-Book on Sound,* Macmillan (1908), p. 61]. The numbers at the left give the relative frequencies of the components. The diagrams in the different columns are for different phase relationships.

Question 35. If one simple harmonic motion has a frequency three times that of another, and an amplitude half as great, how does the appearance of the resultant curve differ when the two components are initially in phase and when they are initially in opposite phases?

In the above cases one body has at the same time two simple harmonic motions, and both of these motions occur along the same line. Such cases are of great importance. There are also many cases in which the directions of the component motions are not the same. When two simple harmonic motions have perpendicular directions some very entertaining and beautiful results occur. Several of these are shown in Fig. 12, and further discussion of them will be given in Art. 50.

Question 36. Can you devise some simple method of checking the frequency ratios that are given at the left in Fig. 12?

CHAPTER FOUR

SIMPLE TONES AND COMBINATIONS OF TONES

16. **Ohm's Law.**—When several sounds are reaching the ear we know that it is often possible to pay attention to some of them to the exclusion of others. When several persons are talking we may follow what one of them is saying. When an orchestra is playing we may follow certain instruments. Even when a single instrument plays a single note it is sometimes possible to recognize component tones which have different pitches. In this last case it seems reasonable to suppose that the components are simpler than the whole sound in which we distinguish the components. Is there a simplest kind of sound? If there is, what type of vibration gives rise to it?

The motion of the air when sounds pass through it may be very complicated. Sometimes this complicated motion can be regarded as produced by combining a number of simple harmonic motions. Sometimes an analysis of the sound into simple harmonic components seems rather artificial. It is possible to regard the complicated motion as made up in other ways, just as it is possible to regard the number 12 as made up by adding 5 and 7, or 2 and 10, or three 4's, or two 6's. There is no reason for regarding any one of these ways of resolving 12 into components as more simple and more fundamental than the others. But in the case of sound the kind of components into which we resolve it does seem to be of importance. A belief gradually developed that there is a simplest kind of sound, and that the simplest sounds are produced by simple harmonic motions.

It can be shown that the vibration caused in the air by
a tuning fork mounted on a resonant box or in front of a
suitable resonator is very nearly simple harmonic. Moreover, the sound from such a tuning fork does, as a matter
of fact, give an impression of being very simple. One
pitch is heard clearly, and if any others are heard at all
they are very faint. But if a note is played on a piano or
an organ, or in fact on almost any musical instrument, it
can be shown that the vibration set up in the air is not
simple harmonic. In these cases it is often possible to
analyze the complicated motion into simple harmonic components; and it is often possible for the ear—especially after
a little training, or with the aid of suitable equipment—to
pick out simple tones [22] that have precisely the pitches of
the simple harmonic components.

There are sounds, like some of those mentioned in Chapter Two, which it is not helpful to regard as produced by
simple harmonic components, and from which the ear does
not pick out simple tones. Even in the cases of many musical sounds there are difficulties in regarding them as the
resultants of simple tones. In spite of these difficulties we
do usually regard sounds which are more or less musical
as consisting, in part at least, of a number of simple tones,
and the credit for clearing up some of the difficulties in
this point of view is usually given to Ohm [23]—the same
Ohm who had stated a famous law for electricity some
seventeen years earlier.

For sound Ohm gave a law which it is not easy to state

[22] In this book we shall often follow Mr. Ellis [English translation of
Helmholtz's *Tonempfindungen* (1912), p. 24.] in distinguishing *simple tones*
from *compound tones*. A simple tone is heard when the vibration that gives
rise to it is very nearly simple harmonic.

[23] Georg Simon Ohm (1787(?)-1854), Pogg. An. 59, 513 (1843); 62, 1
(1844). At this time Ohm was teaching mathematics in the polytechnic
school in Nuremberg. His law for sound was reached theoretically, "da ich
mit dem Ohre in dieser Sache nichts zu thun vermag, weil mir die Natur
ein musikalisches Gehör ganz and gar versagt hat."

accurately and at the same time simply, but of which the gist is contained in the two following sentences. A simple harmonic motion of the air gives to the air an impression of a single pitch. If the motion of the air is more complicated, and if the ear is to hear a component tone of frequency N, two conditions are necessary: First, it must be possible to analyze the complicated motion into motions that are either simple harmonic or very nearly simple harmonic; and second, one of these motions must have the frequency N. This statement of Ohm's law is somewhat awkward and complicated. But the fact which it states seems to be of fundamental importance.

17. **Reinforcement and Interference.**—The simplest combination of tones is doubtless two simple tones of the same pitch. Now it is a remarkable fact that if two simple harmonic motions of the same frequency are combined the resultant motion is also simple harmonic. Moreover, the resultant has the same frequency as the components. Similarly if two or more simple tones of the same pitch reach us at the same time, we hear a single tone of that pitch. When several simple tones have the same pitch the only difference that the ear can detect between a single one and the resultant of all is a possible difference in loudness.

When two simple harmonic motions of the same frequency are in phase with each other the amplitude of the resultant is the sum of the amplitudes of the components, when they are opposite in phase the amplitude of the resultant is the difference between the amplitudes of the components, and when the phases are neither the same nor opposite the amplitude of the resultant lies between these values. Similarly when the vibrations that give rise to two simple tones of the same pitch are nearly in phase with each other the resultant tone is louder than either of the components, and the two tones are said to *reinforce* each other; and when the components are nearly opposite in phase the resultant tone is fainter than the louder of the components, and one tone is said to *interfere* [24] with the other. In the particular case where the two component simple harmonic motions have not only the same frequency but also the same amplitude, and are also just opposite in phase, there is no resultant motion at all. Similarly when two simple tones are of precisely the same pitch and loudness, and are exactly opposite in phase, the two tones combine to give no sound at all.

Question 37. This last statement is difficult to show experimentally. What reasons for the difficulty do you see?

18. Beats.—If the frequencies of two simple harmonic motions are nearly the same, but not quite the same, the resultant bears a close resemblance to a simple harmonic motion. Since the frequencies are not exactly the same the phase relationship between the components cannot remain the same, and so the amplitude experiences a gradual change.

At some instant the motions are in phase, and the amplitude of the resultant has its largest value. Then the phases drift apart, and the amplitude of the resultant decreases. When one component has gained half a cycle on the other the phases are opposite, and the amplitude of the resultant has its smallest value. When one component has gained a whole cycle on the other the motions are again in phase, and the amplitude of the resultant has again its largest value. Thus the amplitude of the resultant grows alternately smaller and larger. A graph of such a resultant is shown in Fig. 13.

If a few of the waves in Fig. 13 are examined it will be seen that, except for the changing amplitude, and excepting the places where the amplitude is least, the curve

[24] The word *interfere* is often used in a wider sense. For our present purposes the above meaning is sufficient.

does look much like that for simple harmonic motion. If the component curves are compared with the resultant (Fig. 14) it is seen that the top of an upward displacement in the resultant lies between the tops of upward displacements

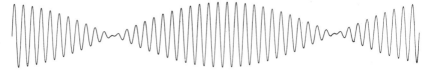

FIG. 13.—Resultant of Two Simple Harmonic Motions Which Have Nearly the Same Frequency [Curve kindly provided by Professor Samuel R. Williams]. In the present case one component makes 24 vibrations in the same time in which the other makes 25.

in the components. In fact, except for the changing amplitude, the resultant is not only much like a simple harmonic motion, but also has a frequency between the frequencies of the components.

Similarly if two simple tones of nearly the same pitch are sounding at the same time, we do not hear them as

FIG. 14.—Frequency of a Beating Tone [From Arthur L. Kimball, *College Physics,* Henry Holt, ed. 3 (1923), p. 215]. The dotted curve represents one component, and the light solid curve the other. The heavy curve is the resultant. In the present case one component vibrates ten times while the other vibrates eleven.

two tones. We hear one tone, of which the pitch lies between the pitches of the components, and of which the loudness increases and decreases periodically. The two tones are said to *beat with each other* or to *give rise to beats.* One beat is regarded as lasting from some instant when the resultant is loudest to the next instant when it is loudest, or from an instant when it is faintest to the next instant when it is faintest. The frequency with which the beats occur can be shown to equal the difference between the frequencies of the components.

Question 38. How can the statement made in the last sentence be shown to hold?

Question 39. In Fig. 13 if the tone of higher pitch has a frequency of 125 cycles per second what is the frequency of the beats?

Question 40. Beats often afford a convenient means of determining the frequency of a tone. A certain note on an organ is found to beat 33 times in 10 sec. with a tuning fork which has a frequency of 256 cycles/sec., and to beat 48 times in 10 sec. with a fork which has a frequency of 264 cycles/sec. What is the frequency of the note on the organ?

If we hear at the same time more than two simple tones of nearly the same pitch we still perceive them as a single tone. The pitch of the resultant is close to an average of all the pitches. But every pair of the component tones gives rise to beats, and the different sets of beats have different frequencies. If there are three components, say A, B, and C, there are beats from A and B, beats from B and C, and beats from A and C—beats which may be of three different frequencies. If there are four components there may be beats of six different frequencies, with five components beats of ten different frequencies, with six components fifteen different frequencies, and so on. With many components the beats may become so confused that we cease to notice them. It has been suggested that these facts have some bearing on the effect of music sung by a chorus or large choir, where it is of course impossible for all those who sing any one part to sing exactly the same pitch.

"The whisper of a tree, whatever its volume, has substantially the same pitch as that of its individual twigs or needles, . . . the hum of a swarm of bees is pitched to that of the average bee, and the concert of a million mosquitoes is only the megaphoned whine of the type." [25]

[25] W. J. Humphreys, *Physics of the Air*, ed. 2 (1929), p 429.

19. Roughness from Beats.—If two or more musical tones are played at the same time the resultant may be smooth and pleasing or it may be rough and unpleasant. In the former case we say that the component notes are *consonant,* and in the latter that they are *dissonant.* Why should some combinations of notes be consonant and others dissonant? An answer to this question is to be found in the varying loudness of sound from tones that beat.[26] Let us see how beats may be concerned in questions of consonance and dissonance.

When the pitches of two tones are very nearly the same the beats are very slow, and as the difference in pitch grows greater the beats grow more rapid. When the beats are moderately slow the effect may be pleasing, and in some organs there is a stop in which each note is produced by two pipes that beat some two to four times a second. When, however, the beats are fairly rapid the effect is a rough jarring rattle which is decidedly unpleasant. As they grow still faster the roughness decreases, and when they are sufficiently rapid the ear no longer detects them at all.

The eye reacts in a similar way to a light that varies periodically in brightness. As the variations in brightness become moderately rapid the flickering effect becomes decidedly unpleasant, but as the variations grow still faster the unpleasant effect decreases, and when the variations are sufficiently rapid the flickering blends into what looks to the eye like a steady light.

The frequency of the beats when the roughness from two tones is most unpleasant depends somewhat on the pitch.

---

[26] According to Lagrange [Oeuvres, I, p. 144] the suggestion that dissonance is caused by beats comes from Sauveur. It was developed by Helmholtz. See *Sensations of Tone,* 4th English edition, pp. 169-173. Although Joseph Sauveur (1653-1716) was never able to hear well, and in fact did not learn to talk until he was seven years old, he did important work in sound. He gave us the words *acoustics, fundamental, harmonics, node,* and he proposed the use of 256 cycles/sec. for the frequency of middle *c.*

For a considerable part of the range used in music Helm-holtz found "the most penetrating roughness" when there were some thirty to forty beats in a second, and he was still able to hear beats when there were more than 130 in a second.

Most musical sounds are not simple. When two com-pound tones are sounding together it may be that some component tone of one has a pitch so near to some compo-nent of the other as to beat with it, and if several compo-nents of one are close to components of the other there may be several sets of beats at the same time. Even when the pitches of two notes differ too much for their funda-mentals to beat, it nevertheless happens frequently that dis-tinct beats from some of their overtones can be heard. We shall see later (Art. 28) how use is made of such beats in tuning pianos and organs.

The various components of a musical sound have dif-ferent strengths. Sometimes beats which occur at a very disagreeable rate may happen to be produced by components so weak that they do not contribute greatly to roughness, and this fact must be taken into account in judging the harshness of any combination. If there are beats which are both strong and of frequencies that are especially annoying there is dissonance, and if there is very little roughness from beats there is consonance.

Question 41. Suppose that we have a musical instrument on which each fundamental tone has overtones that vibrate 2, 3, 4, 5, and 6 times as fast as the fundamental. If we play on this instru-ment two notes whose fundamentals have frequencies of 100 and 101 cycles/sec, what will be the frequencies of the beats that are produced?

Question 42. If we play on this same instrument two notes whose fundamental frequencies are 250 and 255 what will be the frequencies of the beats? What if the fundamentals have frequencies of 250 and 372? If all the overtones are equally strong in which of these cases do you judge that the combination would sound the harsher?

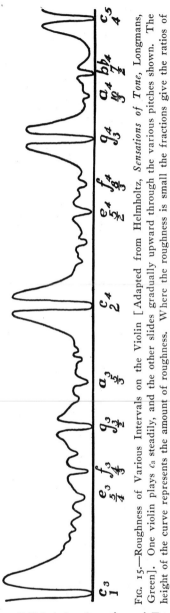

FIG. 15.—Roughness of Various Intervals on the Violin [Adapted from Helmholtz, *Sensations of Tone*, Longmans, Green]. One violin plays c_3 steadily, and the other slides gradually upward through the various pitches shown. The height of the curve represents the amount of roughness. Where the roughness is small the fractions give the ratios of the fundamental frequencies.

Helmholtz [27] made an interesting study of the roughness of the sound from two violins. He used the first ten harmonic partials, he made certain reasonable assumptions about the relative strengths of the components and the roughness due to different frequencies of beats, and he then made calculations for cases where one note had a frequency of 264 cycles/sec. and the other had frequencies running from somewhat less than 264 to somewhat more than 1056. The results are shown in Fig. 15. It will be seen that for many intervals the effect from the two notes is decidedly harsh, but that there are certain intervals for which it is beautifully smooth. The roughness actually heard from two violins fits the predictions of this curve remarkably well, and for various other instruments we may expect that the results would be similar.

27 Helmholtz, *Sensations of Tone,* 4th Eng. ed. (1912), p. 193.

Question 43. If you attempt to arrange the ten or a dozen smoothest intervals in Fig. 15 in the order of their smoothness what order do you find?

20. Consonant Intervals and Triads.

—If we examine the consonance of the intervals in the lower octave of Fig. 15 we see that the perfect octave c_3c_4 and the perfect fifth c_3g_3 are excellent, that the major third c_3e_3, the perfect fourth c_3f_3, and the major sixth c_3a_3 are good, and that the minor third $c_3e\flat_3$ and minor sixth $c_3a\flat_3$ are fair. The frequency ratios that make these intervals the smoothest are these:

perfect octave	1:2	major sixth	3:5
perfect fifth	2:3	minor third	5:6
perfect fourth	3:4	minor sixth	5:8
major third	4:5		

If we attempt to put together three notes to form a *triad* the probability of rough beats is greater than with two notes, so that the number of consonant triads may be expected to be smaller than the number of consonant intervals. To learn whether a triad is consonant we examine the intervals that form the triad. There are three of these intervals: From the lowest note to the middle note, from the middle note to the highest note, and from the lowest note to the highest. If all three of these intervals are consonant the triad is consonant. If any one of the intervals is dissonant the triad is dissonant.

For instance, let us form a triad in which the two lower notes form a perfect fifth, and the two upper form a major third. Then the interval from the lowest note to the middle one and the interval from the middle note to the highest are both of them consonant, and we have only to investigate whether the interval from the lowest note to the highest is consonant. From the above table we see that the frequencies in the two intervals are in the ratios

$$2 : 3$$
and $$4 : 5,$$
or, for the triad, $$8 : 12 : 15.$$

The last line is found by multiplying both terms of $2 : 3$ by 4, and both terms of $4 : 5$ by 3. From this last line we see that the lowest note of our triad vibrates $8/15$ as fast as the highest.

The interval which has a frequency ratio $8 : 15$ is not consonant, and the triad which we have attempted to form is not a consonant triad.

Question 44. If we restrict ourselves to triads in which the interval from the lowest note to the highest is less than an octave, and if we assume that all of the intervals in the list near the beginning of this article are consonant and that no other interval smaller than an octave is consonant, how many consonant triads are there, and what are their frequency ratios?

The solution of the problem set in Question 44 shows that there are six consonant triads, and that they have frequency ratios $3 : 4 : 5$, $4 : 5 : 6$, $5 : 6 : 8$, $10 : 12 : 15$, $12 : 15 : 20$, and $15 : 20 : 24$. But these six triads are not all independent. If we replace the lowest note of $3 : 4 : 5$ by its octave we have $4 : 5 : 6$, and if we replace the lowest note of $4 : 5 : 6$ by its octave we have $5 : 6 : 8$. Thus the three triads $3 : 4 : 5$, $4 : 5 : 6$, and $5 : 6 : 8$ may be regarded as simply different positions of a single triad, which we may represent by $4 : 5 : 6$. This is known as a *major triad*. In the same way we can see that the three other triads may be regarded as different positions of the triad $10 : 12 : 15$, which is known as a *minor triad*. If we restrict ourselves to triads in which no notes are as far apart as an octave there are only two kinds of consonant triads—major triads and minor triads.

Question 45. If we do not restrict ourselves to notes inside of an octave do we find any consonant triads that are not simply new positions of major and minor triads?

Question 46. Notes which have frequencies 100, 125, 150 cycles/sec. form a major triad. The same is true of notes with frequencies 400, 500, 600. One of these triads sounds smooth and the other decidedly rough. Which is the smoother? Why?

CHAPTER FIVE

MUSICAL SCALES

21. **Units for Intervals.**—Before examining our musical scales it is desirable to have some accurate means of describing musical intervals. We already know that an interval is characterized by its frequency ratio, and for many purposes it is entirely satisfactory to describe an interval by giving this ratio. There are other purposes for which frequency ratios prove to be rather awkward. Question 47 may illustrate one of the difficulties that we meet when we attempt to measure intervals by frequency ratios.

Question 47. Five notes have frequencies of 400, 500, 600, 800, 1600 cycles/sec. These notes are to be laid off on a horizontal line in such a way that equal distances shall represent equal intervals. The distance between the 400 and 800 marks is to be 4 cm. How far from the 400 mark should the marks for the rest of the notes be placed? Notice that the interval from 400 to 800 is an octave, and that the interval from 800 to 1600 is also an octave.

A somewhat different consideration is the following. Suppose that the musical interval from c_3 to f_3 is a certain number of small unit intervals of some sort, and that the interval from f_3 to a_3 is another number of these same units. We should like to be able to get the interval from c_3 to a_3 by adding the two numbers. If we measure intervals by means of their frequency ratios we must multiply. We should like to add instead of multiplying.

We recall that if we add the logarithms [28] of two numbers we get the logarithm of their product. This suggests

[28] If the reader has forgotten what a logarithm is he may refer to Appendix Four.

that we measure intervals by the logarithms of their frequency ratios instead of by the frequency ratios themselves. By making use of this idea it is possible to devise systems in which an intervals is given by the sum of the smaller intervals that compose it.

But the logarithms themselves are not entirely satisfactory. Let us see why. We know that among all musical intervals the octave occupies a position of unique importance,[29] and what we should like is a small interval that fits into an octave some whole number of times, and that is also convenient to use in measuring other intervals. Now when two notes are an octave apart the upper vibrates twice as fast as the lower. Moreover, the common logarithm of 2 is 0.30103 · · · ·. So if we measure an interval by the logarithm itself an octave will be represented by the number 0.30103. This number is awkward, and it is not a whole number. But if we multiply all our logarithms by some suitably chosen factor, it turns out, not only that we can add the numbers which represent our intervals, but also that all intervals can be measured in terms of a small interval of any size we choose.

[29] If the partial tones of the notes with which we deal are harmonic it is not difficult to see why notes an octave apart seem to have something in common. Helmholtz [*Sensations of Tone,* 4th Eng. ed., Longmans, Green, p. 253], states the reason as follows. "Let any melody be executed on any instrument which has a good musical quality of tone, such as a human voice; the hearer must have heard not only the primes of the compound tones, but also their upper Octaves, and, less strongly, the remaining upper partials. When, then, a higher voice afterwards executes the same melody an Octave higher, *we hear again a part of what we heard before,* namely the evenly numbered partial tones of the former compound tones, and *at the same time we hear nothing that we had not previously heard.* Hence the repetition of a melody in the higher Octave is a real repetition of what has been previously heard, not of all of it, but of a part. If we allow a low voice to be accompanied by a higher in the Octave above it, the only part music which the Greeks employed, we add nothing new, we merely reinforce the evenly numbered partials. In this sense, then, the compound tones of an Octave above are really repetitions of the tones of the lower Octaves, or at least of part of their constituents. Hence the first and chief division of our musical scale is that into a series of Octaves."

In order to understand how to determine the factor by which we multiply the logarithms suppose that we wish to divide an octave into 1000 equal parts. Let us call one of these parts a *millioctave*. And suppose that we wish to know how many millioctaves there are in an interval which has a given frequency ratio. Let f stand for the given frequency ratio, and n for the corresponding number of millioctaves. Then we may write the proportion

$$\frac{n}{1000} = \frac{\log f}{\log 2}.$$

Whence

$$n = \frac{1000}{\log 2} \cdot \log f.$$

That is, to find the number of millioctaves that correspond to the frequency ratio f we multiply the logarithm of f by the factor $[1000/\log 2 =]$ $3321.93\cdots$. For many acoustic purposes the millioctave is a convenient unit, and it is often used in the current literature.

The factor just found is rather awkward. It would certainly be easier to multiply by some such factor as 1000 instead of by 3321.93. If we use the factor 1000 an octave is divided into $301.03\cdots$ equal parts. One of these parts is sometimes called a *savart*,[30] and although the number of savarts in an octave is not a whole number, it is nevertheless true that for some purposes it is sufficiently accurate to regard an octave as containing 300 savarts, and for such purposes the savart is a convenient unit.

Another division of the octave is into 1200 equal parts. In this case the factor by which to multiply the logarithm is $[1200/\log 2 =]$ $3986.314\cdots$. The 1200th part of an octave is called a *cent*. This interval was introduced by

---

[30] In honor of Félix Savart (1791-1841), French physician and physicist. Much of his work was in the field of sound.

Ellis,[31] and is much used in his translation of Helmholtz's *Tonempfindungen.* For the purposes of music it is one of the most satisfactory of the units that have been proposed.

Question 48. How many millioctaves are there in 100 cents?

Question 49. Yasser [32] has introduced a unit which he calls a *centitone.* It is twice as large as Ellis's *cent.* What is the factor by which the logarithm of the frequency ratio is to be multiplied in order to express an interval in centitones?

Question 50. Making use of the table in Appendix Five how many cents do you find in each of the consonant intervals listed on p. 53?

Question 51. What is the sum of the numbers of cents in a perfect fourth and a perfect fifth? Did you expect this result?

22. The Major Scale.—The major and minor scales that we use in our music are by no means the only possible scales. Others have been used in other ages and are now used in other parts of the world. In an appendix to his translation of Helmholtz's *Tonempfindungen* Ellis [33] gives a collection of 139 different musical scales. Most of these scales have been used only for music in which all voices sing the same melody. With the gradual development of part songs and of music in which chords are employed, our occidental civilization has largely restricted its choice of scales to those in which harmony is possible—that is, to scales in which there are consonant triads.

Now the triads on the keynote, the fifth above the keynote, and the fifth below the keynote are regarded as "the three essential elements of harmony." [34] In the key of *c*, for instance, these are the triads on *c, g,* and *f.* So our

---

[31] Alexander John Ellis (1814-1890), Roy. Soc. Proc. **37,** 368 (1884). Ellis was an English philologist, mathematician, musician, and writer on phonetics.

[32] Joseph Yasser, *A Theory of Evolving Tonality* (1932), p. 14.

[33] Helmholtz, *Sensations of Tone,* 4th Eng. ed., p. 514.

[34] Percy Goetschius, *The Theory and Practice of Tone Relations,* ed. **21,** G. Schirmer, p. 12.

scale ought to include, if possible, the triads based on these three notes.

In the key of c major let us see what the scale will turn out to be if we use no other notes but those in the successive major triads f-a-c, c-e-g, and g-b-d.

In each of these triads the ratio of frequencies is to be $4:5:6$, as is indicated in (1). Let us rewrite in such a

$$
\begin{array}{ccc}
c & e & g \\
4 & 5 & 6
\end{array}
$$

$$
\begin{array}{cccccc}
f & a & c & & g & b & d \\
4 & 5 & 6 & & 4 & 5 & 6
\end{array}
\tag{1}
$$

way as to indicate how many times each note vibrates while c makes one vibration. From (1) we see that e vibrates $5/4$ as fast as c, g $6/4$ as fast as c, b $5/4$ as fast as g, and so on. Thus we find that while c makes one vibration each of the other notes makes the number shown in (2). The

$$
\begin{array}{ccccccc}
f & a & c & e & g & b & d \\
\dfrac{2}{3} & \dfrac{5}{6} & 1 & \dfrac{5}{4} & \dfrac{3}{2} & \dfrac{15}{8} & \dfrac{9}{4}
\end{array}
\tag{2}
$$

notes that we have here range over more than an octave. To bring them into one octave let us multiply the ratios for f and a by 2, thus raising them an octave; let us divide the ratio for d by 2, thus lowering it an octave; and let us add the octave above c. Then the ratios in (2) become those shown in (3).

$$
\begin{array}{cccccccc}
c & d & e & f & g & a & b & c \\
1 & \dfrac{9}{8} & \dfrac{5}{4} & \dfrac{4}{3} & \dfrac{3}{2} & \dfrac{5}{3} & \dfrac{15}{8} & 2
\end{array}
\tag{3}
$$

We have been successful in building up a diatonic scale in which we can play the major triads on the keynote, the fifth above it, and the fifth below it. In fact, the relative frequencies in (3) are those in a "just" or "pure" major scale.[35] We shall see that they are not precisely the frequency ratios in the scale to which we are most accustomed, but they are usually regarded as forming a scale which is more pleasing.

Next let us examine the frequency ratios that we find in passing from any one note of this just scale to the next. e vibrates $5/4$ as fast as c, and d vibrates $9/8$ as fast as c. Consequently e vibrates $[5/4 \div 9/8 =] \; 10/9$ as fast as d. In this way, as the reader should verify, we obtain from (3) the ratios shown in (4).

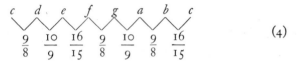

$$\frac{9}{8} \quad \frac{10}{9} \quad \frac{16}{15} \quad \frac{9}{8} \quad \frac{10}{9} \quad \frac{9}{8} \quad \frac{16}{15} \tag{4}$$

Question 52. What should you expect for the product of all the frequency ratios in (4)? What does the product turn out to be?

Question 53. The relative sizes of intervals is probably more easily appreciated if they are expressed in cents instead of frequency ratios. What number of cents corresponds to each of the frequency ratios in (3) and (4)? Make use of Appendix Five.

Question 54. The interval from c to d is how many times as large as that from e to f? The interval from d to e is how many times as large as that from e to f?

Question 55. In the major scale that we have found some of the thirds $c-e$, $d-f$, $e-g$, etc., are major and some are minor. Which are major and which are minor? One of the thirds does not have exactly the frequency ratio for either a major or a minor third. Which one is it? By how many cents does it differ from a just major or minor third?

Question 56. In the major scale that we have found some of the fourths $c-f$, $d-g$, $e-a$, etc., are not perfect. Which ones are not? By how many cents do they differ from a just perfect fourth?

[35] These relative frequencies were not originally obtained by the method employed here. They seem to have been first given by the Egyptian astronomer Claudius Ptolemy (2d century A.D.) in his ʽΑρμονικᾶν Βιβλία Γ (*Three Books on the Theory of Music*).

Question 57. Mr. Redfield has proposed a new scale [36] which differs from the above major scale by having the interval from c to d represented by $10/9$, and the interval from d to e by $9/8$. Show that in Mr. Redfield's scale, and in the key of c, the triads c–e–g and f–a–c are major, and the triad d–f–a is minor.

23. Related Keys.—We know that only very short and simple pieces of music are in a single key. In most compositions there are digressions into other keys. Suppose that we have the notes needed for the key of c major, and that we wish to play in the key of f major. We ask what additional notes are needed.

The relative frequencies of the notes that we already have will not be changed if we multiply all of them by any factor that we choose. If we multiply the ratios in (3) by $3/4$ they become

c	d	e	f	g	a	b	c
$\dfrac{3}{4}$	$\dfrac{27}{32}$	$\dfrac{15}{16}$	I	$\dfrac{9}{8}$	$\dfrac{5}{4}$	$\dfrac{45}{32}$	$\dfrac{3}{2}$

and if we omit the first c, d, and e, and add the octaves of d, e, and f, we have

$$
\begin{array}{ccccccccc}
 & f & g & a & b & c & d & e & f \\
\mathrm{I} & \dfrac{9}{8} & \dfrac{5}{4} & \dfrac{45}{32} & \dfrac{3}{2} & \dfrac{27}{16} & \dfrac{15}{8} & 2
\end{array}
\tag{5}
$$

These are still the relative frequencies of the notes that we already have in the key of c. For any major scale we need notes which have frequencies in the ratios given in (3). On comparing (5) with (3) we see that all but two of the notes that we have in the key of c are also the notes that we need for the key of f. We need a new b and a new d. From (5) we see that the b which we have vibrates $45/32$ as fast as f, and from (3) we see that the fourth note in the scale ought to vibrate $4/3$ as fast

---

[36] John Redfield, *Music a Science and an Art* (1928), p. 191; and a somewhat different treatment in Journ. Acoust. Soc. I, 249 (1930).

as the key note. So the b that we have vibrates $[^{45}\!/_{32} \div \frac{4}{3} =] \ ^{135}\!/_{128}$ as fast as the b that we need. Similarly we find that the d which we have vibrates $81/80$ as fast as the d that we need. Now $135/128 = 1.0547$, which is equivalent to 92.2 cents; and $81/80 = 1.0125$, which is equivalent to 21.5 cents. So if we are to play in both c major and f major we need, in addition to all the notes in the key of c, a new b which is about 92 cents flatter than the b in the key of c, and also a new d about 22 cents cents flatter than the d in the key of c. The two new notes that we introduce may be represented by $b\flat$ and $d\backslash$.

The interval which is represented by the ratio $81/80$ or $80/81$ is theoretically of much importance, and is usually known as a *comma*.[37] In this book the symbol $d\backslash$ will represent a note one comma flatter than d, and $d/$ will represent a note one comma sharper than d. These symbols may be read "d lowered" and "d raised."

Question 58. If we have the notes needed to play in the key of c major, what additional notes do we need to play in g major? Are these new notes sharper or flatter than the notes which they replace? How much sharper or flatter?

24. Minor Scales.—Our "original minor" scale is sometimes regarded as just like the major scale except that the sixth note in the major scale becomes the key note in the minor scale. It is probably better to regard a minor scale as built from three successive triads in a manner similar to that in which we have obtained the major scale. Just how these triads are to be chosen depends on the particular minor scale desired.

---

[37] Sometimes called a "syntonic comma." It is also called the "comma of Didymus," because it appeared in the writings of the Roman Claudius Didymus (1st century A.D.). Two other commas are also recognized, both of them a trifle larger than the comma of Didymus. When the word "comma" is used without some restricting expression it usually refers to the comma of Didymus.

Three forms of minor scale are usually recognized: The *original minor*, the *harmonic minor*, and the *melodic minor*. In forming the original minor scale and the descending form of the melodic minor the three triads chosen are all of them minor; for the harmonic minor scale the two lower triads are minor and the upper triad is major; and for the ascending form of the melodic minor scale the middle triad is minor and both of the others are major.

Question 59. If we build the original minor scale of *a* from three minor triads *d–f–a, a–c–e,* and *e–g–b,* each triad having frequencies in the ratios 10:12:15, how do the frequencies of the notes in this scale compare with the frequency of the key note *a*? How do they compare with the frequency of *c*? To what extent does this minor scale differ from the one obtained by using precisely the notes that are in the just key of *c* major?

25. Temperament.—When we pass from one key to another we have seen that it is necessary to introduce notes that were not in the original key. The more close the musical relationship between the two keys the fewer notes it is necessary to introduce. If we restrict ourselves to major scales the most closely related keys are those on the fourth and fifth of the original scale. For instance, the keys which are most closely related to the key of *c* are *f* and *g*. Now in passing from the key of *c* to that of *f* we have found it necessary to introduce two new notes. Similarly if we pass from *f* to *b♭*, or from *g* to *c*, it is necessary to introduce two new notes. As we continue this process of passing on to other keys we introduce more and more new notes. Table Two shows the notes that are needed if we are to play diatonically—that is, without the use of any additional sharp or flat "passing notes"—in the nine keys indicated.

With only these nine keys we see that there are three or four different pitches for each letter of the scale. If the table is extended to include the fifteen keys from *c♭*\ to *c♯*/ there are five different pitches for each letter. That

Table Two—Notes Needed to Play in Several Major Keys

In this table the symbol ♯ means that the frequency is greater in the ratio 135/128, ♭ that the frequency is smaller in the ratio 128/135, ╱ that the frequency is greater in the ratio 81/80, and ╲ that the frequency is smaller in the ratio 80/81.

Key	Notes Needed						
a♭	c╲	d♭╲	e♭	f╲	g╲	a♭	b♭
e♭	c╲	d╲	e♭	f	g╲	a♭	b♭
b♭	c	d╲	e♭	f	g╲	a	b♭
f	c	d╲	e	f	g	a	b♭
c	c	d	e	f	g	a	b
g	c	d	e	f♯	g	a╱	b
d	c♯	d	e╱	f♯	g	a╱	b
a╱	c♯	d	e╱	f♯	g♯	a╱	b╱
e╱	c♯	d♯	e╱	f♯╱	g♯	a╱	b╱

is, inside of each octave there are thirty-five different pitches. Moreover this is on the assumption that we pass from one key to another only through the most closely related major keys, and that we employ no passing notes that lie outside of these diatonic scales. If the modulation is more abrupt, or if we employ passing notes for which we have not yet provided, more notes may be required. For the purposes of modern music the number of different pitches needed becomes very unwieldy. We should like to modify the scale in some way that will reduce the number of different pitches and yet offend the ear as little as possible. This modification of the just scale is known as *temperament*.

Before considering how the temperament is accomplished it will be worth while to point out that if free modulation through all keys is to be possible some form of temperament is necessary. Suppose that we begin playing in the key of *c* and then modulate to *g*, then to *d,* and so on, always passing into the major key which has for its key note the fifth of the preceding key. Thus each new key note is a fifth above the preceding one, and in order to keep in the same general range of pitches we pass downward an octave whenever it becomes desirable. If x represents the number of fifths upward, and y the number of octaves downward, a precise return to the original pitch would require that the equation

$$\left(\frac{3}{2}\right)^x \cdot \left(\frac{1}{2}\right)^y = 1$$

should be true for some choice of x and y as whole numbers. Since such a choice is impossible it follows that no number of fifths upward and octaves downward can ever lead to a return to the precise pitch at which we started. Some form of temperament is necessary.

Question 60. Can you prove that the above equation is not satisfied by any whole numbers?

Question 61. We cannot go far in the study of musical scales without meeting other ratios beside those already mentioned. One of these is 25/24. Can this ratio be represented by any combination of the symbols used in Table Two?

* **Question 62.** We have the notes needed to play in the key of c major, and we wish to play in the key of a major, where a is the a that we already have in the key of c. What additional notes are needed? How are these additional notes to be represented in terms of the symbols used in Table Two? Does it look to you as if these notes would be found in the extended table that runs from the key of $c\flat\backslash$ to that of $c\sharp\diagup$? Do you see any simple way of answering this question without going through calculations like those you made when answering Question 58?

26. Systems of Temperament.—Various systems of temperament have been suggested, but only two have had any extended use. These two are the Meantone Temperament and the Equal Temperament.

In the meantone system the major thirds are kept pure, and the note which lies between the notes of each major third is put half way between them. For instance, in the key of c each of the thirds c-e, f-a, g-b is adjusted to have frequencies in the ratio of $4:5$; d is put half way between c and e, g half way between f and a, a half way between g and b; and the intervals e-f and b-c are made equal to each other and of such size as to fill out an octave.

On this basis let us find the actual frequency ratios. Since e is to vibrate $5/4$ as fast as c, and d is to be half way between c and e, d must vibrate $\sqrt{\frac{5}{4}}$ as fast as c, and e $\sqrt{\frac{5}{4}}$ as fast as d. In this way we find the frequency ratios shown in (6) except for e-f and b-c. Since (6) covers one octave, the product of all these frequency ratios

$$c \quad d \quad e \quad f \quad g \quad a \quad b \quad c$$

$$\sqrt{\frac{5}{4}} \; \sqrt{\frac{5}{4}} \; x \quad \sqrt{\frac{5}{4}} \; \sqrt{\frac{5}{4}} \; \sqrt{\frac{5}{4}} \quad x \tag{6}$$

must be 2, and it follows that x is close to 1.070. A frequency ratio $\sqrt{\frac{5}{4}}$ is equivalent to about 193.2 cents, and 1.070 to about 117.1 cents. The meantone temperament makes c-d, f-g, and a-b half a comma too small, d-e and g-a half a comma too large, and e-f and b-c about five cents too large.

When the meantone temperament is used, the number of additional notes needed in order to modulate into other keys is not as great as when the scale is just. The reason is seen by comparing (6) with (4). In (4) there are intervals of three different sizes, but in (6) there are only two. If we start with the meantone notes for the key of c, and set out to build up the meantone key of g, we see from (6) that only one note need be changed. We need to interchange the frequency ratios of e-f and f-g, and to accomplish this we introduce instead of f a new note which we shall call $f\sharp$.[38]

---

[38] As employed here the sympols $\sharp$ and $\flat$ do not have precisely the same meaning as in Table Two. See Question 63.

Similarly to pass from the key of *c* to that of *f* we need only one new note. We need to interchange the frequency ratios for *a-b* and *b-c*, and to accomplish this we introduce instead of *b* a new note which we shall call *b*♭.

If we make out in this way a table similar to Table Two, we find that we shall be able to play in the fifteen major keys from *c*♭ to *c*♯ if for each letter of the scale we have three different pitches—the natural note, its sharp, and its flat. We have not gone into keys so distant as to introduce any double sharps or double flats, but we have a considerable range of keys. The octave now includes twenty-one different pitches instead of the thirty-five that are needed under similar circumstances for the just scale.

But not many keyboard instruments have been built with as many as twenty-one different notes in an octave. Each octave has usually contained only the twelve notes to which we are accustomed on pianos and organs. If there is an *f*♯ there is no place for a separate *g*♭, if there is a *b*♭ there is no place for a separate *a*♯, and so on. If an organ in the meantone temperament had a *g*♯ and the organist wanted to play *a*♭-*c*-*e*♭, he had to play *g*♯-*c*-*e*♭ instead. The *g*♯ in the meantone temperament was more than forty cents flatter than the *a*♭, and the effect from *g*♯-*c*-*e*♭ was so horrible that such combinations were known as "wolves" and were avoided.[39]

Occasionally instruments were built in which one or more of the black digitals were divided into two—the front part playing one note, and the back part another. But even this did not provide the desired freedom of modulation. In spite of this drawback the meantone temperament was largely used until about the middle of the nineteenth century. Ellis[40] states that at the Great Exhibition

---

[39] "It is best for the wolf to remain in the wood with its abominable howling, and not disturb our *harmonicas concordantias*." Praetorius, quoted by Helmholtz, *Sensations of Tone*, 4th Eng. ed., Longmans Green, p. 321.

[40] Helmholtz, *Sensations of Tone*, 4th Eng. ed., p. 434.

of 1851 all the English organs were tuned in the meantone system, and he suggests that if the meantone temperament had been carried out to twenty-seven notes in an octave it would probably still be in use.

Question 63. In the meantone temperament how do the frequency ratios represented by ♯ and ♭ compare with the meanings of these symbols in Table Two on p. 65?

Question 64. In the meantone temperament the interval from c to d is how many times as large as the interval from e to f? How does this compare with the answer to Question 54?

Question 65. In the meantone temperament how do the minor thirds compare with those in the just scale? How do the fourths compare? How do the fifths compare?

The equal temperament is the one that is now in general use. In it the octave is divided into twelve equal parts. Two of these parts are taken for a whole step, and one for a half step. Thus each whole step is 200 cents, and each half step is 100 cents. To find the frequency ratios let us call the ratio for a half step x. Then since the octave contains twelve equal half steps, x^{12} must be 2. Consequently $x = \sqrt[12]{2}$, which is about 1.0595. It follows that d vibrates 1.0595×1.0595 as fast as c, e vibrates 1.0595×1.0595 as fast as d, f vibrates 1.0595 as fast as e. A single note is used for both $c\sharp$ and $d\flat$, another for both $d\sharp$ and $e\flat$, and so on.

This very simple method of dividing up the octave does not provide a scale in which the concords are as smooth as in the meantone temperament, but it is really remarkable that the equally tempered scale comes as near to the just scale as it does.

Question 66. How do the sizes of the minor thirds, major thirds, fourths, and fifths in the equal temperament compare with the corresponding intervals in the just scale?

A number of other systems of tempering the scale have

been devised. One of the simplest is due to Woolhouse,[41] who divided the octave into nineteen equal parts. He used one note for both $e\sharp$ and $f\flat$, and one for both $b\sharp$ and $c\flat$, but aside from these two cases the intervals c-$c\sharp$-$d\flat$-d-$d\sharp$-$e\flat$-e ···· were all equal. Thus the successive intervals in his major scale contained 3,3,2,3,3,3,2 nineteenths of an octave. This gave a major third of about 379 cents instead of 386, and a fifth of about 695 cents instead of 702.

A more complicated division of the octave was suggested many years ago by Mercator,[42] in whose system the octave is divided into fifty-three equal parts. The successive intervals of the major scale contain 9,8,5,9,8,9,5 of these fifty-thirds of an octave. This scale is often connected with the name of Bosanquet[43] who devised a "generalized keyboard" based on this division of the octave.

Fig. 16 shows how the Woolhouse, meantone, and equal scales compare with the just scale. Bosanquet's scale is so close to the just scale that the difference between them would hardly be perceptible in this diagram.

Question 67. In Bosanquet's scale how many cents are there in a major third? How many in a perfect fifth?

27. Opinions Regarding Tempered Scales.—A number of instruments have been so tuned as to make it possible to hear a just scale or some scale much closer to it than is provided by equal temperament.[44] It may be of interest

[41] Wesley S. B. Woolhouse, *Essay on Musical Intervals, Harmonics, and the Temperament of the Musical Scale* (1835), p. 50. This same division of the octave has been suggested independently by Joseph Würschmidt, Neue Musikzeitung, 42, 215 (1921).

[42] Nicolaus Mercator (about 1630-1687), Danish mathematician, astronomer, and engineer. Joseph Yasser, in his book *A Theory of Evolving Tonality*, p. 31, states that the manuscript in which Mercator made this suggestion was probably never published, but that Mercator's system was described in a book by William Holder published in 1694.

[43] R. H. M. Bosanquet, *An Elementary Treatise on Musical Intervals and Temperament* (1875), pp. 19, 51.

[44] For a specially tuned reed organ see Appendix Two. See also Helm-

to collect here the opinions of a few authors with regard to the just scale and the equally tempered scale.

"The subject of just intonation is fatally fascinating to people whose mathematical insight has not attained to the notion of approximation." [45]

"The tempered scale has already passed the limit of its usefulness." [46]

"A diatonic passage played on an instrument tuned in this way produces an effect which is a revelation of smooth-

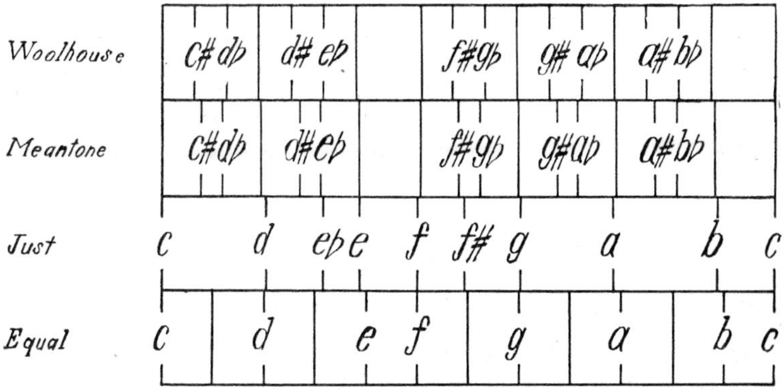

Woolhouse	$c\sharp d\flat$	$d\sharp e\flat$		$f\sharp g\flat$	$g\sharp a\flat$	$a\sharp b\flat$	
Meantone	$c\sharp d\flat$	$d\sharp e\flat$		$f\sharp g\flat$	$g\sharp a\flat$	$a\sharp b\flat$	
Just	c	d	$e\flat e$	f $f\sharp$ g	a	b	c
Equal	c	d	e f	g	a	b c	

FIG. 16.—Comparison of Three Tempered Scales With the Just Scale.

ness to any one hearing it for the first time. . . . If, after listening for some time to the pure chord, the tempered chord is sounded, it is so manifestly out of tune that the listener can only wonder that human beings can be found to tolerate it." [47]

"Whoever has heard one of the few experimental key-

holtz, *Sensations of Tone,* 4th Eng. ed., pp. 316-320, 424-426, 466-483; W. H. Stone, *Elementary Lessons on Sound* (1908), pp. 147-157.

[45] Donald Francis Tovey, Art. HARMONY, in Encycl. Brit. 11 (ed. 14, 1929).

[46] John Redfield, *Music a Science and an Art,* Knopf (1928), p. 184.

[47] Sir Percy C. Buck, *Acoustics for Musicians,* The Oxford University Press (1918), p. 91.

board instruments that have been constructed to play in pure intonation has been entranced with the sweetness of music thus played." [48]

"It must not be imagined that the difference between tempered and just intonation is a mere mathematical subtilty without any practical value. That this difference is really very striking even to unmusical ears, is shewn immediately by actual experiments with properly tuned instruments. And that the early musicians, who were still accustomed to the perfect intervals of vocal music, which was then most carefully practiced, felt the same, is immediately seen by a glance at the musical writings of the latter half of the seventeenth and the earlier half of the eighteenth centuries, at which time there was much discussion about the introduction of different kinds of temperament, and one new method after another was invented and rejected. . . .

"In rapid passages, with a soft quality and moderate intensity of tone, the evils of tempered intonation are but little apparent. Now, almost all instrumental music is designed for rapid movement, and this forms its essential advantage over vocal music. We might, indeed, raise the question whether instrumental music had not rather been forced into rapidity of movement by this very tempered intonation, which did not allow us to feel the full harmoniousness of slow chords to the same extent as is possible from well-trained singers. . . .

"On the other hand, for the harsher stops on the organ, as the mixture and reed stops, the deficiencies of equal temperament are extremely striking. It is considered inevitable that when the mixture stops are played with full chords an awful din must ensue, and organists have submitted to their fate. . . .

[48] William Braid White, *Modern Piano Tuning and Allied Arts*, Bill Brothers (1917), p. 81.

"Whoever has heard the difference between justly-intoned and tempered chords, can feel no doubt that it would be the greatest possible gain for a large organ to omit half its stops . . . and double the number of tones in the Octave, so as to be able, by means of suitable stops, to play correctly in all keys." [49]

"Equal temperament, or what tuners give us for it (a very different thing, generally), has indeed become a temporary necessity. . . . But the discoveries of Helmholtz have sounded the knell of equal temperament, which must henceforth be recognized as a theoretical mistake and a practical makeshift—a good servant dismissed for becoming a bad master, and now merely retaining office till his successor is installed. The human voice, the violin, and the trombone do not require it, and will enable the composer to study the wondrous wealth of just intonation as a means of musical expression, when the laws of just modulation have been laid down. . . . At any rate just intonation, even upon a large scale, is immediately possible. And if I long for the time of its adoption in the interests of the listener, still more do I long for it in the interests of the composer. What he has done of late years with the rough-and-ready tool of equal temperament is a glorious presage of what he will do in the future with the delicate instrument which acoustical science puts into his hands." [50]

It is now more than half a century since Ellis wrote the words last quoted. The equal temperament is still the one that is almost universally employed on keyboard instruments, and there is little evidence that it is likely to be displaced very soon. As suggested by Helmholtz, it is probably on the organ, especially when playing loudly and with many stops drawn, that the faults of the equal tem-

[49] Helmholtz, *Sensations of Tone,* 4th Eng. ed., Longmans Green, pp. 320, 323.
[50] Alexander J. Ellis, Musical Association (London) Proc. I, 163 (1875).

perament are most obvious. It is also doubtless true that
string quartets and choirs that usually sing without accompaniment often give us music which is not equally tempered. There is however some question as to whether
the scales they employ are a closer approach to just intonation.

Before leaving this subject it may be worth while to
add one more opinion regarding equal temperament. A
recent writer says he "believes that the practice of Equal
Temperament not only does not spoil but refines the musical ear which is compelled to develop its adaptability and
thus increases its range of physiologically detectable tones
and sonorities in general. Equal Temperament serves the
ear as a useful stumbling block, which broadens and en-
riches its experience, just as in ordinary life obstacles (and
not their absence) add to our experience, thereby teaching
us how to live." [51]

28. **Tuning in Equal Temperament.**—When tuning a
piano or organ in the equal temperament the first step is to
tune the notes in some one octave near the middle of the
scale. The method of "setting the temperament" or "lay-
ing the bearings" in this octave depends on the beats from
certain partial tones. The second, third, fourth, fifth, and
sixth partials of a piano string vibrate almost exactly two,
three, four, five, and six times as rapidly as the fundamental, and the same is true of most organ pipes. So if the
interval from c to the g above it is not extremely close to a
just fifth the third partial of c will beat with the second
partial of g. And if the interval from c to the f above it
is not extremely close to a just fourth the fourth partial
of c will beat with the third of f. It is the beats from
tempered fourths and fifths that are principally used in
tuning. By long practice the tuner has accustomed himself

[51] Joseph Yasser, *A Theory of Evolving Tonality*, American Library of
Musicology (1932), p. 168.

to these beats, so that he knows fairly well how rapidly they come when the fourth or fifth is equally tempered.

The exact procedure differs somewhat with different tuners, but as a rule if the tuner has gone upward to the last note he tuned he goes downward to the next, upward to the next, downward to the next, and so on—the steps upward being fifths and the steps downward fourths, or else the steps upward being fourths and the steps downward fifths. For instance, he may first tune middle *c,* then the *g* above it, then the *d* below that *g,* then the *a* above the *d,* and keep on in this way until he has tuned *c-g-d-a-e-b-f♯.* If he continued upward from *f♯* to *c♯* he would be outside of the chosen octave. He may now come downward a fourth to *c♯,* and then continue the series *c♯-g♯-d♯-a♯-e♯-b♯.* At each step he has tuned until the beats from the note last tuned and the note being tuned practically disappeared, and then he has flatted the note until the beats came at the proper rate. This has made the fifths a trifle smaller than just fifths, and the fourths a trifle larger. If he has been successful in setting the temperament the *b♯* will now be an octave above middle *c,* and will not beat with it. If there are appreciable beats the process must be repeated. After the temperament has been satisfactorily set the rest of the instrument is tuned by octaves and unisons.

Question 68. In the equal temperament how does the frequency of the beats from the fourth c_3-f_3 compare with the frequency of those from the fifth f_3-c_4?

Question 69. In the equal temperament how does the frequency of the beats from the fifth c_3-g_3 compare with the frequency of those from the fifth f_3-c_4?

Question 70. Some tuners set the temperament by proceeding as indicated in the text until they reach *f♯,* and then tuning the upper c and continuing with *c-f-a♯-d♯-g♯-c♯-f♯.* What advantage does this plan have over that outlined in the text?

Question 71. Some tuners set the temperament by using major thirds and minor thirds instead of fifths and fourths. An equally tempered major third is 400 cents, and an equally tempered minor third is 300 cents. If the frequency of e_3 is about 325 cycles/sec. how many beats per second should be heard from the equally tempered major third c_3–e_3? How many from the equally tempered minor third $c\sharp_3$–e_3?

CHAPTER SIX

TRANSMISSION OF SOUND

29. Running Waves on Strings.—We have seen that sounds are usually brought to us by waves of compression and rarefaction that travel through air. Pianos, violins, and various other musical instruments produce the compressions and rarefactions in the air with the aid of strings. The waves that travel along these strings are easier to understand than the waves of compression and rarefaction in the air, and we shall consider a few matters connected with waves on strings before turning to a fuller study of sound waves in air.

If one end of a rope is shaken waves run along the rope, and in these waves each small part of the rope moves back and forth across the direction in which the waves travel. In air waves the motion is not across the direction in which the waves travel but is in that direction. We distinguish these two types of waves by speaking of the former as *transverse* or *flexural,* and of the latter as *longitudinal* or *compressional.*

Let us begin our study of transverse waves by imagining an extremely long rope which is very flexible and is so far from the earth that there is no need of supporting it in any way. Let the rope be stretched so that it is straight, and let it be lying in a direction which we may call horizontal. If the end A (Fig. 17) is moved up and down with simple harmonic motion the waves that travel off to the right are of a type which we shall call *simple harmonic waves.*

If the curves in Fig. 17 are compared with that in Fig. 10 it will be seen that although their shape is the same their significance is different. Each of the curves in Fig. 17 shows the positions of different particles at a single instant, whereas the curve in Fig. 10 shows the position of a single particle at different instants. Each of the curves in Fig. 17 has the characteristic *wave form* for simple harmonic waves,

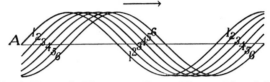

FIG. 17.—Simple Harmonic Waves on a Rope. The particles of the rope are moving with simple harmonic motion up and down, and the waves are traveling to the right. At some chosen instant curve 1 shows the shape of the rope, at an instant a trifle later the shape is shown by curve 2, and at later instants by curves 3, 4, 5, 6.

and the curve in Fig. 10 is the corresponding *vibration curve* for a chosen particle.

Question 72. Select any one of the wave forms in Fig. 17, and compare it in the following ways with the corresponding vibration curve. At what points on each curve are the particles at rest? Moving most rapidly? How do the directions of motion compare?

Question 73. In most types of waves the motions of the particles are not simple harmonic but are more complicated. In such types do you expect the wave form and the vibration curve to have the same shape?

In the case of the following wave form how should you find out whether they have the same shape?

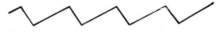

There is an important relation between the speed with which a wave form travels and the frequency with which the particles of the medium oscillate. To get this relation let us introduce the term *wave length* to mean the distance from one point on the wave form to the corresponding point in the next wave. For instance, in Fig. 18 each of the distances marked λ is a wave length. At the instant for which the figure is drawn we see that the particle A is in its highest position. As the wave travels onward A moves alternately downward and upward, and while the wave travels one wave length A describes one complete cycle. If A describes N cycles in one second it follows that the wave travels a distance $N\lambda$ during the second. That is,

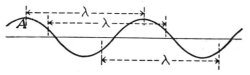

FIG. 18.—Meaning of the Term *Wave Length.*

if c stands for the speed with which the waves travel, we have

$$c = N\lambda. \tag{7}$$

30. **Standing Waves on Strings.**—Suppose that on our long rope there are two trains of simple harmonic waves, just alike except that one train is traveling toward the right and the other with the same speed toward the left. Imagine the two trains represented by simple harmonic wave forms drawn on two transparent pieces of paper. If one paper is laid on the other so that the wave forms coincide, and then the two papers are moved steadily sideways in opposite directions, the sum of the heights of the two curves will give the resultant. Fig. 19 may make this more clear. When the waves coincide in the position shown by the dashed curve the particle at A is displaced upward a distance AB by each train, and so the displacement produced by both is AC, twice as great as AB. At the same time the particle at N is not displaced by either train. When the waves have moved to the positions shown by the dotted curves the particle at A has a displacement somewhat smaller than before. At the same time the particle at N would be displaced upward to M_1 by the train that is moving toward the right, and downward an equal distance to M_2

by the train that is moving toward the left. The resultant of these two displacements is no displacement at all.

At A the two trains are in phase and reinforce each other, whereas at N their phases are opposite and they interfere with each other.

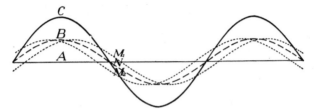

FIG. 19.—The Production of Standing Waves. The dashed curve represents two simple harmonic wave forms which are just alike except that one is traveling to the right and the other to the left. At the instant in question the wave forms coincide, and the full curve represents their resultant. A short time later the wave trains have advanced to the positions shown by the dotted curves, and the resultant is now like the full curve except that its height is less.

A similar study for other particles shows that the shape assumed by the rope changes as indicated in Fig. 20. At

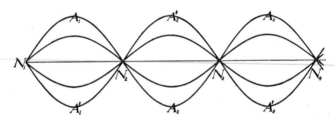

FIG. 20.—Standing Waves. The curve passes alternately from the position $N_1A_1N_2A_2N_3A_3$ . . . to the position with the primed A's and back again. The nodes are at the positions marked with N's.

the *nodes* N there is practically no motion. At the *antinodes* or *loops*, half way between the nodes, the motion is greatest. The resultant waves in Fig. 20 are known as *standing waves* or *stationary waves*, because the resultant form does not travel, as it does in the *running waves* which combine to produce the standing waves.

Question 74. How does the distance from one node to the next compare with the wave length?

Question 75. In running waves how do the phases of the particles, at any given instant, differ from point to point along the wave form? How do they differ in standing waves?

31. Waves in Air.—We turn now to sound waves in air. In Fig. 21 AB is a long tube which extends far beyond B, P is a piston that fits it snugly, and L is a thin layer of the air in the tube. If the piston moves back and forth with simple harmonic motion it causes compressions and rarefactions that travel through the air toward B, and as a consequence L moves back and forth with simple harmonic motion.

We shall find it convenient to draw a vibration curve to represent the motion of L. The vibration curve in Fig. 10 represented an up and down motion, and the distance of the curve above or below the axis represented the displace-

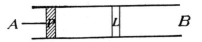

Fig. 21.—Long Tube in Which Air Waves Are Set Up by the Motion of the Piston P.

ment of the particle above or below its position of equilibrium. Now L is not moving up and down, but we may nevertheless represent its motion by a curve like that in Fig. 10 if we agree that distance of the curve above the axis shall stand for the displacement of L to the right of the equilibrium position, and that distance of the curve below the axis shall stand for the displacement of L to the left of the equilibrium position. With this convention a single vibration curve may represent either transverse or longitudinal vibration.

We may imagine the air in our tube divided into a great many thin layers like L. If P is moving with simple harmonic motion, and has been doing so for a long time, each of these layers is also moving with simple harmonic motion. All the layers have the same period and practically the same amplitude, but their phases differ—that is, the vibration curves for the different layers are practically alike except that they are displaced sideways with respect to each other.

With the aid of our convention that back and forth displacements are to be represented by distances up and down, we can apply to sound waves in air some of the results that we have obtained for transverse waves on strings. We can draw curves to represent wave forms, we can deal with both running waves and standing waves, and we see that the equation (7) applies to compressional waves as well as to flexural waves.

Question 76. How is Fig. 17 to be interpreted when it represents compressional waves in air instead of flexural waves on a rope?

Question 77. Let one of the curves in Fig. 17 represent compressional waves in air. At what points is the air at rest? Moving most rapidly? In what direction is it moving? At what points are the particles of air crowded most closely together? At what points are they spread farthest apart?

Question 78. How are Figs. 19 and 20 to be interpreted when they represent compressional waves in air?

Question 79. What is your guess as to the wave length of the sounds that come from a man's mouth when he speaks? If the man's voice is pitched in the neighborhood of 120 cycles/sec., is the wave length larger or smaller than you guessed?

Question 80. The lowest and highest pitches that can be heard have frequencies of about 20 and 20,000 cycles/sec. When these sounds travel in air what are their wave lengths?

32. Distribution of Pressure.—Let us make use of the answers to Questions 76, 77, and 78 to see how the pressure is distributed in simple harmonic compressional waves. For

the running waves represented in Fig. 22 the full curve is the wave form, and the waves are traveling toward the right. The layers at *A, C, E, G* are in their equilibrium positions, the layers between *A* and *C* and between *E* and *G* are displaced to the right, and the layers between *C* and *E* are displaced to the left. The greatest crowding of the layers occurs at *C* and *G*, and the greatest spreading apart at *A* and *E*. That is, *C* and *G* are in the midst of compressions, and *A* and *E* are in the midst of rarefactions. Now the layers *C* and *G* are moving most rapidly forward, and the layers at *A* and *E* most rapidly backward. So we have

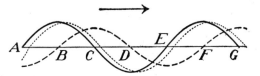

Fɪɢ. 22.—Distribution of Pressure in Simple Harmonic Running Waves. The full curve represents the wave form at some chosen instant. The dotted curve represents it a short time later. The dashed curve shows the distribution of pressure.

arrived at the result stated in Art. 8 that in the compressions the layers are moving forward, and in the rarefactions they are moving backward.

If we choose to represent increased pressures by distances above the axis, and diminished pressures by distances below the axis, we can draw a curve that shows how the pressure is distributed. For the simple harmonic waves in Fig. 22 this curve turns out to be like the wave form except that it is a quarter of a wave length to the right of it. The pressure at any point changes while the waves are passing, and the total change in pressure at any point is the same as that at any other point.[52]

[52] When waves spread outward in all directions they cease to be simple harmonic, so that the above statement is no longer true. In this case the change in pressure is less at greater distances from the source.

In standing waves the situation is very different. Although it is true that at any instant the distribution of pressure is similar to that in running waves, it is no longer true that the total change in pressure at one point is as large as that at all other points. In fact, Questions 82 and 83 will lead us to two important results: First, the pressure experiences its greatest change at nodes, where the air has practically no motion at all, whereas at antinodes, where there is the greatest movement of the air, there is hardly any change in pressure; and, second, the pressure at one node is greatest at the instant when it is least at the node next to it.

Question 81. If the waves in Fig. 22 were traveling to the left, would the pressure curve be a quarter wave length to the right of the wave form or a quarter wave length to the left of it?

Question 82. Let Fig. 20 apply to compressional waves in air. How does the pressure at N_1 compare with that at N_2? How does the pressure half way between N_1 and N_2 compare with that half way between N_2 and N_3? How does the phase of a layer a short distance to the right of N_1 compare with that of a layer a short distance to the left of N_2? To the right of N_2?

33. Intensity of Sound.—It is well known that sound waves, light waves, and radio waves carry energy, and that in the case of sound waves the loudness is in some way connected with this flow of energy. In order to have a measure of the rate at which the energy is transferred it is customary to consider unit area of a surface that lies perpendicular to the direction in which the waves are traveling. Then the *intensity* of the wave train is measured by the amount of energy that crosses this unit area in a unit of time. For instance, if sound waves are carrying 20 ergs across one square centimeter in each second, this quantity is a measure of the intensity of the sound waves. In a rough way we may say that the greater the intensity of the sound the louder it is. (The relationship between loudness and intensity will be considered more fully in Chapter Nine.

If a small source is producing a steady sound which spreads uniformly in all directions, it is easy to find out how the intensity differs at different distances. Suppose that the source gives out E ergs in each second. If we draw a sphere with the source at its center the intensity of the sound will be the same at all points on the surface of the sphere. If r is the radius of the sphere the area of its surface is $4\pi r^2$. So if none of the sound energy is lost as it passes outward, and if I stands for the intensity of the sound at the surface of the sphere, we have

$$I = \frac{E}{4\pi r^2}. \qquad (8)$$

This equation tells us that the intensity of the sound is inversely proportional to the square of the distance from the source.

Question 83. If the intensity of sound is 20 ergs/cm.^{2} sec. at a distance of 10 ft. from a singer what is the intensity at a distance of 100 ft.?

If the answer to Question 83 is found by using Eq. (8) it is altogether probable that actual measurement would show the result to be considerably in error. This is principally because (8) assumes that the sound spreads out uniformly in all directions, and this assumption is one that it is almost impossible to realize in practice. A source is never very far from surfaces that reflect and absorb part of the sound. If the singer is in a hall the walls and ceiling reflect a large amount of sound, and so prevent it from dying away to the extent that (8) indicates.

If sound waves travel in a tube that has smooth hard walls and a uniform cross section there is no opportunity for the waves to spread out as they travel, and there is very little decrease in the intensity of the sound. It is this fact, of course, that is put to use in speaking tubes.

Question 84. If sound travels along a tube that changes abruptly in diameter there is some reflection where the change in size occurs. If, however, the change in diameter is gradual most of the energy is transmitted. The diameter of one part of a certain tube is 6 inches, and of another part is 2 inches. The two parts are joined by a long connector that flares gradually. If sound travels through this tube how does the intensity in the 2-inch part compare with that in the 6-inch part?

34. Reflection of Sound.—It is well known that echoes are due to sound which is reflected from some distant surface. If the original sound is much prolonged, or if the reflecting surface is so near that the reflected sound returns very quickly, no separate echo is heard. But if the original sound is produced suddenly and is quickly over, and if the reflecting surface is far enough away, an echo may be heard. If there are several reflecting surfaces the sound may be sent from one to another in such a way as to give rise to multiple echoes.[53]

[53] "One of the most remarkable multiple echoes ever known was one formerly heard in the Chateau of Simonetta, near Milan. According to Father Kircher, a sound was here reflected no less than forty times. An echo in Woodstock Park, in England, repeats a sound seventeen times during the day, and twenty times at night. All European travelers are familiar with the celebrated echoes at the Gap of Dunloe, at Killarney, and that which is heard between Bingen and Coblentz, where the waters of the Nahe flow into the Rhine. The most remarkable echoes I know of in this country are found in the cañons of the Rocky Mountains. These deep chasms, as one might imagine by reason of their precipitous and oftentimes parallel cliffs are particularly well adapted to reflecting sound and to furnishing echoes of all kinds. I have also heard in the Grand Cañon of the Colorado River, in Arizona, some most extraordinary echoes, comparable, I think, with any that are to be heard elsewhere."

J. A. Zahm, *Sound and Music,* McClurg (1900), p. 120.

"Visitors to Killarney will remember the fine echo in the Gap of Donloe. When a trumpet is sounded in the proper place in the Gap, the sonorous waves reach the ear in succession after one, two, three, or more reflections from the adjacent cliffs, and thus die away in the sweetest cadences. There is a deep *cul-de-sac,* called the Ochsenthal, formed by the great cliffs of the

Question 85. If you clap your hands twice with an interval of a fifth of a second between the claps, how far from a reflecting wall must you be in order to hear the four sounds—first the two original and then the two reflected—follow each other at equally spaced intervals?

If two smooth parallel walls are not too far apart, any sudden sound produced between them is reflected back and forth and may reach an observer between the walls at such regular and frequent intervals as to produce a note of fairly definite pitch. Similarly, if a sudden sound is made at a sufficient distance in front of a grandstand the echoes from the successive risers may reach an observer one after another and give a more or less definite note.

Question 86. If the walls of a corridor are two meters apart, and a man standing half way between them claps his hands, what is the frequency of the note that he hears? How does the pitch of the note differ if he is not half way between the walls? How would the effect differ if the corridor were only one meter wide?

Question 87. In a certain grandstand the distance from one riser back to the next is 70 cm. If a man stands in front of this grandstand and claps his hands, what is the frequency of the note that comes back to him?

35. Whispering Galleries.—If a reflecting surface is properly shaped it may cause the sound that spreads out

Engelhörner, near Rosenlaui, in Switzerland, where the echoes warble in a wonderful manner. The sound of the Alpine horn, echoed from the rocks of the Wetterhorn or the Jungfrau, is in the first instance heard roughly. But by successive reflections the notes are rendered more soft and flute-like, the gradual diminution of intensity giving the impression that the source of sound is retreating farther and farther into the solitudes of ice and snow."
John Tyndall, *Sound,* Appleton, ed. 3 (1876), p. 47.

An interesting multiple echo is found at Echo Bridge over the Charles River at Newton Upper Falls, Massachusetts. Just beneath the arch of the bridge there is a platform which is easily accessible. If an observer stands on this platform and claps his hands the echo comes back to him about a dozen times before it dies out. It may be that the sound is focused in a rough way by the inner surface of the arch, and so reflected back and forth from one side of the river to the other.

from one point to ~~converge to a~~ focus at another point some
distance away.   The sea wall built at Galveston after the
disastrous hurricane and flood of 1900 focuses sound in this
way.   A vertical section through the wall is an arc of a
parabola, and a ladder rises from the beach to the top of
the wall.   "Though at low tide a person ascending the ladder may be several hundred feet from the water, the roar
of the surf when his ear reaches the focus is greater than
when actually at the water's edge." [54]

A similar focusing action is in considerable part the ex-
planation of the whispering galleries in the Hall of Statues
in the Capitol at Washington, in the Mormon Tabernacle at
Salt Lake City, in the Cathedral of Girgenti in Sicily, in the
Church of Saint John Lateran in Rome, in the Salle des
Cariatides in the Louvre in Paris, and in Salle Echo in the
Conservatoire des Arts et Métiers in Paris.[55]

A simple focusing of the sound does not appear to be
adequate to explain the whispering galleries in Saint Paul's
Cathedral in London, the State Capitol at Jefferson City,
Missouri, and the whispering galleries in certain buildings
in India.[56]   In each of these cases there is a gallery with a
dome above it.   With regard to St. Paul's Rayleigh says,
"The abnormal loudness with which a whisper is heard is
not confined to the position diametrically opposite to that

[54] Leigh F. J. Zerbee, Scientific American, 113, 235 (1915).

[55] On these and the whispering gallery at St. Paul's in London and the Ear
of Dionysius in Sicily see a very interesting article by Wallace C. Sabine,
Collected Papers on Acoustics (1922), pp. 255-276.

[56] In addition to the reference in footnote 55 see Rayleigh, Theory of
Sound, ed. 2, vol. 2 (1896), art. 287; Phil. Mag. 20, 1001 (1910); 27, 100
(1914); Roy. Inst. Proc. (Jan. 15, 1904) or Sci. Papers of Lord Rayleigh, 5,
p. 171; and C. V. Raman, Indian Assn. Cult. Sci. 7, 159 (1922).

John William Strutt (1842-1919), Third Baron Rayleigh, had extraordinary skill in accomplishing important results with modest equipment.   He
contributed to all branches of physics.   In collaboration with William Ramsay
he discovered the element argon.   He was awarded the Nobel Prize in physics
in 1904.   For nine years he was secretary, and for three years president, of the
Royal Society.   His two volume work The Theory of Sound is a masterpiece.

Regarding Raman see foot note 18 on p. 34.

occupied by the whisperer, and therefore, it would appear, does not depend materially upon the symmetry of the dome. The whisper seems to creep round the gallery horizontally, not necessarily along the shorter arc, but rather along that arc toward which the whisperer faces."

Rayleigh's explanation of the effect may be made more clear with the aid of Fig. 23, where we are not thinking so much of the sound waves themselves as of the directions in which they travel. AB represents part of a circular wall. If the whisperer is at W_1 the part of the sound that leaves him in the direction W_1C_1 is repeatedly reflected along $C_1D_1E_1 \cdots$, and never gets farther from the wall than s.

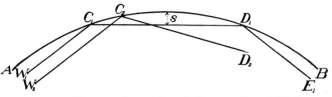

FIG. 23.—The Creeping of Sound Along a Curved Wall.

If the whisperer is at W_2 the sound that leaves him in the same direction as W_1C_1 is reflected along $C_2D_2 \cdots$, and does at times reach a greater distance from the wall than s. Moreover the distance W_2C_2 is greater than W_1C_1; and therefore the sound that reaches the wall along W_2C_2 is fainter than that which reaches it along W_1C_1. So we see that the sound which leaves the whisperer in a given direction stays closer to the wall when the whisperer is close to the wall, and that the sound which travels in the given direction is louder on reaching the wall if the whisperer is close to the wall. For both of these reasons it is to be expected that a sound produced close to the inside surface of a circular wall will tend to travel along the wall, somewhat as if it were in a speaking tube.

Another factor which may possibly contribute slightly to

the whispering gallery effect is the increase of speed with loudness. We know that very loud sounds travel faster than ordinary sounds. Now both reflection at a rigid boundary and the concentrating action that we have just been considering make the whisper somewhat louder close to the wall than a little farther from it. So the part of the sound wave close to the wall travels a little faster than the part farther out in the room. This difference in speed would tend to keep the wave front perpendicular to the wall, and so make the path of the sound follow the curve of the wall.[57]

In water of uniform depth Russell[58] called attention many years ago to a similar effect. If a wave on the surface of water is approaching a vertical wall, and if the crest of the wave makes an angle of more than about 60° with the wall, the inner end of the wave piles up and travels faster than the rest of it. The inner end speeds up until it is perpendicular to the wall, and the wave sweeps along the wall without the formation of any reflected wave. With the bow and stern waves from a bullet Boys[59] has detected a similar effect in air. With light waves Roy[60] has found a slight curving of the path to follow the inside of a curved mirror. With the sound waves from electric sparks Barton and Kilby[61] have been able to show this curving of the path most beautifully, even when the wall curves rather rapidly.

These various cases seem to show clearly that under fa-

[57] The possibility of the wave front turning so as to be always perpendicular to the wall seems to be really assumed in the last two Rayleigh references in footnote 56.

[58] John Scott Russell (1808-1882), British engineer and naval architect, Brit. Assn. Report, p. 358 (1844).

[59] Charles Vernon Boys, Nature, 47, 441 (1893).

[60] Bidhu Bhushan Roy, Ind. Assn. Cult. Sci. Proc. for 1918, p. 75 (1920).

[61] Edwin H. Barton and Walter B. Kilby, Phil. Mag. 24, 728 (1912).

Edwin Henry Barton (1859-1925) was Professor of Experimental Physics at University College, Nottingham. He was the author of a widely known Text-Book on Sound (1908). For nearly twenty years he wrote most of the summaries on sound for Science Abstracts.

vorable circumstances waves of different types may be guided by concave surfaces. But there may still be some question as to whether the intensity of a whisper is sufficient for the somewhat greater intensity close to the wall to be an important factor in actual whispering galleries. Moreover Rayleigh's theory would lead us to expect that the sound would become steadily fainter as we move away from the wall, and that the loudness would not differ greatly when we stay close to the wall and pass around the gallery. It is found that neither of these expectations is correct.[62] As the ear is moved away from the wall the loudness decreases and increases several times before the sound is lost, and there is a similar change in loudness in passing around the gallery.

Very likely Rayleigh's theory is correct as far as it goes, but it will be necessary to modify it in some way. The complete explanation of such a whispering gallery as that in Saint Paul's seems to involve at least one more factor: "There are many circular walls as high, as hard, and as smooth as that in St. Paul's Gallery, but in which the whispering gallery is not to be compared in quality. The rear walls of many semi-circular auditoriums satisfy these conditions without producing parallel results. . . . A feature of the whispering gallery in St. Paul's, contributing not a little to its efficiency, is the inclination of its wall. [The wall slopes slightly inward as it ascends.] . . . The result is that all the sound which passes the quarter point of the gallery, the point half way around between the foci, is brought down to the level of the observer, and, combined with the reflection from the ledge which constitutes the broad seat running entirely around the gallery, confines and intensifies the sound."[63]

[62] C. V. Raman and G. A. Sutherland, Nature, 108, 42 (1921); Roy. Soc. Proc. A100, 424 (1922).
[63] Wallace Clement Sabine, p. 273 in the reference in footnote 55.

Question 88. The diameter of the whispering gallery in St. Paul's is 108 ft. If sound at the wall is to travel around the gallery in the same time as sound 6 inches out from the wall how much faster must it travel?

36. Reflection at the Ends of Tubes.—Various musical instruments consist in part of tubes, and the end of a tube is sometimes closed and sometimes open. If sound coming along a tube arrives at an end which is closed we should expect a large amount of reflection. But if the tube is open we may not feel so sure: Will some of the sound be reflected, or will it all spread outward from the open end? In the present article we shall consider what becomes of the sound when it reaches the end of a tube.

Suppose first that the end of the tube is closed, and suppose that the closing surface is very hard and rigid. As the waves pass along the tube the various layers of air vibrate back and forth, but the layer at the closed end is prevented from vibrating—ahead of it is the rigid wall, and if the layer were to move backward the wall would not follow.

Although this end layer cannot move there is nothing to prevent the pressure in it from changing. When a compression approaches the closed end the layers farther from the end crowd forward against it, and the pressure rises more than it would if the wall were not there. Similarly when a rarefaction follows the compression the layers farther from the end swing backward away from it, and the pressure drops more than it would if the end layer could follow. Thus the pressure at the wall changes to a greater extent than it would if there were no wall. It is this excess in change of pressure that sends the reflected waves traveling backward along the tube.

Since the surface that closes the end of the tube has been assumed very hard and rigid there is practically no loss of energy in the reflection. It follows that the intensity and the amplitude of the waves are the same after reflection as before. The incident waves that travel toward the closed end and the reflected waves that travel back from it combine to form a system of standing waves. Since the air at the closed end cannot have any displacement, it is necessary for the standing waves to take up such a position that a node is situated at the closed end.[64]

Next suppose that the end of the tube is wide open. When a compression is traveling along the tube the walls keep the compressed air from spreading sideways, but at the end of the tube the air is free to expand outward in many directions. So when a compression reaches the end of the tube the compression becomes smaller than it was well back in the tube. Similarly when a rarefaction travels along the tube the walls maintain the rarefaction by keeping the outside air from rushing in, and when the rarefaction reaches the open end it, too, becomes smaller than it was well back in the tube. Thus at an open end the compressions and rarefactions are smaller than they would be if the tube continued farther. This decreased change in pressure sends reflected waves traveling backward along the tube.

The incident waves that travel toward the open end and the reflected waves that return from it combine to form a system of standing waves. But the conditions are not the same as when the end is closed. At a closed end a compression is increased, and so is reflected as a compression. At an open end a compression is decreased and reflected as a rarefaction. These facts are sometimes put briefly by saying that at a closed end the pressure is reflected *without change of phase,* and that at an open end it is reflected *with change of phase.*

At a closed end practically all of the sound is reflected. But at an open end part of it escapes from the tube, so that

[64] This node is of course not a point. It is spread out over the end of the tube, and it would be more accurate to speak of it as a *nodal surface.* We shall meet other cases of nodal surfaces, and also cases of nodal lines.

the reflected waves are less intense than the incident waves which they meet. The incident waves may be regarded as broken up into two component trains which are just alike except that one component has the same intensity as the reflected waves and the other has whatever intensity is left over. The first component combines with the reflected train to form standing waves. The second component carries the part of the energy that spreads outward from the open end of the tube. Such a superposition of standing waves and running waves occurs in many musical instruments.

In a tube with a closed end we have seen that the standing waves adjust themselves to such a position that a node lies at the closed end. In a tube with an open end there is not much change in pressure at the open end, and the standing waves adjust their position so that an antinode lies near the open end. The exact position of the antinode will be considered further in Arts. 53 and 61.

37. **Interference in Tubes.**—We have seen that when two similar trains of waves run through a tube in opposite directions they combine to form standing waves, and that in these standing waves there is interference at certain points and reinforcement at others. Is there any way in which we can produce interference at all points in a considerable length of tube? It would seem that we ought to be able to attain this end if we can cause two similar trains of simple harmonic waves to run through the tube in the same direction, and make the conditions such that one train is half a wave length behind the other. About a century ago John Herschel [65] suggested a method by which this might be accomplished.

Herschel was seeking an explanation of the dark (Fraunhofer) lines in the spectrum of the sun, and it occurred to him that the lines might be due to interference

---

[65] Sir John Frederick William Herschel (1792-1871), English astronomer, Phil. Mag. 3, 401 (1833).

of light waves.   Herschel's explanation of the lines in the
solar spectrum has not been accepted, but an illustration
which he employed has led to an interesting means of
measuring the wave length of sounds.

Herschel's suggestion is this.   Let simple harmonic
waves of sound travel along the tube shown in Fig. 24, and
let the branch C_1 be half a wave length longer than the
branch C_2.   The wave trains in the branches are in phase
with each other where they separate at B, but after they
reunite at D one is half a wave length behind the other.
Consequently the reunited trains are opposite in phase at
all points of DE.   That is, no sound travels on through DE.

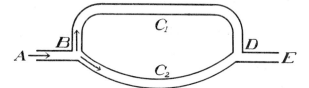

Fig. 24.—One Type of Herschel-Quincke Interference Tube.

With regard to this experiment Herschel says in a footnote, "I ought to observe, that I have not *made* the experiment described in the text, nor am I aware that it has ever
been made; but it is easy to see that it ought to succeed."
A third of a century later Quincke [66] tried the experiment,
and found that it did succeed.   He wrote an interesting
paper on results he had obtained with the apparatus suggested by Herschel, and with some modifications of it.   For
this reason we often speak of the apparatus as a "Herschel-
Quincke interference tube."

Question 89.   In Fig. 24 how does the sound heard at E compare with that at A when C_1 is a whole wave length longer than
C_2?   When the difference is three half wave lengths?   What general statement can be made?

[66] Georg Hermann Quincke (1834-1924), Pogg. An. **128**, 177 (1866).
Quincke taught physics successively at the universities in Berlin, Würzburg,
and Heidelberg.

Question 90. If the length of one of the branches in Fig. 24 is adjustable how might the apparatus be used to measure the wave length of a sound?

Question 91. In Fig. 24 the waves that run in along AB carry energy. When C_1 is half a wave length longer than C_2, so that no waves go along DE, what becomes of this energy?

After the Herschel-Quincke interference tube had been known and used for a good many years G. W. Stewart[67] discovered that the usual explanation of its action is not adequate. It had been generally supposed that the transmitted sound vanished when the difference in the lengths of the branches was any odd number of half wave lengths (Question 89) and that it vanished under no other circumstances. Stewart found that it also vanishes when the sum of the lengths of the branches is a whole number of wave lengths, provided that the difference is not at the same time a whole number of wave lengths. For instance, if the lengths of the branches are respectively 2.6λ and 1.4λ no sound will be transmitted, even though the difference between the lengths of the branches is not an odd number of half wave lengths.

What is the matter with the earlier theory? Why should there be no transmission in the new cases that Stewart has discovered? A clue is to be found in the answer to Question 91. When the difference in the lengths of the paths is not exactly an odd number of half wave lengths the sound that arrives at D (Fig. 24) along the path C_2 divides into three parts. One part goes on along DE, one is reflected in C_2, and the other goes through C_1 toward B. When this last part arrives at B it too divides into three parts, and so on. Similar statements hold for the sound that comes along C_1. The resultant effect at D is made up of the sounds that have come directly along C_1 and C_2, and

[67] George Walter Stewart, Phys. Rev. **31**, 696 (1928). Stewart is Professor of Physics in the State University of Iowa.

also of the sounds that have been one or more times around the circuit. These latter are weaker and weaker because of the loss each time that they pass B or D. The mathematical development by which Stewart reached his result is not sufficiently simple to include here, but Fig. 25 shows how well his observations agree with the predictions of the theory.

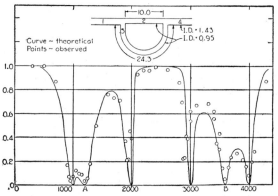

Fig. 25.—Transmission of Sound Through a Herschel-Quincke Interference Tube [Stewart]. Instead of changing the length of one branch and keeping the wave length of the sound the same, Stewart kept the lengths of the branches the same and changed the frequency. The wave lengths can be obtained from the relation $c = N\lambda$. The speed of sound was taken as 343 m/sec. The inset in the upper part of the figure gives the dimensions of the apparatus in centimeters. *I.D.* stands for "inner diameter." According to the usual theory the only frequencies for which no sound should be transmitted are those indicated by A and B. The new theory indicates four additional frequencies at which the transmission should be very small, and the experimental results confirm these new minima.

38. Interference in Wider Spaces.—In most cases the waves are not confined in tubes but are free to spread out in many directions, and the resulting interference patterns may become very complicated. A simple case in which the sound pattern may be easily understood is found in the region around a vibrating tuning fork. In Fig. 26 we are looking at the end of the fork, and P_1P_2 are its prongs. When the prongs move toward each other they compress

the air between them and rarefy that beyond them. This starts compressions traveling outward toward A and A', and rarefactions traveling toward B and B'. When the prongs move away from each other they start rarefactions moving toward A and A', and compressions toward B and B'. These waves of compression and rarefaction spread outward, and along the diagonal lines D they are in opposite phases. Consequently if a tuning fork is struck and then turned around while it is held near the ear, there are four positions in which the sound is heard clearly, separated by four positions in which it is not heard.

A more complicated case is that of an organ pipe sounding steadily in a closed room. The sound is reflected by the

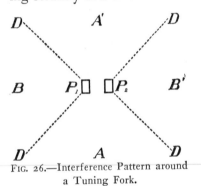

FIG. 26.—Interference Pattern around a Tuning Fork.

walls, floor, and ceiling, and a person moving about in the room may find certain positions where the sound is loud and others where it is fainter. If the pipe is replaced by one of different pitch the pattern may be entirely different. Since the sounds from most organ pipes are complex it is to be expected that the sound

patterns for the different components will be different. As a matter of fact, it is sometimes possible to find positions such that if the head is moved a short distance the pitch that is heard changes—one component being more prominent in one position and another in the other.

Another case, not so easy to understand, is the following.[68] If a person stands near a wall from which the sound

[68] See Nature, 65, 129, 174, 273, 317 (1901-1902); 107, 490, 586, 623, 652 (1921); a paper by Nicolas Savart (1790-1853), brother of Félix, Comptes Rendus, 7, 1068 (1838); a paper by F. A. Schulze, An. der Physik, 49, 683 (1916); and several references given by E. G. Richardson in his book on Sound (1927 and 1935), pp. 59-60.

of a waterfall is reflected he may notice that on moving toward the wall or away from it he hears a soft tone superposed on the splashing and dashing of the fall. As he moves toward the wall the pitch rapidly rises, and as he moves away it falls, sounding somewhat like a faint moaning wind. Similarly when an airplane is overhead a person who bends over so as to bring his head closer to the ground may notice a pitch which rises as he bends downward and falls as he rises again.

How are these changes in pitch to be explained? If two vibrations are sufficient to give a sense of pitch we might suppose that when the distance to the reflecting surface is small the reflected sound reaches the ear at a shorter interval after the direct sound and so gives rise to a higher pitch. It is however doubtful whether two waves are sufficient to give any definite impression of pitch.

If we think of the noise as a very complex one, made up of many simple tones, it might seem that the incident sound and the reflected sound set up a complicated pattern in which there are positions where certain components are strengthened and others weakened. One trouble with this point of view is that the compressions and rarefactions in the noise from the waterfall are so irregular that it is not particularly helpful to regard the noise as containing any simple harmonic components at all.

In front of the wall there is of course a rapidly shifting sound pattern which is made up of the incident sound and the reflected sound, and in this pattern the reflection in some way emphasizes or produces the pitch that is observed. Suppose that two compressions happen to follow each other at such an interval that the second compression reaches the ear with the reflection of the first. Then the reflection of the second will follow after an equal interval, so that instead of two compressions we get three. If there are frequent occasions when we get three—always following each other at the same rate—this may have something to do with our perceiving the tone.

It is also possible that in some situations the head of the observer may reflect sufficient sound to give rise to a number of back and forth reflections between the head and the wall, and therefore to a tone similar to that obtained from clapping hands in a corridor between parallel walls.

Question 92. If one of the prongs of the tuning fork in Fig. 26 has a stiff paper tube slipped over it so as not to touch the prong, how should you expect the sound pattern to be affected? Would the sound pattern probably be affected in the same way by a large sheet of cardboard put in the position AA'?

Question 93. An "open" organ pipe has an opening at the mouth and another at the top of the pipe. If compressions come from both openings at the same time what sort of a sound pattern should you expect around the pipe?

Question 94. If an observer walks along a railroad platform while steam is escaping from a locomotive not far away, he may notice a change in pitch as he approaches the locomotive. The hissing of the escaping steam reaches him directly and also by reflection from the platform. Is the pitch higher when he is near the locomotive or farther from it?

39. Diffraction and Scattering.—It is well known that in a uniform medium light travels practically in straight lines, whereas sound passes readily around corners. A clock, a piano, a radio can be heard when it cannot be seen—and when the sound reaches the auditor only after spreading out around various obstacles. This spreading around obstacles is known as *diffraction*. Since waves set the small parts of the medium into vibration, and the vibrations of these small parts start new wavelets that travel out in all directions, it is not surprising that trains of waves pass around obstacles. The really surprising fact is the possibility of shadows.

The reason why diffraction is so readily observed with

sound, but is somewhat difficult to detect with light, lies in the vast difference in wave lengths. If an obstacle is small in comparison with wave length the waves spread readily around it, reunite behind it, and pass on very much as if the obstacle were not in the way. A vertical pole rising above the surface of water has little effect on the water waves that roll past it. A man standing on a lawn does not offer much obstruction to ordinary sound waves.

Nevertheless when waves, whether of sound or light or of other types, meet an obstacle a part of the energy is deviated from its course. If the obstacle is small in comparison with the wave length only a small part of the energy is deviated, and most of it travels onward. The deviated part spreads out from the obstacle in many directions, and we say that this part is *scattered* by the obstacle. When sound waves in air meet a solid obstacle the scattering occurs because the obstacle is not so yielding and compressible as the air. The compressions and rarefactions in the air are slightly increased, somewhat as they are at the closed end of a tube, and it is the increased variation in pressure that gives rise to the scattered waves.

If a sound contains tones of a number of wave lengths an obstacle will be larger in comparison to some of the waves than to others. So the longer waves will pass the obstacle more readily, and the shorter will be more largely scattered. Rayleigh [69] tells of a case where "the sound of a woman's voice was returned from a plantation of firs, situated across a valley, with the pitch raised an octave," and he quotes a number of other statements about cases of similar "harmonic echoes." [70]

Question 95. In the case just quoted from Rayleigh why should the pitch be raised by the reflection? Why should the rise

[69] Lord Rayleigh, Nature, **8**, 319 (1873).

[70] For interesting cases of "analyzed sounds in nature" see papers in Science, **60**, 5, 245, 282 (1924); **61**, 540 (1925); **62**, 204 (1925); **66**, 109, 280 (1927).

in pitch be an octave? If you do not see how to answer the second part of this question at present you may wish to return to it after reading Chapter Nine.

If an obstacle is large in comparison with the wave length a greater proportion of the energy is deviated from its course. The direction in which the deviated energy travels depends in this case on the shape of the obstacle, and the deviated waves constitute what we usually have in mind when we speak of reflected waves. Behind the obstacle the waves do not close in so rapidly as when the obstacle is smaller. In fact, if the size of the obstacle is very large compared with the wave length there may be a considerable region which is largely shaded from the waves. The width of a lead pencil may be more than ten thousand times the wave length of light, and a distant arc lamp casts a sharp shadow of the pencil. Sound waves may be a million times as long as light waves, and an obstacle has to be a large one if it is to cast a marked acoustic shadow.

Next consider waves that meet a very large wall which has an opening in it. If the opening is small compared with the wave length the waves beyond the opening spread outward in many directions, much as if the opening were a place at which waves were being produced. The smallness of an opening through which sound will spread is really remarkable. A crack under a door permits the passing of considerable sound. A piece of cloth held between a watch and the ear of an observer does not greatly reduce the intensity of the sound—the little openings between the threads of the cloth transmit a large part of it. But if the cloth is wet these openings become filled with films of water, and the ticking of the watch sounds much fainter.

If an opening in a wall is large compared with the wave length the waves pass through the opening in much the same way as if there were no wall, but behind the wall itself there is a definite shadow. "Some few years since a powder hulk exploded on the river Mersey. Just opposite the spot there is an opening of some size in the high ground which forms the watershed between the Mersey and the Dee. The noise of the explosion was heard through this opening for many miles, and great damage was done. Places quite close to the hulk, but behind the low hills through which the opening passes, were completely protected, the noise was hardly heard, and no damage to glass and such like happened. The opening was large compared with the wave-length of the sound." [71]

40. Transmission in Other Media than Air.—Sound can be transmitted by other media beside air. If one end of a long wooden rod is held against the teeth, and the stem of a vibrating tuning fork is pressed against the distant end of the rod, the fork is heard clearly. The sound is transmitted by the wood, the teeth, and the bones of the head. If the stem of the tuning fork carries a small wooden foot, and if this foot is brought down to the surface of water in a tall jar standing on the lecture table, the sound is carried through the water to the top of the table, and can be heard by an audience.

Tyndall [72] tells of an experiment in which the lower end of a long wooden rod rested on the sounding board of a piano, and the rod extended upward through another room and into a lecture room above that. On the top of the rod was a wooden tray, and when the piano was played an audience in the lecture room heard the music carried up through the wooden rod.

A demonstration that sound can be carried by a stretched string is afforded by the string telephone. In this telephone there was nothing electrical. Each end of a long string was attached to the middle point of a rather tightly stretched

[71] R. T. Glazebrook, *Physical Optics*, Appleton (1883), p. 149.

[72] John Tyndall, *Sound*, ed. 3 (1876), p. 108. A similar experiment, as Tyndall points out, was first performed by Sir Charles Wheatstone, Roy. Inst. Journ. 2 (1831). Reprinted in *Wheatstone's Scientific Papers*, pp. 53-57.

membrane, and the string itself was supported so as to be rather taut. A person speaking to one of the membranes could be understood by a person listening at the other, even over a distance of several hundred feet.

Pupin [73] tells of learning to signal through the ground when he was a boy in Serbia. "Each boy had a knife with a long wooden handle. This knife was stuck deep into the ground. A sound was made by striking against the wooden handle, and the boys, lying down and pressing their ears close to the ground, had to estimate the direction and the distance of the origin of sound. Practice made us quite expert in this form of signalling."

41. Flexural, Compressional, and Surface Waves.—We have seen that sound waves in the air are compressional, and that on a stretched string there may be flexural waves. By what type of waves is sound transmitted in other media? And what happens when waves traveling in one medium meet the boundary of another medium?

In a rope the different parts are strongly attached to each other, so that when flexural waves travel along it the displacement of any part of the rope gives rise to forces that pull on the neighboring parts. Thus when one part of the rope is moved sideways it pulls its neighbor sideways, that neighbor pulls its neighbor, and so on. It is by means of these pulls sideways that flexural waves are transmitted.

Parts of the air have only a very slight attraction for each other. If a layer of air is moved sideways it exerts very little side pull on a neighboring layer. Consequently any flexural waves that might be started in the air would die out in a very short distance. We usually say that flexural waves are not transmitted by air, water, or other fluids.

In an extended solid, like the earth or a very thick wall,

[73] Michael Pupin (1858-1935), *From Immigrant to Inventor,* Scribner's (1923), p. 15. Pupin was Professor of Electro-Mechanics at Columbia University. He is best known for an invention which greatly extended the range of long distance telephony.

there may be both flexural waves and compressional waves. When waves of either one of these types reach a boundary at which the medium changes, the waves that leave the boundary are likely to be of both types. To see why there should be a change in the type of the waves let SS' (Fig. 27) represent the upper surface of a large mass of rock. If the waves reach the surface in the direction AO they are reflected in some such direction as OB. If the incident waves are compressional, the displacements in them are back and forth in the direction AO, and if the displacements continue to be in this same direction the waves reflected along OB are, in part at least, flexural. Waves that have been reflected in a solid are usually in part compressional and in part flexural. It is possible, however, for these two parts to become separated from each other.

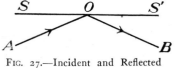

FIG. 27.—Incident and Reflected Waves in a Solid.

The compressional waves travel faster than the flexural waves, and if the medium is homogeneous and isotropic, and the train of waves a short one, the compressional waves may get ahead of the flexural waves and travel independently until they reach some other boundary.

When waves in a solid reach a boundary, like the surface SS' in Fig. 27, another type of waves is often produced.[74] These are waves that are guided by the surface. They travel along the surface somewhat as ordinary water waves travel over the surface of a lake. Since most of the energy in these waves spreads outward close to the surface—that is, principally in two dimensions—the intensity does not fall off with distance as rapidly as if the waves were spreading uniformly in three dimensions.

These "Rayleigh waves" are best known in connection with earthquakes. When an earthquake is caused by a dis-

[74] Lord Rayleigh, Math. Soc. Proc. **17**, 4 (1885).

turbance many miles away, the first tremor comes more or less directly from the focus of disturbance, and is brought by compressional waves. Before the first tremor is over it may be followed by a second, which also comes more or less directly, and which is brought by flexural waves. A third part of the quake, often the most violent, is brought along the surface by the Rayleigh waves.

These compressional waves, flexural waves, and surface waves all of them depend on the elasticity of the medium. There are other kinds of waves in which an actual mechanical elasticity is not concerned. Such are the ordinary gravity waves on the surface of water, the little capillary ripples on the surface of water, and the electromagnetic waves that bring us heat and light from the sun and carry our radio programs.

42. Refraction when the Medium changes Gradually.— When waves arrive at a boundary where there is a change in the medium, part of the energy is usually reflected while part of it travels on into the new medium. The direction in which the waves travel in the new medium is in most cases different from that in the old, and so the waves are said to be *refracted* where they cross the boundary.

The change in the properties of the medium is often gradual instead of abrupt. In such cases the change in the direction of propagation is also gradual. One such case is found where waves on the surface of water roll in on a sloping beach. These waves travel faster where the water is deeper. Consequently the parts of a wave that are farther from the shore travel faster than the rest of the wave. So the waves gradually swing around and tend to come in with their crests more or less parallel to the shore.

Similar cases frequently occur with sound waves in air. The temperature is often warmer near the ground, and decreases with altitude. Consequently waves that leave a source S (Fig. 28) in the direction SA do not continue to

travel in that direction. Since sound travels faster in
warmer air, the lower parts of the waves travel faster than
the upper parts, and so the wave swings around as indicated.
The path of the waves is not straight but curves upward.

There are times when a "temperature inversion" occurs.
That is, for some little distance the temperature rises with
altitude instead of falling. It is now the upper parts of the
waves in Fig. 28 that travel the faster, and the path of the
waves bends downward instead of upward. Under these
circumstances most of the sound that leaves the source at a
sufficiently small angle to the horizontal spreads outward
somewhat as if it were reflected back and forth between the

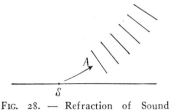

FIG. 28. — Refraction of Sound
Waves When the Temperature Decreases Upward.

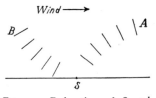

FIG. 29.—Refraction of Sound
Waves by Wind.

ground below and another surface not very far above the
ground. That is, a considerable part of the sound spreads
out principally in two dimensions instead of three, and so
the intensity at a distance does not fall off nearly as rapidly
as it usually does. It is often the case that on a calm frosty
night the temperature is low at the ground and rises for
some little distance upward. We doubtless have here the
explanation of the considerable distance at which voices can
be heard at such times, especially over quiet water or a
frozen lake.

A wind may also have an effect on the distance to which
sounds can be heard. Near the ground the wind meets
more obstacles than it does higher up. So the speed of
the wind usually increases somewhat with altitude. In Fig.

29 the wind is blowing toward the right. If it is going faster at greater heights, the sound waves are swung around as indicated, so that the sound which leaves S in the direction SA has its path curved downward, whereas sound which leaves S in the direction SB has its path curved upward. It is for this reason that sounds can be heard farther when they come with the wind than when they come against it.[75]

Question 96. If you were at sea and listening for a signal from shore, should you be more likely to hear it if you were on the deck or in the crow's nest?

Question 97. Why is it better to have a church bell in a steeple instead of nearer the ground?

43. Abrupt Change in Medium.—In the cases that we have already considered the change of medium is gradual, and the bending in the path of the sound is also gradual. When the change of medium occurs in a small fraction of a wave length the bend in the path is more abrupt. Moreover, the energy of the incident waves is usually divided into two parts: One part is reflected back—usually in a new direction—in the medium in which it had been traveling, while the other is refracted and passes on in a new direction in the new medium.

The fraction of the energy that is reflected can be cal-

[75] On refraction by wind and temperature see two very interesting papers by Osborne Reynolds (1842-1912), British engineer and physicist, Roy. Soc. Proc. (1874); Phil. Trans. **166**, 315 (1876). Reprinted in the *Scientific Papers of Osborne Reynolds,* 1, (1900), pp. 89, 157. See also John Tyndall, *Sound,* ed. 3 (1876), pp. 338-341.

The difference in the distance to which sounds can be heard with the wind and against it appears to have been first explained by George Gabriel Stokes (1819-1903) [p. 22 in the Notices of Miscellaneous Communications, Report of the British Association for 1857]. Stokes was born in Ireland. In his student days he turned one of his rooms into a physical laboratory. When he was thirty-five he was elected to the Lucasian Chair of Mathematics at Cambridge—the chair which was filled 180 years earlier by the election of Sir Isaac Newton. In 1880 Stokes introduced the *solidus* notation—writing a/b to represent the quotient obtained when a is divided by b. In 1889 he was made a baronet.

culated by methods which are beyond the scope of this book. The fraction depends on the relative densities and elasticities of the two media, and it also depends on the angle which the original path of the sound makes with the interface between the two media. A decrease in this angle leads to an increase in the energy reflected, and if the angle is sufficiently small, and the speed of sound in the second medium is greater than in the first, "total reflection" occurs—that is, practically none of the sound travels on into the second medium.

When the properties of the two media differ as much as do those of air and water most of the sound energy is reflected. Even when a sound in air strikes a water surface perpendicularly all but about a thousandth of the energy is reflected, and when the angle between the surface and the path of the sound is less than about 77° there is total reflection.[76]

The statements that have just been made have to do primarily with compressional waves passing from one fluid to another. When there is a solid on one side of the interface the situation is more complicated. Even if the original waves are entirely compressional they are almost sure to give rise at the interface to flexural waves and to surface waves.

44. Absorption of Sound at a Boundary.—Why does not a sound last indefinitely when it is produced inside of a

[76] "After forty years of study and observation, Henry W. Fowler, curator of fish and reptiles at the Philadelphia Academy of Natural Sciences, states that loud talking does not disturb fish, and that the old idea that one must keep still while fishing is without scientific foundation. What really drives the fish off, says Mr. Fowler, is unusual moving shadows upon the surface of the water. Fish have keen eyes, and moving shadows cause them to flee or seek protection in the depths. What really happens is that people who talk and shout move about. Mr. Fowler has also observed that the black plume of smoke issuing from the funnel of an oil-burner will cast shadows that will cause fish to go far below the surface."

Quoted from p. 14 of the supplement to Science, **74** (October 2, 1931).

Perhaps it should be added that sounds produced against the bottom or sides of a rowboat are transmitted to the water with great ease.

room? The walls, floor, and ceiling reflect the sound back and forth, and back and forth, but for some reason the sound soon dies out. If doors or windows are open, part of the sound escapes through them; but even if all doors and windows are closed the sound is soon over. We say that the sound has been absorbed. But what is the process of absorption? How does it occur?

When sound waves meet a boundary, such as the surface of a wall or a rug, part of the energy is reflected, part of it may be transmitted into the material beyond the boundary, and perhaps pass on to other substances, and part of it is changed from the energy of audible sound waves to the disordered energy of molecular motion that constitutes heat. When we are dealing with sound the word *absorption* refers primarily to this turning of sound energy into heat, but the meaning is very often extended to include all of the sound that is not reflected. With this latter use of the word an open window is said to be an excellent absorber of sound. The sound that travels out through the window is still sound, but since it has been lost from the room it is customary to say that the window has absorbed it.

When sound waves meet a baundary, such as the surally makes the partition bend a little. Each compression in the air bends the partition in one direction and each rarefaction bends it in the opposite direction. This bending has two results. The bending itself turns part of the incident energy into heat, and the vibration of the partition sets up sound waves beyond it. The former is a real absorption of sound. As to the latter, the ear is so extremely sensitive that it is often difficult to build partitions so rigid as not to transmit in this way a considerable amount of sound. Whether the sound has been used in warming the partition slightly or has been transmitted to the room beyond, all of it that has left the room is usually said to have been absorbed.

When sound is turned into heat, how does the conversion take place? When a layer of any fluid—air, water, steam, gasoline—moves sideways in its own plane it exerts a small drag on the layers next to it. It is this dragging action that determines the property known as the *viscosity* of the fluid. The viscosity of air and other gases is usually extremely small. The principal reason why gases have any viscosity at all goes back to the incessant motion of their molecules. Between any two neighboring layers of gas there is a continual interchange of molecules, and when one layer moves over another this interchange serves to oppose the relative motion. If the motion does nevertheless occur, it can be shown that there is an average speeding up of the molecules—that is, some of the applied energy is turned into heat.

What does this have to do with the absorption of sound? When sound waves come to a small opening, like the opening between the threads in a piece of cloth, the air in the opening has to swing back and forth as the waves pass. Now the air in contact with a solid clings to it very tenaciously. So the air at the boundary of an opening does not move, and consequently exerts a drag on the layer next to it, that layer exerts a drag on the next layer, and so on. The result is that the air near the boundary of the opening does not move as far as the air at the middle of it, and even the air well out in the opening does not move quite as far as if there were no bounding surface. This moving of layers of air over other layers of air causes a part of the energy of the sound to turn into heat.

For any one opening this effect is exceedingly minute, but when there are vast numbers of openings—and especially if the openings are deep—there may be considerable absorption. This is probably in large measure the manner in which rugs, draperies, and clothing absorb sound. A very simple illustration of the amount of sound that may be absorbed in this way is provided by bringing a large wad of cotton batting down to the top of an open organ pipe while it is speaking. The effect is very striking.

Question 98. If it is desired to absorb the energy of standing waves would it be better to put the absorbing material near a node or an antinode?

Question 99. If it is desired to absorb sound waves that might give rise to echoes in an auditorium would it be better to mount the absorbing material on the wall or out a little distance from it?

Question 100. If a room has the shape of a complete sphere ten meters in diameter, and if a sound is produced at the center of this room, how many times is the sound reflected from the wall in one second? Take the speed of sound as 340 m./sec.

Question 101. If the wall of the room in Question 100 absorbs 5 per cent of the sound at each reflection, how long a time is required for the sound to die to one millionth of its original intensity? How long if the wall absorbs 30 per cent at each reflection?

Question 102. When sound waves reach an observer's ear the drum of the ear responds by vibrating back and forth. Does the ear drum absorb sound?

Question 103. Surfaces like leather upholstery and the skin on an observer's hands and face are soft and yielding. Why do they absorb more sound than if they were hard and rigid?

45. Absorption in the Medium.—We have been considering the absorption of sound at a boundary, like the wall of a room. What about materials distributed in the air itself? Do fog, smoke, rain, snow absorb sound? We have already seen that an obstacle which is very small compared with the length of the waves that pass has very little effect on the waves. But it is entirely possible that effects which are extremely minute with a single particle may become of importance when there are an enormous number of them. If there are a great many particles in one wave length, and if the particles simply swing back and forth with the air as the compressions and rarefactions travel past, the particles might produce a slight change in the speed of the sound but we should hardly expect them to cause any appreciable decrease in its intensity. On the other hand, if the particles have sufficient inertia to prevent them from vibrating readily with the air, we might expect that at each vibration there would be some drag on the air as it moved back and forth past the particle. If there is much drag part of the energy of the sound waves must be turned into heat, and for this reason there would be a falling off in the intensity of the sound.

For sounds of ordinary wave lengths observations made by Tyndall [77] showed that air may contain large amounts of hail, rain, snow, or fog without any noticeable decrease in loudness. In fact, the sound was often heard at a greater distance when filled with such particles than when free from them. Tyndall attributed this increased acoustic transparency to a greater uniformity in the temperature of the air rather than to any direct effect of the particles themselves. It is only when the wave length becomes extremely short that the presence of large numbers of particles in the air is found to cause an appreciable absorption of sound.[78]

Even if the air were entirely free from dust and other particles, a slight amount of absorption is to be expected, especially for sounds of short wave length. The molecules of the air are continually bounding about in one direction after another. The shorter the wave length the more likelihood there is of molecules passing from the warmer regions where air is compressed to the cooler regions where it is rarefied, and also from those parts of the wave where the air is moving more rapidly to those where it is moving less rapidly, thus tending to destroy the compressions and rarefactions and leading to the absorption of sound.

The expectation that sounds of short wave length might

[77] John Tyndall, *Sound*, ed. 3 (1876), pp. 320-338.
[78] W. Altberg and M. Holtzmann, Physikal. Zeitschr. **26,** 149 (1925).

be appreciably absorbed by ordinary air appears to be borne out by the facts. Rayleigh [79] has found that the pitch of a hiss or the sound of the letter *s* has a wave length in the neighborhood of 25 or 30 mm., and that such a sound is inaudible at some distance. He says, "I suppose it must have been noticed before now that the *s* sound is badly returned by an echo. Standing at a distance of about 150 yards from a large wall, I found that there was scarcely any response to even the most powerful hiss. . . . The failure of the hiss seems to be the fault of the air rather than of the wall, for a powerful hiss heard directly at a distance of 200 yards had very little *s* left in it."

Question 104. In studies of the transmission of sounds in the water of the Baltic, H. Barkhausen and H. Lichte [Ann. der Physik, **62**, 485 (1920)] found that the intensity fell off much more rapidly than if it were inversely proportional to the square of the distance. According to the inverse square law they should have been able to pick up the sound at a distance of 1000 km. Sometimes they could detect it to 100 km., at other times not more than 2 km. They could usually detect it to about 10 km. in summer and 20 km. in winter. What possible explanations can you suggest? How might your explanations be tested?

46. Distance at which Sounds may be Heard.—The very short distance to which thunder can be heard is surprising. Other very loud sounds, such as those from volcanic outbursts and from the firing of heavy guns, may be heard to distances of a great many miles. But an interval as great as thirty seconds between a flash of lightning and the thunder that follows it is unusual, and an interval of thirty seconds would mean a distance of about six miles. Thunder is probably seldom heard at a distance as great as ten miles. Why is it not heard farther?

Registering apparatus has been used to obtain vibra-

[79] Lord Rayleigh, Phil. Mag. **3**, 459 (1877); **16**, 244 (1908); Nature **95**, 645 (1915).

tion curves for thunder.[80] These curves show that the compressions and rarefactions follow each other in a very irregular manner, and that much of the energy is carried by long waves that have frequencies of from 2 to 5 cycles/sec. Waves of such low frequencies are inaudible, but we are sometimes made aware of them by the rattling of windows or the shaking of objects in the room. The very low frequencies are interspersed with others up to something like 100 cycles/sec., and it is by means of some of these that the thunder is heard. It has been estimated that the energy which the compressions and rarefactions in thunder carry through the air may be as great as if more than 200 million cornets were distributed along the path of the lightning discharge, and were all playing loudly at the same time.

Although the audible part of the energy carried by the waves is only a small fraction of the total it is nevertheless true that thunder is sometimes very loud. Why is it not heard farther? One suggested explanation[81] is that the fall in temperature with increasing elevation bends the path of the sound upward as in Fig. 28, so that much of it passes well above us and is not heard, and that the winds in the neighborhood of the storm are often such as to aid in producing this effect. A calculation on the basis of a reasonable fall in temperature and reasonable change in wind velocity with height shows that these causes may well be important ones. Another probability is that in the turmoil of up and down air currents and of winds that vary rapidly in strength there is considerable irregular bending of the path of the waves, so that the sound which reaches an observer is spread out over an appreciable time—and over greater times at greater distances. Any such increase in the duration of the sound involves a decrease in its intensity. Per-

[80] Wilhelm Schmidt, Meteorol. Zeitschr. 31, 487 (1914).
[81] Wilhelm Meinardus, Meteorol. Zeitschr. 12, 14 (1895).

haps all of these factors contribute toward reducing the loudness at a distance.

In contrast to thunder there are sounds which can be heard at very great distances. The most stupendous noise of which anything is known occurred in August, 1883. The volcano Krakatoa, which lay between Java and Sumatra, had been in eruption, and during the 27th and 28th of August a large part of the mountain was blown to pieces. The most intense air wave traveled several times entirely around the earth. At many stations the instruments showed seven records of this wave, four on its passage outward and three as it returned from the other side of the earth. The sound was actually heard at a distance of nearly three thousand miles. During a considerable part of a day the detonations were heard in the Philippines, in Australia, in Burma, and in Ceylon.

47. Zones of Audibility.—During the past thirty years there have been many cases where the reports from cannon or from explosions have been heard for considerable distances, not heard at greater distances, and then heard again at still greater distances. Fig. 30 shows positions at which the sound was heard after an explosion at Moscow. The question why there should be a zone in which the sound is not heard, followed by a zone in which it is heard, has been the subject of many studies.[82]

Before attempting any explanation it will be worth while to state some of the facts that have been discovered. Surrounding the point at which the explosion occurs there is an inner zone of audibility, which may extend outward some 50 km. (30 miles). The second zone of audibility begins at a distance which is sometimes as small as 100 km., and sometimes as great as 200 km. There is some indication

[82] For excellent summaries with bibliographies see Alfred Wegener in Müller-Pouillet, *Lehrbuch der Physik,* ed. 11, vol. 5, part 1 (1928), pp. 184-198; and H. Benndorf, Physikal. Zeitschr. **30,** 97-115 (1929). See also a brief summary by E. H. Gowan, Nature, **124,** 452 (1929).

of a possible third zone of audibility, at a distance about twice that of the more common second zone. The inner edge of the second zone appears to be a circle, or arc of a circle, with the source of sound at its center. Usually the second zone is incomplete—or, at any rate, there is a large sector in which there are no reports that the sound was heard. In summer there are likely to be more reports of

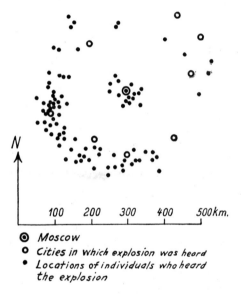

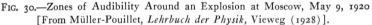

⊙ Moscow
○ Cities in which explosion was heard
• Locations of individuals who heard
   the explosion

FIG. 30.—Zones of Audibility Around an Explosion at Moscow, May 9, 1920 [From Müller-Pouillet, *Lehrbuch der Physik,* Vieweg (1928)].

audibility from the western part of the second zone, and in winter from the eastern part. In summer the inner edge of the second zone is farther away than in winter. In the inner zone the time at which the sound arrives is about that to be expected from the known speed of sound. In the second zone the sound arrives later than is to be expected— as if the sound had traveled more slowly than usual, or else had not come by the most direct route.

This last fact suggests that the path by which the sound reaches the second zone may be a curve that rises to a considerable height and then bends over and comes back to the ground. It is now believed that this is the case, but there has been considerable question as to just why the path should curve in this way. If the effect is due to refraction by wind it is difficult to explain a fairly complete second zone, with observations in such different directions from the source as there are in Fig. 30. If the temperature rose with increasing height above the ground the path would curve in the proper direction. But it is well known that the temperature usually falls with increasing elevation—at any rate for the first few miles of ascent.

In order to understand the explanations that have been proposed let us consider briefly the structure of the atmosphere. There is probably no definite upper boundary. The atmosphere thins out gradually, and there seems to be evidence that there is at least a trace of matter at heights as great as 1000 km. But long before any such heights are reached the air becomes extremely tenuous.

A third of a century ago Teisserenc de Bort began a long series of studies of the atmosphere by means of small balloons that carried meteorological instruments. These balloons are known as *ballons-sondes* or *sounding balloons*. Observations made with these balloons show that the density of the air has fallen to a tenth of that at the ground by the time that an elevation of 17 or 18 km. has been reached, and that it has probably fallen to a hundredth of that at the ground when the elevation is 32 or 33 km.

When we examine the temperature the instruments in the sounding balloons tell a different story. They show that the temperature does not continue to drop as greater and greater heights are reached. Up to a height of about a dozen kilometers the temperature falls, and above that, as high as sounding balloons have gone, the temperature does not change greatly with elevation. It is fairly steady at about $-55°$ C.

The lower part of the atmosphere, in which the temperature falls with increasing elevation, is a region of winds and up and down currents that keep the atmosphere well mixed. It is known as the *troposphere*. The higher part of the atmosphere is called the *stratosphere,* because it soon came to be supposed that it is not much disturbed, and that in it the different constituents are more or less arranged in layers according to their density.

We turn now to explanations of the second zone of audibility. One of the first explanations was given by von dem Borne.[83] If the gases in the stratosphere are arranged more or less in the order of their densities the upper part of the stratosphere might well consist largely of the lightest gas there is. The lightest gas is hydrogen, and in hydrogen sound travels nearly four times as fast as it does in the air of the troposphere. von dem Borne assumed that the proportion of hydrogen in the gases of the stratosphere increases rapidly above an elevation of about 50 km., and that above some 80 km. the atmosphere is mostly hydrogen. In the region where the composition varies rapidly the path of sound would bend downward, and von dem Borne was able to explain not only the existence of a second zone of audibility but also the distance at which it occurred.

At the time when von dem Borne stated his hypothesis it seemed very plausible, but since that time several objections to it have been raised. It was not long before one of these objections was satisfactorily answered, but others have proved more serious. One objection was raised by Schrödinger.[84] We have seen (Art. 45) that the viscosity

[83] G. von dem Borne, Physikal. Zeitschr. **11**, 483 (1910).
[84] Erwin Schrödinger, Physikal. Zeitschr. **18**, 445 (1917). The 1933 Nobel prize in physics was divided between Schrödinger and Paul A. M. Dirac.

of the air and the transfer of heat from regions where the air is compressed to regions where it is rarefied may have some effect in decreasing the intensity of sound when the waves are very short. With ordinary sounds, and under the conditions we usually meet, any effect from these causes is extremely minute. But Schrödinger pointed out that when the density is greatly reduced the molecules travel so far between collisions with each other that viscosity and heat conduction become very important. His calculations led him to think it very likely that sound which had traveled as high as 70-100 km. would be much stifled in the upper rarer parts of the atmosphere—so much so, in fact, that nothing audible would return to the ground.

As time went on and more cases of the second zone of audibility were studied, it became possible to make fairly reliable estimates of the heights attained by the sound waves before they turned downward. These heights proved to be in the neighborhood of 40 km., whereas von dem Borne had assumed very little change in the speed of sound until after it had reached heights of more than 50 km. The evidence now available seems to be opposed to any explanation of the second zone of audibility in terms of refraction in an upper layer of hydrogen.

But it has become increasingly clear that the sound waves do travel upward along a path which curves until it brings them down again. What is there that can produce this effect? Studies of an entirely different matter made by Lindemann and Dobson [85] have suggested an explanation. These studies are concerned with "shooting stars" or meteors, which are particles of foreign matter that enter our atmosphere and are vaporized by their passage through the air. These bodies often travel much faster than sound. As a result the air immediately ahead of the meteor becomes

[85] F. A. Lindemann and G. M. B. Dobson, Roy. Soc. Proc. A102, 411 (1923); A103, 339 (1923).

highly compressed before it has time to escape at the side. This compression heats the compressed air, and consequently heats the meteor.

From a study of several hundred meteors Lindemann and Dobson have made calculations of the density and temperature of the outer part of the atmosphere. Between elevations of 30 km. and 50 km. their results agree with an extrapolation of the results obtained directly with sounding balloons. That is, throughout this region the temperature is not far from $-55°$ C. Between elevations of 50 and 60 km. few meteors have been observed. Between elevations of 60 and 160 km. many meteors have been seen, and in this region all the records that Lindemann and Dobson examined indicated densities and temperatures much higher than $-55°$. They conclude that the temperature probably rises rapidly with elevation between 50 and 60 km., and reaches some such temperature as $+25°$ C.

There are other facts which make such a rise in temperature seem reasonable, and if the temperature does rise at these higher elevations the speed of sound must also increase. It is now believed that the rise in temperature really occurs, and that it occurs at an elevation somewhat lower than that suggested by the work of Lindemann and Dobson. In fact it seems likely that when the rise of temperature begins there is in some 10 km. a change from a subarctic temperature to a tropical temperature. It is now probable that a rapid rise in temperature at some 30 to 40 kilometers above the ground provides an important part of the explanation for the second zone of audibility. Probably the complete explanation involves both wind and temperature effects, and perhaps other factors.

Question 105. For how large a part of the facts stated in the second paragraph of Art. 47 do you now see a reasonable explanation?

48. Doppler's Principle.—We have seen (Art. 37) that the Herschel-Quincke interference tube was devised to explain a certain optical effect, and that Herschel's explanation of that effect is not now accepted. The story of Doppler's principle is somewhat parallel. This principle occurred to Doppler [86] as a means of explaining certain facts about the colors of double stars. Doppler's explanation of those colors is not now accepted, but in spite of that his principle is of interest in sound, and in its application to light has become of enormous importance in the study of celestial objects.

The idea is really very simple. The number of sound waves that travel past an observer in a second is greater when he is moving toward the source of sound than when he is not moving. Consequently the pitch that he hears is higher than it would be if he stood still. Similarly, when he is moving away from the source the pitch that he hears is lower than it would be if he stood still. If the source is moving there is a change in the length of the waves. The waves ahead of the source are crowded together and made shorter, and the waves behind it are spread out and made longer. This change in wave length does not change the speed with which the waves travel, but it does change the number of waves that pass a given point in a second. So if the source is approaching an observer who is at rest, the

[86] Christian Doppler (1803-1853), Abh. d. Böhm. Ges. d. Wiss. 2, 467 (1842). Reprinted in Ostwald's *Klassiker der exakten Wiss.* 161 (1907), p. 1. At the time when this paper was published Doppler was teaching in Prague. In 1851 he became Professor of Experimental Physics and Director of the Physical Institute in the University at Vienna.

Although usually connected with the name of Doppler, the effect seems to have been discovered independently by other investigators. Six years after Doppler's first paper on the subject was published J. Scott Russell [Brit. Assn. Report for 1848, Transactions of the Sections, p. 37] reported the effect to the British Association, and Hippolyte Louis Fizeau [Ann. de chim. et de physique, 19, 211 (1870)] read a paper on it before the Société Philomathique. The published summary of Russell's report gives no indication that he knew of Doppler's paper. Fizeau's paper (not published in full for nearly twenty years after he read it) contains no reference to Doppler, but does state that the effect had been noticed by a number of experimenters. Fizeau mentions Babinet and Scott Russell.

pitch which the observer hears is higher than it would be if the source were at rest. And if the source is moving away from a stationary observer the pitch that is heard is lower than it would be if the source were at rest. This change in pitch due to motion of either the source or the observer, is known as the *Doppler effect,* and the statement that this effect occurs is known as *Doppler's principle.*

When the motion is along the line that joins the source and the observer, it is not very difficult to set up an equation that shows how much the pitch is changed. If N stands for the frequency of the vibration at the source, N' for the frequency of the pitch that is heard, c for the speed of sound, v_s for the speed with which the source is moving toward the observer, and v_o for the speed with which the observer is moving toward the source, the equation is

$$\frac{N'}{N} = \frac{c + v_o}{c - v_s}. \tag{9}$$

If either the source or the observer is moving in the direction away from the other, the sign before the v_s or the v_o is to be changed.

A famous experimental test of the equation (9) was carried out in Holland by Buijs Ballot.[87] On the Rhine Railroad between Utrecht and Maarsen he secured the use of a locomotive and one car for two days in June of 1845. In one set of experiments musically trained observers at three points along the road listened to trumpets played in the car as it sped past. In another set of experiments the men who played the trumpets were at the side of the track, and the observer was carried rapidly past them. The Rhine Railroad had only a single track, so that it was not possible to have the source and the observer move in opposite directions. The changes in pitch were estimated by ear, the noise from the locomotive was very disturbing, and various

[87] Buijs Ballot, Pogg. Ann. 66, 321 (1845).

difficulties were met. Ballot's results are not as reliable as we should wish, but they agree with the theory as well as can be expected. Other experimenters have also put the theory to a test, and the equation (9) is now regarded as well established.

Question 106. What does Eq. (9) become when the observer is at rest? When the source is at rest? Without using (9) can you devise a way of obtaining one or both of the equations that you have just found from (9)?

Question 107. If a source of sound could move toward a stationary observer with a speed half that of sound how would the pitch be affected? If an observer could move toward a stationary source with a speed half that of sound how would the pitch be affected?

Question 108. If a source of sound could move away from a stationary observer with a speed equal to that of sound how would the pitch be affected? If an observer could move away from a stationary source with a speed equal to that of sound how would the pitch be affected?

Question 109. If an observer could move away from a stationary source with twice the speed of sound what would he hear?

Question 110. Perhaps you have found the answers to questions 107, 108, and 109 by using Eq. (9). Do the answers you have found seem reasonable?

Question 111. Two railway trains are traveling in opposite directions at the same speed. On one locomotive the whistle is sounding. How fast must the trains be going if a passenger on the other train hears a drop of a minor third as the locomotive passes?

Question 112. If a freight engine is puffing four times a second is it likely that a passenger on an express that passes the freight would notice any change in the frequency of the puffs?

Question 113. If a tuning fork mounted on a resonant box is struck and then moved quickly toward a wall, the sound that reaches an observer consists of two parts: One part comes directly from the fork, and the other after reflection from the wall. Since the fork is moving away from the observer the pitch of the direct sound is a trifle flat, and since the fork is moving toward the wall the pitch of the reflected sound is a trifle sharp. With any speed that is readily imparted to the fork the changes in pitch are too slight to be noticed separately, but the changes may nevertheless be sufficient to cause the direct and the reflected waves to beat with each other. If this experiment is tried with a fork that has a frequency of 1024 cycles/sec., how fast must the fork be moved if the observer is to hear beats at the rate of four in a second?

Question 114. On pp. 26-29 in Fritz Kreisler's book "Four Weeks in the Trenches" (1915) he tells of noticing that shells which are rising, before they reach the highest point of their more or less parabolic path, sound dull, with a falling cadence, whereas shells that are on the downward part of the path sound shrill, with a rising cadence. Can this difference be explained by means of Doppler's principle?

CHAPTER SEVEN

FREE VIBRATION

49. Free Vibration, Forced Vibration, Maintained Vibration.—It is convenient to divide vibrations into three classes. The vibration of a body is said to be *free* when no outside force urges the body alternately back and forth. When the body is subject to an outside force that does urge it alternately back and forth, and when the body swings with the frequency that is thus impressed upon it, the vibration is said to be *forced*. When an outside force keeps the body vibrating, and does not impose a frequency of its own but keeps the vibration going at a frequency close to that of free vibration, the vibration is said to be *maintained*.

Illustrations of free vibration are found in the motion of a pendulum that is drawn aside and then released, a piano string that has been struck by the hammer, a harp string that has been plucked, a bell that has been struck. In each of these cases the body was displaced from a position of equilibrium, and then was released and allowed to vibrate after the outside force had ceased.

A simple illustration of a forced vibration is provided by the Savart wheel.[88] This is simply a toothed wheel against which a card is held. Savart used it when examining how high a pitch can be heard. When the wheel is turning steadily and the card is held against it the card gives a note of rather definite pitch. Each tooth lifts the card a little and then lets it drop onto the next tooth. Thus the card is

[88] Félix Savart, Ann. de chim. et de physique, **44**, 337 (1830).

forced to vibrate, and the frequency of the vibration is that with which the teeth pass it.

One form of automobile horn is very similar to the Savart wheel. An electric motor turns a wheel that carries on its rim a series of small radial elevations—like teeth that have been much rounded off. On the middle of the diaphragm in the horn is fastened a small boss. As each elevation on the wheel passes the boss it forces the diaphragm to bulge outward. So the diaphragm executes a forced vibration. Another illustration of a forced vibration is found in the drum of the ear. As the sound waves in the air beat upon the ear the varying pressure makes the ear drum bulge alternately more and less. Thus the ear drum is forced to vibrate with the frequency of the waves that fall upon it.

As illustrations of maintained vibration we may think of the pendulum of a clock, a string on a violin, the air in an organ pipe. In the clock the pendulum swings with almost the same period as if it were free. The spring or weight causes the escapement to give the pendulum a little push at each swing, so that the vibration does not die down but is maintained. In the violin and organ pipe the vibration is maintained by the bow or blowing wind in ways which we shall consider later. In each of these cases the vibration has nearly the same frequency as if the vibration were free, but some outside force maintains the vibration.

Question 115. Sometimes the pitch obtained from a Savart wheel is an octave below that to be expected. Why?

50. Damped Vibration.—When a vibration is free it does not last indefinitely, it always dies out. Part of the energy is often carried away by sound waves, part of it may be turned into heat by the bending of the vibrating body, and part may be carried off in other ways. The loss of mechanical energy shows itself by a gradual decrease in the amplitude of vibration, and this decrease is known as *damp-ing*. When the amplitude dies rapidly we say that the *damping is large,* and when the amplitude dies slowly we say that the *damping is small.*

The interesting patterns formed by combining two simple harmonic motions in perpendicular directions were mentioned in Art. 15. In some forms of apparatus for demonstrating these effects the motions are free, and so are damped instead of being strictly simple harmonic. The gradual damping adds considerably to the beauty of some of the effects that can be obtained.

One of the simplest means of showing these patterns is known as a Blackburn pendulum.[89] In this pendulum the bob is supported by two strings. The upper ends of the strings are fastened at the same level and a foot or so apart. The lower parts of the strings are kept close together by a small ring that can be adjusted to different levels. Thus the supporting strings form a letter *Y*. If the bob of the pendulum swings sideways, in the plane of the *Y*, its frequency is determined by the vertical length of the lower part of the *Y*. If the bob swings in a plane perpendicular to that of the *Y*, the frequency is determined by the heights of the whole *Y*. If the pendulum is started in a diagonal direction it swings with both of these frequencies at the same time, and the bob describes a pattern similar to one of those in Fig. 12 except that the vibration is damped.

The bob of the Blackburn pendulum is a funnel that

[89] The first description of such a pendulum seems to be in a single paragraph in a paper on The Apparent Motion of the Earth Viewed from the Moon, written by James Dean, Professor of Mathematics and Natural Philosophy at the University of Vermont [Am. Acad. Arts and Sciences, Memoirs, 3, 241 (1815)]. A study of some of the figures that might be described by the pendulum was soon written by Nathaniel Bowditch of Salem, Massachusetts [ibid, p. 413]. In the papers by Dean and Bowditch there is no mention of sand or funnel. Hugh Blackburn (1823-1909), Professor of Mathematics at Glasgow, invented the pendulum independently some twenty-nine years later— probably in 1844, the year before he took his B.A. at Cambridge—and added the funnel and sand.

contains sand. The sand trickles out through a small opening in the bottom of the funnel, and forms on a paper below it a record of the path that has been followed by the funnel. By setting the ring at different levels it is possible to obtain different frequency ratios.

Another device for showing these figures is Wheatstone's "kaleidophone." [90] One form of the kaleidophone consists of a slender steel rod which is mounted so as to stand upright above a heavy support to which the lower end is fastened. If the cross-section of the rod is not circular it bends most easily in one direction and least easily in a perpendicular direction. Consequently its period of free vibration in one of these directions is different from that in the other. At the top of the rod is a bead which may be illuminated. When an observer looks down at the bead and sets the rod vibrating he sees a figure which depends on the relative frequencies of the two perpendicular vibrations. Unless the dimensions of the rod have been adjusted with extreme care the ratio of the frequencies is likely to deviate somewhat from the exact ratio intended. It follows that the figure changes gradually, going through a series similar to one of those in Fig. 12.

Another means of obtaining these figures is due to Lissajous.[91] If a beam of light is reflected from a mirror to a wall it is well known that turning the mirror moves the spot of light on the wall. If the mirror is mounted on the end of one prong of a tuning fork the vibration of the fork gives to the mirror a slight back and forth rotation.

[90] Sir Charles Wheatstone, Quarterly Journal of Science, Literature, and Art, 1 (1827). Reprinted in *Wheatstone's Scientific Papers* (1879), p. 21. The name "kaleidophone" comes from the Greek καλός, beautiful, εἶδος, form, φωνή, sound.

[91] Jules Antoine Lissajous (1822-1880), Ann. de chim. et de phys. 51, 147 (1857). Lissajous had already described his apparatus and given some of his results, but without the mathematical theory, in the Bulletin de la Société d'Encouragement pour l'Industrie nationale, 3, 699 (1856). For a considerable number of years Lissajous taught physics at the Lycée St. Louis in Paris.

With a suitable lens the spot of light reflected from the mirror may be focused so as to be small and bright. When the fork vibrates it causes the spot of light to swing back and forth with a motion that is nearly simple harmonic, and if the fork vibrates rapidly the spot of light appears to be drawn out into a bright line.

Suppose that a second fork is also provided with a mirror, and that the beam of light is made to fall on both mirrors, one after the other, before it reaches the wall. If the forks are so placed that the vibration of one draws out the spot of light into a line that is vertical, and the other into a line that is horizontal, the vibration of both makes the spot describe the resultant of two simple harmonic motions in perpendicular directions.

Lissajous made a considerable study of the patterns that can be obtained, and they are now usually called *Lissajous figures*. In addition to the method with tuning forks there are various other means of obtaining Lissajous figures and similar curves. Six photographs that may give some idea of the wide variety of the resulting patterns are shown in Fig. 31.

Question 116. How would the curves in Fig. 31 be changed if the damping were increased? If it were decreased?

Question 117. In Wheatstone's kaleidophone one of the two component vibrations is sometimes more strongly damped than the other. How does this affect the figure?

51. Conditions for Free Vibration.—If a body is to execute free vibrations two conditions must be satisfied. In the first place there must be some force that tends to restore the body to a position of stable equilibrium. When a uniform ball lies on a horizontal table it has no position of stable equilibrium: If the ball is moved a short distance from the position in which it happens to be resting there is no tendency for it to roll back. But if the ball is inside

FIG. 31.—Curves Similar to Lissajous Figures [From Goold, Benham, Kerr, and
Wilberforce, *Harmonic Vibrations and Vibration Figures,* Newton and Company, London (about 1915)].

of a bowl there is a force that urges it toward the lowest point in the bowl. If the ball is moved away from this equilibrium position and then released, its weight makes it roll back and forth. And however the ball may be rolling, whether toward the lowest point or away from it, a part of its weight urges it back toward this position of stable equilibrium.

When a body is displaced to different distances from a position of stable equilibrium it is known that the restoring force is greater when the displacement is greater. If the displacement is sufficiently small the restoring force is proportional to the displacement—at twice the distance the force is twice as great, at three times the distance it is three times as great. In dealing with vibration we shall find it convenient to use a quantity which is known as *stiffness,* or as a *stiffness coefficient.* This coefficient is measured by the restoring force that is called into play by a unit displacement.

Question 118. The bob of a pendulum is drawn aside until it is 2 cm. from its equilibrium position, and it is found that a force of 4000 dynes is needed to hold it there. How large is the stiffness coefficient? When the bob is 1 mm. from its equilibrium position how large is the restoring force?

The second condition for free vibration is that the damping must be sufficiently small. An ordinary pendulum hanging in air is not greatly damped. It swings to-and-fro many times before the vibration dies out. If the bob hangs in water the damping is much greater, and the vibration is soon gone. If the bob hangs in a viscous oil or in cold molasses there is no vibration: When the bob is displaced and then released it simply settles gradually back to its equilibrium position but never swings beyond it. There can be no free vibration unless the damping is sufficiently small.

Perhaps we ought to add a third condition for free vibration: The body which vibrates must have inertia. If the body had no inertia it would swing back to its equilibrium position, but it would not go beyond it. Until a body reaches its equilibrium position the restoring force aids the motion, but after the equilibrium position is passed the restoring force opposes the motion. If the body had no inertia the least trace of an opposing force would stop it. Since inertia is a fundamental property of all actual bodies it may seem unnecessary to specify this third condition. We shall however find it convenient to deal with an *inertia coefficient,* which in simple cases is nothing more or less than the mass of the vibrating body.

52. The Frequency of a Simple Harmonic Motion. Application to Strings.—It is shown in Appendix Three that the frequency of a simple harmonic motion is given by the equation

$$N = \frac{1}{2\pi}\sqrt{\frac{K}{m}}, \qquad (10)$$

where N stands for the frequency, K for the stiffness coefficient, and m for the inertia coefficient. Damping makes the frequency slightly less than that given by (10). But unless the damping is large the change which it produces in the frequency is so small that for many purposes it is entirely proper to neglect it. We shall assume that (10) gives the frequency for free vibration.

Let us apply this equation to the vibration of strings. It is known that a string half as long as another gives a pitch an octave higher. Let us see whether (10) leads us to expect this result. In Fig. 32 AB is a string which is drawn aside at C and then released. $A'B'$ is a string stretched with the same force as AB, and just like AB except that it is half as long. $A'B'$ is drawn aside to C' and then released, and C' is so chosen that the triangle $A'B'C'$ is similar to the triangle ABC. Since these triangles are similar, and the stretching forces the same, it follows that the forces which pull upward at C and C' to hold the strings at rest in the positions shown must be equal. But the displacement of the string $A'B'$ is half that of the string AB. So the stiffness coefficient for $A'B'$ is twice that for AB. Let us indicate this fact by writing $K' = 2K$. We see also that the mass of $A'B'$ is half that of AB. So we may write $m' = m/2$.

Now let us write (10) twice, first for the string AB, and then, with the letters primed, for $A'B'$. Then let us substitute for K' and m' the values we have just found. On comparing the results we find that $N' = 2N$.

This last equation shows us that (10) does lead to the result that we expected. As a matter of fact, experiment

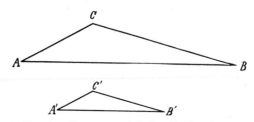

Fig. 32.—Frequency of String Half as Long.

shows that the result is very nearly correct, but not exactly. We shall now see why it is not exactly correct. When we draw the string aside we bend it at A and B and C, and when the string vibrates other parts of it bend. The string may be a steel piano wire. Whatever it is, it is not perfectly limp and flexible. Some force is needed to bend it, and the shorter it is the greater is the force required. This means that instead of writing $K' = 2K$ we ought to state that K' is a trifle greater than $2K$. Then instead of $N' = 2N$ we find that N' is slightly greater than $2N$. Other conditions being the same, a string half as long gives a pitch a trifle sharper than the octave.

Does the diameter of a string have any effect on its pitch? Consider two strings made of the same material, stretched with the same force, and just alike in every way except that one has a diameter half that of the other. If we neglect the very small effect that comes from the natural stiffness of the string we may write $K' = K$. If the diameter of one string is half that of the other its cross-sectional area is a quarter as great, and therefore $m' = m/4$, where the prime refers to the thinner string. The relation between the frequencies is to be found in the answer to Question 119.

Question 119. If we set $K' = K$ and $m' = m/4$, what do we find about the frequency of a string that has half the diameter of another?

Question 120. If we take account of the natural stiffness does the frequency of a string that has half the diameter come out a little larger or a little smaller than that found in Question 119?

Question 121. The lower strings of a piano are "wound" with another steel wire that is twisted round and round the whole vibrating length of the string. The g string on a violin is also wound, and so are the c and g strings on a cello, and various strings on other instruments. What is the purpose of this winding?

Question 122. The e string on a violin is stretched with a force of about 20 lb. If the force is reduced to 16 lb. how much will the pitch be affected?

Question 123. If a steel string and a gut string have the same length and the same diameter and are stretched with equal forces, how do their pitches compare? The density of steel is about six times that of gut.

The manner in which the frequency of a perfectly flexible string depends on its length, diameter, density, and the force that stretches it, has been known for about three centuries. It may well be that Mersenne and Galileo independently made experiments from which these relations were found. At any rate both of them tell of such experiments.[92] The

[92] As already mentioned on p. 6 Mersenne's *Harmonie Universelle* was published in Paris in 1636. It is a voluminous work, and one part of it contains an account of experiments from which Mersenne obtained the relations just mentioned. Two years later the *Discorsi e Dimostrazioni matematiche intorno a due nuove Scienze,* by Galileo Galilei, was published in Leiden. It is known that Galileo wrote this book a number of years before it was

mathematical theory that leads to the relations was developed by Taylor [93] about seventy-five years later. Taylor's work leads to the equation

$$N = \frac{1}{ld}\sqrt{\frac{F}{\pi\rho}},\tag{11}$$

where N stands for the frequency, l for the length of the string, d for its diameter, ρ for its density, and F for the stretching force.

Question 124. If you answer questions 119, 122, and 123 by using (11) do you find the same answers as when you employed (10)? Which equation do you prefer to use?

53. Application to Pipes.[94]—If we blow across the end of a piece of glass tubing we may set the air in the tube to vibrating. The vibration is so strongly damped that the sound dies out very quickly after we stop blowing, but it lasts long enough for us to get some idea of the pitch. The pitch is almost the same as that produced while we blow. If we try a second tube, half as long as the first, we find that the pitch is about an octave higher. Let us see whether the equation (10) leads us to expect this.

Probably the air in the tube vibrates in such a way as to set up standing waves, with a node some place in the tube. If so, the distance from one end of the tube to the node is probably half as great in the tube that is half as long. If equal forces act on thin layers of air near the

published. It was reprinted in 1855 as volume 13 of the *Opere Complete di Galileo Galilei*. The statements of the relations in question are to be found on pp. 103, 106 of this latter volume, or on pp. 100, 103 of the English translation which has been made by Henry Crew and Alfonso de Salvio under the title *Two New Sciences* (published in 1914). It is interesting to know that a French translation of the *Due Nuove Scienze* was made by Mersenne and published in Paris in 1639, the next year after the book was first published in Italian at Leiden.

[93] Brook Taylor, Phil. Trans. **28**, 26 (1713), or Phil. Trans. Abridged, **4**, 391 (1700-1720).

[94] In this connection the words "pipe" and "tube" are used more or less interchangeably.

ends of both tubes it seems reasonable to suppose that a layer would be pushed in half as far in the tube that is half as long. That is, it seems likely that $K' = 2K$, where the prime refers to the shorter tube. Moreover, if the diameters of the tubes are the same, the mass of air in the shorter tube is half that in the longer, and so we may probably write $m' = m/2$.

If we write (10) twice—once for the longer tube, and once for the shorter one—and then substitute for K' and m' the expressions we have just found, we are led to the relation $N' = 2N$. This is the result that we anticipated.

Here, too, as in the case of the string, the result is only approximately correct. A tube half as long does not give exactly the octave. This is because the air that vibrates does not end abruptly at the ends of the tube—it extends outward a little distance beyond the ends. Perhaps the air that vibrates may be represented, in a very rough way, by the air that vibrates in the tube plus the air in a hemispherical cap at each end (Fig. 33). If we change the

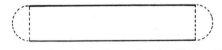

FIG. 33.—The Inertia Coefficient for the Air in a Tube.

length of the tube we do not change the mass of air in these caps. If m_s stands for the mass of air that vibrates inside of the shorter tube, and m_c for the mass of air in one of the caps, we see that the mass of air which vibrates when the shorter tube speaks is $m' = m_s + 2m_c$, and that the mass which vibrates when the longer tube speaks is $m = 2m_s + 2m_c$. Instead of $m' = m/2$ we ought then to write $m' = (m/2) + m_c$. Thus if we are correct in writing $K' = 2K$, we find that $N' < N/2$.

According to this result a tube half as long should give a pitch a little flatter than the octave. Experiment shows that this result is correct, and that the effect is large enough to be observed easily.

Next consider the diameter of the tube. A string of half the diameter gives a note close to an octave higher. Is the same true for a tube? If the diameter of the tube is half as great, its cross-sectional area is a quarter as great. So the force that acts on a thin layer near one end of the tube need be only a quarter as great. That is, $K' = K/4$, where the prime refers to the narrower tube. Since the cross-sectional area of the tube is a quarter as great, we have also $m' = m/4$. Our usual procedure leads to the result $N' = N$. We find that the diameter of the tube has no large effect on the pitch, and experiment shows that this result is correct.

Is there however some small change in pitch which depends on the diameter of the tube? Let us again use the same rough approximation as in Fig. 33. The volume of air in each cap is $2\pi r^3/3$, where r stands for the radius of the tube. For a tube of half the diameter the volume in each cap is one eighth as great. If m_n stands for the mass of air that vibrates inside of the narrow tube, and m_c for the mass of air in one cap of the narrow tube, we have therefore $m' = m_n + 2m_c$ and $m = 4m_n + 16m_c$. So instead of $m' = m/4$ we have $m' = (m/4) - 2m_c$. It follows that $N' > N$.

According to the result just obtained a narrow pipe is sharper than a wide one. Experiment shows that this result is correct, and that the effect is large enough to be observed easily. In fact, the effect has been known to organ builders for many years. When we calculate the frequency to be expected from a pipe it is customary to add to the measured length two "end corrections"—one for each end of the pipe. If the ends of the pipe are alike the two end corrections are equal. Each end correction allows for the vibrating air that is just beyond that end. The importance of end corrections lies in the fact that after the corrections have been applied it is no longer necessary to consider the diameter: If the corrected length of one pipe is half that of another similar pipe its pitch is an octave higher.

The magnitude of the end correction depends on the conditions near the end of the pipe, but the calculation of just how large the correction should be is a matter of very great difficulty. Both Helmholtz [95] and Rayleigh [96] attacked the problem with some success. Suppose that the end we are considering is open and is provided with an infinite flange. That is, suppose that in a hard, smooth wall of vast extent there is a hole just large enough to let the tube slip in snugly, and suppose that the end of the tube is flush with the face of the wall. For a tube which is cylindrical, and is provided with such an infinite flange, Rayleigh was able to show that the end correction must be in the neighborhood of 0.41 of the diameter of the tube. Of course no pipe is provided with an infinite flange. For pipes as they are actually used it is found by experiment that the end correction is about 0.3 of the diameter.

Question 125. When open at both ends a glass tube 5 cm. in diameter and 60 cm. long gives a certain pitch. It is desired to cut another tube to such a length that it will give a pitch an octave higher. If the second tube has a diameter of 2 cm. how long a piece is needed?

Question 126. To how large an end correction are we led by assuming that all of the air inside the tube vibrates, and that the mass of the vibrating air outside of the tube is equivalent to that contained in a hemispherical cap at each end?

54. Application to Other Air Cavities.—In Art. 72 we shall consider the use of an important piece of acoustic apparatus known as a Helmholtz resonator. One common

[95] Hermann von Helmholtz, Journ. f. reine u. angew. Math. **57**, 1 (1860). Reprinted in Helmholtz's *Abhandlungen,* I, p. 303, and as vol. 80 of Ostwald's *Klassiker der exakten Wiss.*

[96] Lord Rayleigh, Phil. Trans. **161**, 77 (1871) ; or *Theory of Sound,* vol. 2, appendix A.

form of Helmholtz resonator is a hollow brass ball with two openings. The sound to be examined enters through the mouth A (Fig. 34), and the smaller opening B is put into the observer's ear. Instead of using the resonator to pick up sound it is possible to make it produce sound. It may be caused to speak by directing a stream of air across the mouth. When the stream is discontinued the sound from the resonator dies quickly, showing that the free vi-

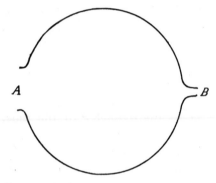

FIG. 34.—Section of a Helmholtz Resonator.

bration is strongly damped, but it lasts long enough for us to get some idea of the pitch. In fact the pitch is almost the same as that produced while the resonator is being blown.

We wish to apply (10) to the free vibration of the air in a Helmholtz resonator. For the present let us imagine the nipple at B (Fig. 34) closed, so that the only opening is that at the mouth. When a sound comes from the resonator the air near the mouth swings in and out, and the air inside of the resonator is alternately compressed and rarefied. The stiffness coefficient depends principally upon the varying pressure inside of the resonator. The inertia coefficient depends principally upon the air that moves back and forth near the mouth.

How does the diameter of the resonator affect the frequency? Suppose we have two resonators. Let the diameter of one be twice that of the other, and let the mouths be of the same size. Since the mouths are alike the inertia coefficients are equal. But the resonator that has twice the diameter has eight times the volume. Consequently if we consider a thin layer of air extending across the mouth we see that the force needed to press this layer a given distance inward in the smaller resonator is eight times as great as in the larger. If we follow our usual reasoning, (10) tells us that the frequency of the smaller resonator is $\sqrt{8}$ times that of the larger.

This result is not as simple as the approximate expressions we have found for strings and pipes. We notice however that the larger resonator, as we might have expected, is the flatter, and that there is nothing in our reasoning which restricts greatly the shape of the resonator. For a given mouth it is the volume of the resonator that is important rather than the shape. All that is necessary is that no dimension of the cavity shall be great enough to permit much difference in pressure in different parts of the cavity. In fact, so long as every dimension is considerably less than quarter of a wave length it is found that the pitches obtained from cavities of very different shapes are the same, provided only that the mouths are alike and not too large, and that the volumes of the cavities are the same.

This fact is employed in varying the pitch when a person whistles. It is possible to whistle different pitches without change in the position of the lips. The pitch is determined, in large measure, by the volume of the cavity in the whistler's mouth, and this volume depends on the position of the tongue. The change in pitch of the mouth cavity can be observed without whistling. If the mouth is set successively for the desired pitches and the cheek is patted with a finger, it is not difficult to play a simple tune that can be recognized by persons at a distance of several feet.

Let us now return to the resonator and ask how the pitch depends on the size of the mouth. This question is more difficult than those we have been considering. Suppose that we have two resonators with circular mouths, and that the resonators are of the same size except that one mouth has twice the diameter of the other. Let us examine first the stiffness coefficient. The area of the larger mouth is four times that of the smaller. When a thin layer of air at the mouth is pushed a given distance inward, four times as much air enters the resonator. It follows that the pressure inside rises four times as much, and therefore that the pressure which would be needed to hold the layer in the displaced position is also four times as great. Now pressure is measured by the force that acts on a unit area. When the pressure is four times as great, and the area is also four times as great, the force needed is sixteen times as great. That is, $K' = 16K$, where the prime refers to the resonator with the larger mouth.

Next consider the inertia coefficient. The air that moves is not simply that in the mouth itself. In the mouth the air moves faster near the middle and more slowly near the edges. In addition there is some appreciable movement for a short distance inside the mouth and for a short distance outside of it. Perhaps we shall not be far in error if we imagine a spherical cap inside of the mouth and another outside of the mouth (Fig. 35), somewhat as we did for the pipe in Fig. 33, and if we take for the inertia coefficient the mass of air in the sphere that is bounded by these caps. Then for a mouth with twice the diameter we have $m' = 8m$, where again the prime refers to the resonator with the larger mouth.

If we now use (10) in the usual way we find that $N' = \sqrt{2}N$, another result which is not as simple as those for strings and pipes. However, we notice that the resonator with the larger mouth has the higher pitch.

Long before the development of the reasoning that we have just been following Sondhauss [97] carried out experiments from which he concluded that the frequency of free vibration of an air cavity which is small compared with the wave length of sound is proportional to the fourth root of the area of the mouth, and inversely proportional to the square root of the volume of the cavity. The conclusions which we have just obtained are in agreement with the results found by Sondhauss. Ten years after the paper by Sondhauss, Helmholtz obtained the same results theoretically. Helmholtz's method is long and difficult. Rayleigh was able to simplify it, but even Rayleigh's treatment is much beyond the scope of this book. For the

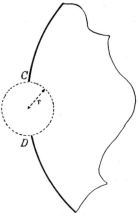

FIG. 35.—Inertia Coefficient for a Resonator. CD is the mouth, and r is the radius of the mouth.

case of a resonator with a round mouth and no neck, Rayleigh's result may be put in the form

$$N = \frac{c}{2\pi} \sqrt{\frac{d}{V}}, \qquad (12)$$

where N stands for the frequency of free vibration, c for the speed of sound in air, d for the diameter of the mouth, and V for the volume of the resonator.

Question 127. How can it be shown that the results obtained in Art. 54 from Eq. (10) agree with the conclusions that Sondhauss drew from his experiments?

Question 128. In Art. 54 we made use of Eq. (10) to obtain two results for resonators. Do you find that you get the same results by using (12)? Which equation do you find it easier to use?

[97] Carl F. J. Sondhauss, Pogg. An. 81, 235, 347 (1850).

Question 129. The diameter of a Helmholtz resonator is 8 cm., and the diameter of its mouth is 2 cm. What is its free frequency? How does the diameter of the resonator compare with the wave length for this frequency?

Question 130. A Helmholtz resonator is to be used in a large box that is filled with hydrogen at atmospheric pressure. How does the frequency of the free vibration of the resonator when in this box compare with its frequency when in air? The density of air is about 14 times that of hydrogen.

Question 131. We have two Helmholtz resonators which are just alike except that one is an enlarged copy of the other. The diameter of the larger is twice that of the smaller, and the diameter of its mouth is also twice that of the smaller. How do the periods of free vibration compare?

Question 132. If you have had a course in physics you may be interested in seeing whether you can obtain Eq. (12) from (10) by making the rough assumption we have used (Fig. 35) regarding the inertia coefficient. You will need to know that the speed of sound in air is given by $c = \sqrt{1.41p/\rho}$ where p stands for the atmospheric pressure and ρ for the density of the air. You will not reach exactly (12). How does your result differ from (12)?

55. Effect of Shading an Opening.—In Art. 54 we saw that if two resonators are just alike except for size of mouth, the resonator with the larger mouth has the higher natural pitch. This fact illustrates a principle which has many applications. If the opening to an air cavity is made smaller the natural pitch of the cavity is made lower. The pitch of a Helmholtz resonator is perceptibly flatter when the nipple is closed than when it is open. A Helmholtz resonator is readily tuned by rolling a finger to a greater or less extent over the mouth. By this simple means the natural pitch is easily lowered more than half an octave— or even, if necessary, a whole octave. A musical instrument which has finger holes may have the pitch lowered gradually by bringing a finger gradually over one of the holes. It has been suggested that the low pitch which can be obtained with a small opening has something to do with the deep note that may come from a small frog.

This same principle has application to organ pipes. Any solid object brought near to either the mouth or the open end lowers the pitch of the pipe. If a large wooden pipe is a trifle sharp it may be tuned by covering the open end to the proper extent with a small board. If pipes are mounted very close to each other they may be a trifle flatter than when farther apart. Thus when an organ is assembled the pitches may be slightly affected by the presence of neighboring pipes.

Question 133. An organ tuner is at work on an organ. Two pipes which ought to be of the same pitch are beating. When he brings his hand near the mouth of the one he is tuning he finds that the beats become more rapid. Should he raise or lower the pitch of the pipe?

Question 134. Should you expect the end correction for a pipe to be greater when the pipe has an infinite flange or when it has no flange? Is your answer in agreement with the result given at the end of Art. 53?

Question 135. The mouth of a Helmholtz resonator may be simply a hole in the thin wall of the resonator, as shown in Fig. 35. More often there is a short "neck" projecting at the mouth, as shown in Fig. 34. If two resonators are just alike except that one has a neck and the other has not, how should you expect their natural pitches to compare?

56. The Principle of Dynamic Similarity.—The answer to Question 131 is an illustration of a law which was discovered more than a century ago by Savart. As the result of a series of experiments Savart found that the periods of vibration of the air in cavities of the same shape are proportional to the linear dimensions of the cavities.[98]

[98] "Lorsque des masses d'air sont renfermées dans des tuyaux de forme semblable, les nombres de vibrations qu'elles exécutent sont entre eux réciproquement proportionnels aux dimensions linéaires de ces masses d'air." Félix Savart, Ann. de chim. et de physique, 29, 416 (1825).

Savart found that this principle applies to organ pipes and other cavities as well as to those which are small compared with the wave length of the sound. We may call this law the *Principle of Dynamic Similarity of Air Cavities.*

Question 136. How can it be shown that Eq. (12) is in agreement with the principle of dynamic similarity of air cavities?

57. Other Applications.—Rods or bars [99] may vibrate either longitudinally or transversely. Longitudinal vibrations of rods have not been much used in music, although a quaint instrument known as Marloye's harp does employ them. This harp consists of a heavy wooden base from which rise a series of slender wooden rods of different lengths. The performer gets his thumbs and forefingers well rosined, and then rubs them up and down over the rods. The tone is soft and gentle. The stiffness and inertia coefficients depend on the lengths of the rods in much the same way that they do for the longitudinal vibration of the air in a tube.

The transverse vibration of rods is employed in such instruments as the xylophone. The conditions here are very different from those for the transverse vibration of strings. A string is usually stretched so tightly that its natural stiffness is not very important. But a rod is not usually stretched at all, and the natural stiffness becomes of great importance. The longer the rod the easier it is to bend it. Not only so, but a rod twice as long requires much less than half the force—more nearly an eighth of the force. Since the inertia coefficient for a rod twice as long is probably about twice as great, (10) leads us to suppose that if one rod is twice as long as another its pitch will be in the neighborhood of two octaves lower. If the bars on a xylophone are

---

[99] In this connection the words "rod" and "bar" are used almost interchangeably.

measured it will be found that this result is not exactly correct, but that it is not widely in error.

Before taking up the next cases that we shall consider it will be worth while to emphasize the fact that the inertia coefficient of a vibrating body does not always equal its mass. We know that the different parts of a body may have different amounts of motion. Material at a point where the amplitude is large makes its full contribution to the inertia coefficient, whereas material that remains nearly at rest has little effect on the inertia coefficient.[100] If we move matter from a point where it vibrates with considerable amplitude to a point where the amplitude is less we decrease the inertia coefficient, and if we move matter the other way we increase the inertia coefficient—even if we do not change the total mass of the body at all. Similarly, if we add or take away matter at a point where there is no bending, and no change in pressure, we do not affect the stiffness coefficient.

Let us apply these statements to tuning the bars of a xylophone. The greatest motion of the bars occurs near the ends, and the greatest bending near the middle. Consequently the inertia coefficient of a bar will be most affected by changing the mass near its ends, and the stiffness coefficient by changing the thickness near the middle. If the pitch from a bar is too flat we may cut the bar a trifle shorter. This decreases the inertia coefficient, but does not greatly affect the stiffness, and so raises the pitch. If the bar is too sharp we may cut away a little of the wood near the middle of the bar. This decreases the stiffness to a greater extent than it does the inertia, and so lowers the pitch.

---

[100] Students who have had a course in physics will recall that kinetic energy is given by the expression $\frac{1}{2}mv^2$, where m stands for the mass that is moving, and v for its speed. The inertia coefficient is closely related to kinetic energy, and the stiffness coefficient to potential energy.

As a last example let us consider one of the several kinds of reeds that are used in musical instruments. In such instruments as the reed organ, the accordion, and the mouth organ the sound is produced by a *free reed* like that shown in Fig. 36. In these reeds the *tongue,* or reed proper, is a thin piece of spring brass *TR*, which plays through a slot in a brass block *BK*. The root *R* of the tongue is fastened to the block, and the tip *T* swings freely. The tuning is done by filing near the root or tip of the tongue, according as the reed is sharp or flat. In a musical instrument that uses reeds of the above type different notes

FIG. 36.—Longitudinal Section of a Free Reed.

are produced by different reeds—the lower notes by the longer reeds. For the lowest notes the reeds are often loaded. A load near the tip of the tongue increases the inertia coefficient to such an extent that these low pitched reeds do not need to be as large as would otherwise be necessary.

Question 137. Two rods are made of the same material, have the same diameter, and are supported in the same way, but one is twice as long as the other. How do the frequencies of their free longitudinal vibrations compare?

Question 138. Two rods are made of the same material and have the same length, but the diameter of one is twice that of the other. How do the frequencies of their free longitudinal vibrations compare?

Question 139. In a tuning fork the greatest vibration occurs at the tips of the prongs, and the least vibration is down near the roots of the prongs. If a tuning fork is too sharp where should you file off a little of it? If the fork is too flat where should you file it? How is the pitch of a tuning fork affected by applying little wads of wax to the tips of the prongs?

Question 140. The cross-section of the rod in a Wheatstone kaleidophone (Art. 50) is a rectangle 2 mm. × 4 mm. In which direction does it vibrate with the longer period?

Question 141. How does Eq. (10) apply to the tuning of a kettle drum?

Question 142. When playing a horn the lips of the performer fit into a mouthpiece, and vibrate with a small opening between them. When so used, the lips are often spoken of as "membranous reeds." How does Eq. (10) apply to these reeds? The vocal cords act in a similar way when we sing. How does (10) apply to them?

58. Normal Modes of Vibration.—We have been speaking as if the free vibration of any body gave rise to a single musical tone. As a matter of fact we know that a vibrating body usually gives a whole series of simple tones. According to Ohm's law (Art. 16) each of these tones is produced by a simple harmonic motion. It must be then that the body often vibrates in a number of different ways at the same time, each mode having its own stiffness coefficient, its own inertia coefficient, and its own frequency. There are means by which a body may be caused to vibrate in a selected one of these various ways, and consequently to give rise to a single simple tone. In such a case we speak of the body as vibrating in one of its "normal modes." We may make a more formal statement by saying that a *normal mode of vibration* is one in which (1) all the particles that make up the body vibrate with simple harmonic motion, (2) all the particles have the same frequency, (3) this frequency is that of a free vibration of the body, and (4) all the particles reach the ends of their paths at the same time. Normal modes of vibration are of great importance, and the rest of this chapter is devoted to them.

When we try to get a mental picture of a normal mode of vibration we see that it has much in common with standing waves. In fact, when a body is vibrating in one of its normal modes there are standing waves upon it. Now we

know that standing waves may be set up by incident waves
that run toward some boundary, and reflected waves that
return from the boundary. Moreover the type of reflection
depends on the conditions which obtain at the boundary. A
stretched string may be fastened so that its ends cannot
move, or one end may be fastened to something that makes
it move in some definite way. The end of a pipe may be
closed, may be wide open, may flare, may be partly closed,
or may be closed by a piston that forces the air at the end
to move in some prescribed manner. These are different
kinds of *boundary conditions*. Normal modes of vibration
are determined in part by the constitution of the vibrating
body itself, and in part by the conditions at its boundaries.

59. Normal Modes of Stretched Strings.—Let us begin
with the normal modes of vibration of a stretched string
which has its ends fastened so that they cannot move. Since
the ends cannot move it follows that every normal mode
must have a node at each end of the string. In the fundamental mode these are the only nodes (Fig. 37). The

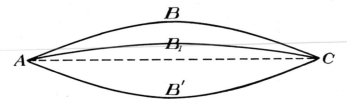

FIG. 37.—Fundamental Mode of Vibration of a Stretched String.

string swings back and forth between the positions ABC and
$AB'C$. All the particles of the string execute simple
harmonic motions of the same frequency, but with differing
amplitudes. All reach the tops of their paths at the same
time, and all reach the bottoms of their paths at the same
time. In short, all the particles vibrate in phase with each
other. The shape of the curve AB_1C which the particles
form at any instant is perfectly definite. In fact, if the

length of the string, AC, corresponds to 180°, it can be shown that the displacement of each particle is proportional to the sine of the angle which represents its distance from A.

We may notice here that when a stretched string is curved there is always a force that acts toward the inside of the curve. When the string is above the straight line from A to C all parts of the string are concave downward. Consequently every part of the string experiences a force that increases its speed when it is moving downward, and decreases its speed when it is moving upward. It is this force that stops the upward motion and starts the string moving downward. Similar statements apply when the string is below the straight line from A to C.

FIG. 38.—Second Normal Mode of Vibration of a Stretched String.

In its second normal mode (Fig. 38) the string vibrates in two parts, with a node at the middle in addition to those at the ends. Here, again, all the particles execute simple harmonic motions of the same frequency, and with differing amplitudes. All reach the ends of their paths at the same time,

FIG. 39.—Third Normal Mode of Vibration of a Stretched String.

but they are not all in phase with each other. All in the left half of the string are in phase with each other, but they are opposite in phase from those in the right half. In the third mode (Fig. 39) the string vibrates in three parts, in the fourth mode in four parts, and so on. In each mode the particles on opposite sides of a node have opposite phases.

A part of the string between two consecutive nodes—that is, a part in which all the particles have the same phase —is called a *ventral segment*. Thus the second mode has two ventral segments, the third has three, and so on. For each normal mode the stiffness coefficient and the inertia coefficient are those for a single ventral segment. So the second normal mode of a string has a frequency a shade higher than twice that of the fundamental mode, the third has a frequency very slightly greater than three times that of the fundamental, and so on. If the string is stretched tightly the natural stiffness has little effect, and the frequency ratios for the normal modes of vibration are close to $1 : 2 : 3 : 4 : 5 : 6 \cdots$. That is, the normal modes of vibration of a tightly stretched string have frequencies that are nearly harmonic.

The vibration of a string usually consists of a number of its normal modes, all occurring at the same time. If the vibrating string is touched lightly with a finger, a feather, or any other soft narrow object, any mode of vibration which has an appreciable amplitude at the point touched will be very quickly damped out, but any mode which has a node at the point touched will not be much affected. If the string is plucked or bowed and then touched at the middle, the modes damped out are the first, third, fifth, etc., whereas the second, fourth, sixth, etc. are hardly affected. Under these circumstances the pitch that is noticed usually jumps upward an octave.

A very pretty way of illustrating the division of a string into vibrating segments was described by Sauveur.[101] Small strips of paper bent to form "riders" are placed on the string in chosen positions. The string is then touched with a feather and bowed. If the feather is, say, a quarter of

---

[101] Joseph Sauveur, Histoire de l'Acad. Roy. des Sciences, p. 479 (1701). Quoted in part in English translation by William Francis Magie, *A Source Book in Physics* (1935), p. 121. See also John Tyndall, *Sound*, ed. 3 (1876), p. 130.

the way from one end of the string to the other, and if the shorter part of the string is bowed, the riders at the half and three quarter positions will be at nodes for all of the modes that are elicited, and will be little affected, whereas riders at other positions may be "unhorsed" and thrown from the string.

A stretched string may also vibrate longitudinally. In a steel string longitudinal vibration may be set up by stroking it with a rosined chamois skin. The normal modes for longitudinal vibration of a string, like those for its transverse vibration, are very nearly harmonic.

Question 143. In the case of a stretched string should you expect the fundamental mode for transverse vibration or for longitudinal vibration to have the higher pitch? Why?

Question 144. "Harmonics" on a violin are produced by touching a string lightly instead of pressing it down against the finger board. If the *a* string is touched at its middle point and then bowed, what pitch will be heard? What pitch will be heard if the *a* string is touched at one third of its length? At two fifths of its length?

60. Normal Modes of Pipes.—We turn now to the normal modes of vibration of the air in pipes or tubes. The cases that we shall consider are those in which the entire vibratory motion is parallel to the length of the tube, and in which every part of a very thin layer that lies directly across the tube vibrates in the same way. We shall take up first the somewhat artificial case of a tube that is closed at both ends, so that there is no opportunity for sound to get out into the surrounding air. Both ends of the tube must be nodal surfaces, and in the fundamental mode these are the only nodes. If use is made of the convention adopted in Art. 31, Fig. 37 may be interpreted as representing the vibration in this case. All the layers of air swing back and forth to the right and left with simple harmonic motions of the same frequency, and all are in phase with each other, but they have different amplitudes. The layers near the ends of the tube move hardly at all, and those near the middle have larger amplitudes. At the instant represented by *ABC* in Fig. 37 all the layers have come to rest at the right hand end of their vibration, and the pressure at the right of every layer is greater than the pressure at the left of it. It is this difference in pressure that starts the layers swinging back toward the left. A quarter of a period later the displacements are represented by the straight line from *A* to *C*, the layers are all in their equilibrium positions, they have their most rapid motion toward the left, and there is no longer any compression or rarefaction in the tube. An instant later the pressure begins to pile up to the left of the advancing layers, and their motion begins to slow down. At the end of a second quarter of a period the displacements are represented by *AB'C,* the air is again at rest, and the pressure is now greatest at *A* and least at *C*.

In the second mode there is one node in addition to the two at the ends, in the third mode there are two beside those at the ends, and so on. Figs. 38 and 39 may be interpreted as representing the second and third modes. From one node to the next the layers are all in phase with each other, and the layers on opposite sides of a node are opposite in phase. The stiffness and inertia coefficients are those for the part of the air between one node and the next. The series of frequencies is practically harmonic.

We turn next to a tube which is wide open at both ends. In Art. 36 we have seen that an open end is not far from an antinode. Since there must be a node between two antinodes the fundamental mode of the tube has a single node, and this is at the middle of the tube. The vibration may be represented by Fig. 40. When the air at one end of the tube is displaced to the right the air at the other end is displaced to the left. The air swings inward at both ends and then outward at both ends. The second and third modes may be represented as in Fig. 41. The second mode has two nodes, the third three, and so on.

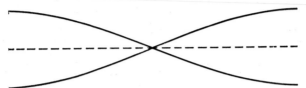

FIG. 40.—Fundamental Mode of Air in a Tube Which Is Open at Both Ends.

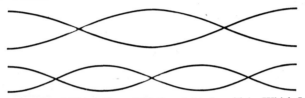

FIG. 41.—Second and Third Normal Modes of Air in a Tube Which Is Open at Both Ends.

The stiffness and inertia coefficients are those for the part of the air between two consecutive nodes, or between two consecutive antinodes. So we see that the frequencies of the second, third, fourth, modes are not far from those for the air in tubes half, a third, a quarter as long as the real tube. The normal modes of vibration of the air in a tube which is open at both ends have frequencies that are not far from harmonic.

Consider lastly a tube which is closed at one end and wide open at the other. Every mode must have a node at the closed end, and an antinode not far from the open end.

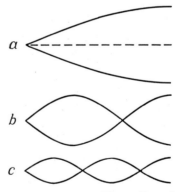

FIG. 42. — First Three Normal Modes of Vibration of Air in a Tube Which Is Closed at the Left End and Wide Open at the Right End. *a* represents the fundamental mode, *b* the second, and *c* the third.

The first three modes are represented in Fig. 42. By reasoning similar to that which we have been using we see that the frequencies of the successive normal modes have ratios not far from $1:3:5:7\cdots$. That is, the frequencies are not far from these of the odd numbered members of a harmonic series of pitches.

Question 145. In the modes of vibration represented in Fig. 41 how can you show that the inertia coefficient is the same whether it is reckoned from one node to the next or from one antinode to the next? How can you show this for the stiffness coefficient?

Question 146. Two tubes have the same length. One is closed at both ends and the other is wide open at both ends. How do the frequencies of their fundamental modes compare?

Question 147. Two tubes are of the same length. One is wide open at both ends. The other is wide open at one end and closed at the other. How do the frequencies of their fundamental modes compare?

Question 148. If l stands for the length of a tube that is open at both ends, and c for the speed of sound in the contained air, what expression gives approximately the frequency of the fundamental mode of vibration? How long should the tube be to have a fundamental pitch in the neighborhood of an octave below middle c?

Question 149. On account of an end correction the frequencies of the normal modes for a tube which is wide open at both ends may not be strictly harmonic. Do you guess that they are strictly harmonic or increasingly sharp or increasingly flat? If you assume that the end corrections are the same for all the modes, and that the corrections are those suggested in connection with Fig. 33, does your guess appear to be correct?

Question 150. After answering Question 149 does it seem to you likely that a tube which is closed at one end and open at the other has natural frequencies that are strictly in the ratios $1:3:5:7\cdots$ or increasingly sharp or increasingly flat? If you make assumptions similar to those in Question 149 does your expectation appear to be justified?

Question 151. Does it seem likely that the material in this article has any bearing on the answer to Question 12 on p. 27?

Question 152. If a piece of glass tubing a few millimeters in diameter is held in a vertical position and the lower end plunged quickly into water a sound is heard. How is the sound probably produced? How could you test your explanation?

61. Experimental Tests of These Results.—There are various experimental means of testing the results at which we have arrived. If a hand is clapped over the end of a glass tube the air in the tube is set into vibration. The vibration is so strongly damped that the sound dies out quickly, but it lasts long enough for us to get some idea of the pitch. If the end of the tube is struck a quick blow, and the hand not allowed to remain in contact with the tube, the vibration is that of a tube which is open at both ends. If the hand is not removed from the tube after the blow the vibration is that of a tube which is open at one end and closed at the other. In the latter case the pitch is heard to be about an octave below that in the former.

Question 153. In the experiment just described should you expect the difference in pitch to be exactly an octave or more or less than an octave?

Some of the experimental means of testing our results make use of organ pipes. When an organ pipe is blown the vibration of the air is maintained, and the frequencies of the lower component tones do not deviate widely from the frequencies of free vibration. An *open pipe* is wide open at the top, but at the mouth, where it is blown, the opening is of only moderate size. A *closed* pipe is closed at the top, and has a mouth like that of an open pipe.

Savart [102] devised a simple way of showing that when an open pipe is speaking its fundamental there is considerable vibration of the air above and below the middle part

[102] Félix Savart, Ann. de chim. et de phys. **24,** 56 (1823).

of the pipe, and little vibration near the middle. A light membrane stretched on a small horizontal frame is strewed with a little sand and lowered into the pipe. At the node the sand is not disturbed, but at a short distance above the node or below it the sand dances so wildly that all of it may be tossed from the membrane. If one side of the pipe is of glass the dancing sand may be seen as well as heard.

Question 154. Savart found that the node for the fundamental mode of vibration of the air in an open organ pipe is not precisely half way up the pipe. Do you suppose it is above the middle or below the middle?

If a hole is made about half way up the wall of an open organ pipe the pipe will not speak its fundamental. At a node, as we already know, the pressure varies considerably, and the hole permits the outside air to swing in and out so easily that the changes in pressure near the middle of the pipe are not sufficient for the fundamental to be produced with any appreciable intensity.

A simple piece of apparatus which is sometimes called Bernoulli's flute provides an entertaining means of demonstrating that at antinodes the pressure does not change greatly and is not very different from that in the air outside of the pipe. This flute is really a small organ pipe that is blown by the demonstrator's mouth. The body of the pipe can be separated into a number of sections, each joint coming at one of the antinodes for a certain normal mode, say the fourth. If the pipe is blown in such a way as to elicit this mode the pitch is practically unaffected by taking off one after another of the removable sections.

Koenig [103] made a careful experimental study of the lo-

---

[103] Karl Rudolph Koenig (1832-1901), Wied. An. **13**, 569 (1881). Reprinted in French translation in his book *Quelques Expériences d'Acoustique*, p. 206.

Koenig was a very skillful and widely known maker of acoustic apparatus of precision, and he was also a careful and thoughtful investigator. Although born and educated in Germany he spent most of his adult life in

cation of the antinodes in an organ pipe. The pipe that he used was 2.33 m. long and 12 cm. × 12 cm. inside. In part of the work it was used as an open pipe, and in part of it the end was closed. The upper lip at the mouth of the pipe was adjustable, and for each mode of vibration the best position of the lip and the best pressure of the blowing wind were found by trial. Most of the front face of the pipe was of glass, and in the back there was a slit 1 cm. wide. The pipe was laid with the glass face upward on supports in a trough, and the slit was closed by water in the trough. Through the water and the slit passed a bent brass tube. The inner end of the tube was on the axis of the pipe, and the outer end was connected by rubber tubing to the observer's ear.

The pipe could be explored by moving the brass tube along from one end of the trough to the other. Near a node the sound was loudest, because it is the varying pressure of the air that affects the ear. At an antinode the sound was very faint. "Während es daher sehr schwer halten würde, mit dem Ohre die Knotenstellen mit einiger Präcision zu finden, kann man auf diese Weise die Lage der Bäuche mit der grössten Leichtigkeit and Genauigkeit bestimmen. Gleitet man mit der Suchröhre durch eine Bauchstelle hin und her, so lässt sich das plötzliche Auftreten der Verstärkung des Tones auf beiden Seiten derselben wie Glockenschläge vernehmen." [104] The first two modes could perhaps not be obtained under Koenig's conditions. For a number of the higher modes Fig. 43 shows his results. So far as the antinodes are concerned, the re-

Paris. He succeeded Marloye, and he lived and had his shop on the Ile St. Louis, the island just east of the Ile de la Cité on which stands the Cathedral of Notre Dame.

[104] "Thus while it would be difficult to find the positions of the nodes by ear with any precision, it is entirely possible in this way to find the positions of the antinodes with the greatest ease and accuracy. If the exploring tube is moved back and forth through an antinode, the sudden increase in the strength of the tone on each side of the antinode is heard like the strokes of a bell."

sults are what we might expect. The spacing from one antinode to the next is nearly uniform. The wide open end of

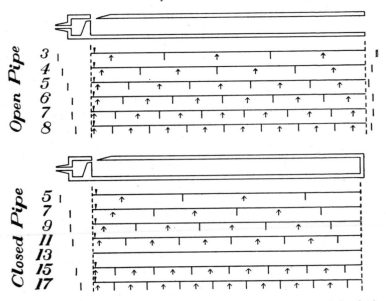

Fig. 43.—Results Obtained by Rudolph Koenig for the Positions of the Antinodes in an Open Pipe and in a Closed Pipe. Each horizontal line shows the
results for one mode. The number at the left end of the line indicates the
mode. The position of the slit through which the pipe was blown is shown
by the dotted line at the left. The other end of the pipe is shown by the
dotted line at the right. The wedge above each line shows the position of
the upper lip [105] during the experiment in question. The vertical marks
under the horizontal lines give the positions at which antinodes were found.
The vertical marks beyond the ends of the pipe give the positions of the
next antinodes if the spacing continued to be the same as in the pipe. The
arrows show the positions of certain nodes as determined from the spacing
of the antinodes.

the pipe is not far from an antinode. The end correction
at this end seems to be not quite the same for all the modes,

[105] Fig. 43 is drawn from tables given in Koenig's paper. The distance
in the figure from the blowing slit to the upper lip is given as a tenth of
the size stated in Koenig's paper. The values he gives seem entirely too
large, and it is probable that there is an error in the position of the decimal
point.

but it does not vary greatly. At the mouth, where the pipe is not wide open, the end correction is larger than at the open end.

The results for the nodes are more surprising. If we assume that the nodes are equally spaced and are half way between the antinodes it is easy to find the position of the node that is nearest to each end of the pipe. At the closed end the position thus found is not exactly at the end of the air in the pipe. In every case it is a trifle beyond it. The explanation is probably found in the fact that the stopper at the closed end cannot be perfectly rigid, but must vibrate to a small extent.

It is near the mouth that we find the greatest surprise. There seems to be a node rather close to the mouth, where the air is doubtless vibrating vigorously. How can that be? No doubt it is in part because the mouth is considerably constricted. Perhaps another part of the explanation may be found in the shape of the pipe at the mouth. If we look at Fig. 111 or examine an actual organ pipe we see that the mouth is in the side of the pipe, and that the mouth end is closed except for the mouth and blowing slit. The vibrations which we have been considering are longitudinal— back and forth parallel to the length of the pipe. At the mouth any vibration in this direction is prevented by the languid that lies directly across the pipe. Any vibration of the air in this neighborhood must be a transverse vibration—in and out through the mouth. It follows that so far as longitudinal vibration is concerned there might well be a node near the mouth.

Question 155. The explanation just given may not be very satisfactory because it deals only with the motion of the air and not with the changes in its pressure. At a node there is a periodic change in pressure. Should you expect any variation in pressure just inside the mouth of an organ pipe? You may find it helpful to read again the paragraph before the last in Art. 36.

The accuracy of Koenig's work is not sufficient to show clearly whether the end correction at the open end of a pipe is the same for all the normal modes. With the development of more modern means of examining acoustic problems it has become possible to carry out a more accurate investigation of this question.[106] If the corrections for different normal modes are not precisely the same it appears at least to be true that they do not differ greatly.

62. Normal Modes of the Air in Spherical Cavities.— We now leave pipes and turn to the normal modes of vibration of the air in other cavities. The nodes that we meet are in most cases not points, as they practically are on strings. In pipes we often spoke as if the nodes were points, although, as pointed out in footnote 64 on p. 93, they are in reality spread out over some area, so that they form nodal surfaces. In many cavities these surfaces become so extended that we can no longer regard them, even approximately, as points. In an ideal nodal surface there is no vibration, and when the waves are compressional the vibration near a nodal surface is almost exactly perpendicular to the surface. Throughout this article and the next we shall assume that the solid walls of the cavity are very hard and rigid, so that the only vibration which can occur in the air at a wall is parallel to the wall. Thus when the vibration is entirely perpendicular to a wall that wall must form part, at least, of a nodal surface.

The simplest cavity is probably a sphere. In this case the normal modes of vibration fall into a number of different classes. In one class the motion of the air is entirely radial. In another class the motion is in part from one side of the sphere to the other. In other classes the motion is more complicated. The mathematical investigation of these modes lies beyond the limits set for this book, but some of

---

[106] S. Herbert Anderson and Floyd C. Ostensen, Phys. Rev. **31**, 267 (1928).

the results are of sufficient interest to warrant a few words about them.

In the radial modes the wall of the cavity must be a nodal surface, and any other nodal surfaces must be concentric spheres. In the fundamental radial mode the only nodal surface is the one at the bounding wall. There is in addition, however, a nodal point at the center of the sphere. During one half period the air swings outward in all directions from the center, and during the next half period it swings inward from all directions toward the center. When it reaches its farthest limit outward there is a compression at the wall and a rarefaction at the center, and both of these have their largest values. It is the resulting difference in pressure that reverses the motion and sets the air swinging inward. At the end of the inward swing there is a compression at the center and a rarefaction at the wall, and this distribution of pressure sets the air swinging outward. So the vibration continues.

Since the motion converges toward the center we may expect the pressure to change more at the center than at the wall, and the antinodal surface to be more than half way out. Calculation shows that these expectations are correct. The variation in pressure at the wall is only a little more than a fifth of that at the center, and the antinodal sphere—at which there is no change in pressure—has a radius about 0.70 that of the cavity. The frequency of the vibration is the same as that of running waves which are not confined in the cavity and which, strangely enough, have a wave length precisely equal to the diameter of the antinodal sphere. That is, instead of the diameter of the cavity being equal to the wave length it is about 1.43 times the wave length.

In the second radial mode there is a nodal surface which has a radius about 0.58 that of the cavity. This of course is in addition to the nodal surface at the wall and the nodal point at the center. During one half period the air swings outward from the center and inward from the wall, and during the next half period it swings the other way. The compressions at the wall and at the center are now greatest at the same time. The variation of pressure at the wall is only about an eighth of that at the center, and only about 0.6 of that in the new nodal sphere. The antinodal spheres have radii about 0.4 and 0.8 that of the cavity. The wave length equals the diameter of the inner antinodal sphere, and the diameter of the cavity is about 2.46 times the wave length.

The higher radial modes have more nodal spheres, and the general type of vibration in any of them is now readily pictured. In the higher modes the variation of pressure at the center becomes much greater than that at the wall. In the tenth mode, for instance, it is about thirty times as great.[107]

In a second class of normal modes for a spherical cavity the air swings back and forth with nodal points at opposite ends of a diameter. In the fundamental mode of this class there are no other nodes, and the vibrations are in directions perpendicular to the lines in Fig. 44. The pressure is highest at N_2 when it is lowest at N_1, and *vice versa*. In this mode the distance from one node to the other is twice as great as in the fundamental radial mode, and we therefore expect the frequency of this fundamental "diametral" mode to be the lower. The mathematical theory shows that the frequency is in the neighborhood of an octave lower, and that the diameter of the sphere is very close to two thirds of the wave length of this mode.

[107] The numerical values given for a spherical cavity are calculated from the customary theoretical expressions, which are to be found, for instance, in *The Dynamical Theory of Sound* by Horace Lamb (1910), pp. 255-256. These expressions neglect viscosity and heat conduction, and they assume that the amplitude is everywhere small. It may be that near the center of a spherical cavity the equations do not apply very accurately. If so, it is probable that the above values are somewhat in error.

In another diametral mode there are nodal points at N_1 and N_2, and there is a nodal plane AB, which lies half way between N_1 and N_2. In this mode the pressure at N_1 is greatest at the same instant at which it is greatest at N_2. Since the average distance of the points in the nodal surface AB from the points N_1 and N_2 is greater than the

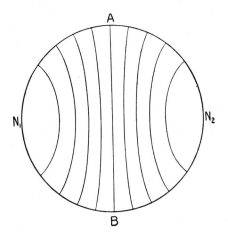

FIG. 44.—Fundamental Diametral Mode of Vibration of the Air in a Spherical Cavity [From Horace Lamb, *The Dynamical Theory of Sound,* Edward Arnold (1910), p. 259]. The directions of vibration are perpendicular to the lines that are drawn, the nodal points are at N_1 and N_2, and there is an antinodal surface at AB.

radius of the sphere we may expect the frequency of this mode to be less than that of the fundamental radial mode. The theory shows that this expectation is correct, and that the diameter of the sphere is about 1.06 times the wave length.

Beside the normal modes that have been mentioned there are various others. The mode which has the lowest frequency is the diametral one shown in Fig. 44. Rayleigh[108] gives a table showing the frequencies of all the modes that

[108] Lord Rayleigh, *Theory of Sound,* ed. 2, vol. 2 (1896), p. 268.

have pitches within two octaves above this gravest mode. There are ten of them, and the relative frequencies are as follows:

1.000	2.712	3.502
1.606	2.854	3.711
2.159	3.246	3.772
2.169		

It will be seen that these frequencies deviate widely from a harmonic series.

Question 156. A spherical cavity is 20 cm. in diameter and contains air. What is the frequency of its fundamental diametral mode?

Question 157. Is the frequency of the fundamental diametral mode of a spherical cavity more or less than an octave below the fundamental radial mode? What fact may have led you to expect this result?

Question 158. What are approximately the relative frequencies of the modes that are described in the text of Art. 62? Why do you not get exactly certain of the values in the above list of frequency ratios?

63. Normal Modes of Air in Other Cavities.—If we return to the radial modes of vibration of the air in a spherical cavity, and recall that we are neglecting any effects of viscosity, we realize that the motion will not be affected if we insert any number of very thin partitions running radially in any directions we please. As a particular case we may cut out from the sphere a cone, with its vertex at the center of the sphere. We have then a conical pipe, closed at the vertex and also at the base of the cone. Since we are considering only the radial modes of vibration, the nodal surfaces are parts of the nodal spheres that existed in the complete sphere. The relative frequencies of the first six modes are found to be 1.000, 1.719, 2.427, 3.129, 3.833, 4.534. Here again the frequencies deviate rather widely from a harmonic series.

If we cut off the solid boundary at the large end of the cone we have a conical pipe with its large end open instead of closed. In this case it is found,[109] both theoretically and experimentally, that the antinodes are equally spaced and that the nodes are not equally spaced. Although the cone is closed at the vertex, the frequencies, curiously enough, are the same as those of a narrow cylindrical tube of length equal to the slant height of the cone, and wide open at both ends! That is, the frequencies of the normal modes in this case are harmonic.

Let us next consider briefly the normal modes of vibration of the air in a Helmholtz resonator. If the resonator is more or less spherical, like that shown in Fig. 34, we might expect the normal modes to be related to those of a spherical cavity. Of course the mouth of the resonator must modify these modes to a large degree. Doubtless the fundamental mode of the resonator has some similarity to the fundamental diametral mode of the spherical cavity. But in the resonator the antinodal surface AB (Fig. 44) is shifted to a position somewhat outside of the mouth, and only one of the nodal points remains. If the volumes are the same the fundamental frequency of the resonator must be much lower than the fundamental diametral mode of the spherical cavity.

The second mode of the resonator may have some similarity to the second diametral mode of the spherical cavity. If the mouth of the resonator is located where the node N_1 is in Fig. 44, the antinodal surface between N_1 and AB must be shifted to the mouth or just beyond it, and the nodal surface AB must be curved and shifted some distance toward the mouth. This will mean that the second mode of a resonator will be flatter than the second diametral mode of the spherical cavity. If the volumes are the same the second mode of the resonator will probably be less than an

109 Edwin H. Barton, *A Text-Book on Sound* (1908), p. 258.

octave flatter than the second diametral mode of the
spherical cavity—perhaps half an octave flatter. At any
rate, on comparing with what we have found for the fundamental mode of a resonator we judge that the second normal
mode of vibration of the air in a Helmholtz resonator has
a frequency several times as great as that of the fundamental
mode. This is correct,[110] and it is one reason why a
resonator is so useful an acoustic instrument.

Question 159. Why does the series of numbers given at the
end of the first paragraph in Art. 63 differ from the series at the
end of Art. 62?

Question 160. In Question 129 you found the fundamental
frequency of a certain Helmholtz resonator. Suppose that the second mode has a frequency seven times as great. How does the frequency of the second mode of this resonator compare with the frequency of the second diametral mode of a spherical cavity of the
same size?

Question 161. How does the fundamental frequency of the
resonator in Question 129 compare with that of the fundamental
diametral mode of a spherical cavity of the same size? Why do
these frequencies differ so widely?

64. Normal Modes of Rods and Tuning Forks.—We
know already that rods may vibrate either longitudinally or
transversely. For given boundary conditions each of these
types of vibration has its own set of normal modes. There
are a number of possible boundary conditions. Any short
part of a rod may be *free* from constraints external to the
rod; it may be *clamped,* so that it can neither vibrate from
side to side nor change its direction; or it may be *supported,*
so that it cannot vibrate sideways but is free to change its

---

[110] In two Helmholtz resonators I find (Results not previously published)
that the second mode has a frequency seven or eight times that of the fundamental. The frequencies of the two modes are about 125 and 1016 cycles/sec.
with one resonator, and about 260 and 1828 with the other. The 125 resonator has more neck in proportion than the 260 resonator.

direction.[111] The number of possible normal modes of vibration is therefore not small.

The longitudinal modes of uniform rods are similar to the longitudinal modes of air columns and the longitudinal modes of stretched strings. The nodes and antinodes are equally spaced, and the frequencies are practically harmonic. But certain of the harmonic components may be missing, just as certain components are missing in a narrow tube that is open at one end and closed at the other.

An interesting way of demonstrating these longitudinal modes is to hold a piece of glass tubing tightly with one hand and stroke it with a wet cloth held in the other hand. The sound produced is loud enough to be heard throughout any ordinary room. If the tube is held at the middle there has to be a node at the middle. If it is held at a quarter of its length there are nodes at one quarter and three quarters of the length, and the pitch is an octave higher than when held at the middle. It has been possible to get a glass tube to vibrating so vigorously that little rings actually break off from it (Fig. 45).

For transverse vibration it is necessary that at least one short length of the rod be clamped or at least two points

FIG. 45. A Piece of Glass Tubing Shivered into Annular Fragments by Intense Longitudinal Vibration. [From John Tyndall, *Sound*, Appleton.]

[111] A more technical statement would be that an element which is supported has freedom of angular motion but no freedom of transverse linear motion.

of it supported. In the bars of the xylophone, for example, two points are supported. On account of the natural stiffness of the bars the points of support are not at a
quarter and three quarters, but a little nearer to the ends.
If the ends of such bars are kept free, and the points of
support are moved to the appropriate positions for the
different modes, the first five transverse modes have relative
frequencies 1.000, 2.756, 5.404, 8.933, 13.345.

If a bar which is free at both ends is bent a little at the
middle it is found that the two nodes for the fundamental
flexural mode have moved a short distance toward each

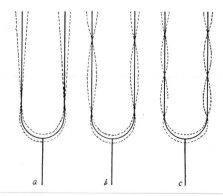

FIG. 46.—First Three Normal Modes of Vibration of a Tuning Fork.

other. If the bar is bent more the nodes move farther inward. If the bending is continued until the bar has the
shape of a U, and if a stem is then attached so as to extend
downward from the bottom of the U, the bar has become a
tuning fork.

The tuning fork is said to have been invented by John
Shore, a trumpeter for Handel and one of a group of
twenty-four musicians that played for Queen Anne. Its
exact form varies somewhat. For ordinary pitches the two
prongs are now usually made straight and parallel. For
the higher pitches they sometimes thicken toward the base.

In its fundamental mode (*a* in Fig. 46) a tuning fork vibrates with two nodes, one close to the base of each prong. In the second mode (*b* in Fig. 46) there are two pairs of nodes, in the third (*c*) there are three pairs, and so on. The sideward vibration of the prongs is accompanied by an up and down vibration of the stem. It is this longitudinal motion of the stem that transmits the vibration to any object upon which the fork is placed. The base of the *U* is often more massive (Fig. 47) than if the fork were made by bending a straight bar. This results in shifting the lower pair of nodes a short distance downward, so that they are still closer to the base.

On a fork of some size it is not difficult to find the nodes for the second and third modes, and also to bring out clearly

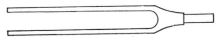

FIG. 47.—Shape of an Ordinary Tuning Fork.

either of these modes at pleasure. One way of accomplishing this is to strike the fork at a suitable level, and then damp out the modes not desired by touching one of the prongs lightly with a finger. A few trials suffice to show where to strike and where to damp.

The frequencies of the normal modes of a tuning fork, like those for the transverse vibration of a straight bar, are far from being harmonic. The precise ratios depend on the particular fork. For a certain fork in the Department of Physics at Smith College the frequencies of the first three modes are about 128, 810, and 2185 cycles/sec. That is, these first three partials have frequencies in the ratios $1 : 6.33 : 17.07$.

When a manufacturer makes a tuning fork he tunes its fundamental. If he pays no attention to the other components it sometimes happens that two forks which have the same fundamental may have somewhat different frequencies for their second modes. If that is the case beats may be heard when the forks are struck in such a way that the second mode of vibration is prominent.

Question 162. Two uniform rods are just alike. One is clamped at the middle, and the other is clamped at one quarter and three quarters of its length. While the rods are subject to these constraints do the longitudinal normal modes of either form a complete harmonic series?

Question 163. In the normal modes of vibration of the rods in Marloye's harp (Art. 57) which of the harmonic components are missing?

Question 164. The relative frequencies given at the end of the fourth paragraph in Art. 64 go up more rapidly than if they were harmonic. Why?

Question 165. If you wish to bring out the third partial of a tuning fork where should you expect to find it desirable to strike the fork and where to damp it?

65. Normal Modes of Plates.—A thin plate of metal or other elastic substance has a great variety of normal modes of vibration. A beautiful and well-known method of finding the positions of the nodal lines on such a plate when it is vibrating transversely was devised by Chladni.[112] The plate

---

[112] Ernst Florens Friedrich Chladni (1756-1827), German lawyer and physicist. He is best known for the sand figures formed on vibrating plates. His first publication that dealt with these figures appeared at Leipzig in 1787. The following account of his discovery of the figures is copied from Tyndall, *Sound*, Appleton, ed. 3 (1876), p. 168. It is a translation from the preface of the French edition of Chladni's book *Traité d'Acoustique* (1809).

"As an admirer of music, the elements of which I had begun to learn rather late, that is, in my nineteenth year, I noticed that the science of acoustics was more neglected than most other portions of physics. This excited in me the desire to make good the defect, and by new discovery to render some service to this part of science. In 1785 I had observed that a plate of glass or metal gave different sounds when it was struck at different places, but I could nowhere find any information regarding the corresponding modes of vibration. At this time there appeared in the journals some notices of an instrument made in Italy by the Abbé Mazzochi, consisting of bells, to which one or two violin-bows were applied. This suggested to me the idea of employing a violin-bow to examine the vibrations of different sonorous

is mounted in a horizontal position, free except over a small region where it is either clamped or held between the thumb and middle finger. A small amount of sand is sprinkled over the plate, and a violin bow is used to set the plate singing. One or more nodal lines must pass through the clamp, and a finger or two held against the plate may determine just where they lie. The sand dances about and is soon thrown from the vibrating parts of the plate and collects at the nodal lines. Fig. 48 shows a few of the more than 250 figures that Chladni obtained and described.

Question 166. In Fig. 48 when some selected ventral segment is moving toward you in what direction is each of the other ventral segments on the plate moving?

Question 167. In some of the modes of vibration that Chladni found on circular plates a number of nodal lines radiated from the center of the plate. What general statement can be made regarding the number of nodal lines that might radiate from one point on a plate?

What makes the sand move toward the nodal lines? The first suggestion that occurs to us may involve little more than the fact that the nodes are at rest, and other parts of the plate in motion. The sand is dancing about irregularly, and when a grain of it happens to fall on a nodal line it stays there. When it falls on any other part of the plate it is soon tossed into the air again. In time it collects where there is the least motion. This appears to have been Chladni's view.

bodies. When I applied the bow to a round plate of glass fixed at its middle it gave different sounds, which, compared with each other, were (as regards the number of their vibrations) equal to the squares of 2, 3, 4, 5, etc.; but the nature of the motions to which these sounds corresponded, and the means of producing each of them at will, were yet unknown to me. The experiments on the electric figures formed on a plate of resin, discovered and published by Lichtenberg, in the memoirs of the Royal Society of Göttingen, made me presume that the different vibratory motions of a sonorous plate might also present different appearances, if a little sand or some other similar substance were spread over the surface."

Fig. 48.—Sand Figures on a Vibrating Plate [From John Tyndall, *Sound,* Appleton, ed. 3 (1876), p. 172].

But if the vibration of a small part of the plate simply carries it up and down, we may ask why the sand should be thrown sideways at all. Why should it not, on the average, come down just where it went up? A part of the answer to this question is found in the fact that, except at an antinode, the motion of the plate is not simply up and down. From Fig. 49 we see that a part of the plate near a nodal line does not remain horizontal, but is inclined first in one direction and then in the other.

Even so, it has been suggested that if the sand is tossed into the air and then simply rebounds from the plate we might expect it to bounce toward a nodal line or away from it according to which way the plate happened to be tipped at the instant when the sand hits. It is not yet obvious why the sand should wander toward the nodal lines.

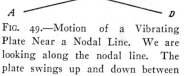

Fig. 49.—Motion of a Vibrating Plate Near a Nodal Line. We are looking along the nodal line. The plate swings up and down between the positions *AB* and *CD*.

But the direction in which the sand bounces is probably not as important as the direction in which it is actively thrown. When a part of the plate is below its equilibrium position the sand on it is likely to be held closely to the plate, and it is only when the plate is above its equilibrium position that it is likely to toss the sand from it.[113] So the direction in which the sand is tossed is not only upward, but it is usually somewhat toward a nodal line.

If this explanation is correct we should expect that when

[113] When a part of the plate is below its equilibrium position its acceleration is upward. So a grain of sand that is lying on this part of the plate presses against the plate with a force greater than the weight of the grain. When a part of the plate is above its equilibrium position its acceleration is downward. The force with which the grain of sand presses on the plate is now less than the weight of the grain, and if the acceleration of the plate is sufficient the sand does not lose its upward motion as rapidly as the plate does. That is, unless the sand is in some way held to the plate it is thrown from it.

the amplitude of vibration is small the sand would not be tossed from the plate at all and would not wander toward the nodal lines. Now the amplitude near a nodal line is smaller than it is farther away. If a plate could be kept vibrating steadily it is quite possible that the sand might

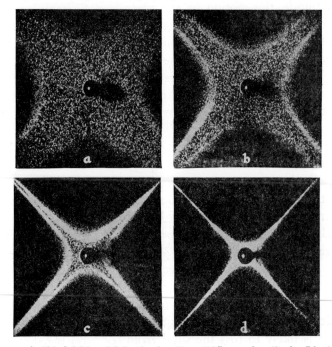

Fig. 50.—A Chladni Plate Maintained at Four Different Amplitudes [Andrade and Smith].

move toward the nodal lines but never reach them. The sand might move rapidly from parts of the plate where the amplitude was large, but it would move more and more slowly as it came to parts where the amplitude was smaller. It would stop its wandering when it reached a region where the amplitude was not sufficient to free it momentarily from the plate.

These expectations have been beautifully verified by

Andrade and Smith.[114]   The Chladni plate was maintained
steadily in one of the normal modes of vibration, and Fig.
50 shows the results.   In a the amplitude was small, and
the sand did not travel far before it stopped moving.   In
b the amplitude of the plate was greater, and the sand
moved in farther before coming to rest on the plate. c and
d show the figures when the amplitude was still greater.

66. Light Powder Instead of Sand.—If the sand on a
Chladni plate is replaced by a very light or very fine powder
it is found that the powder moves away from the nodal
lines instead of toward them.   This effect was first observed
by Chladni himself,[115] and is easily shown by sprinkling the
plate with a small amount of lycopodium powder.[116]   When
the plate is bowed the lycopodium powder collects in small
circular heaps in the neighborhood of the antinodes.

Why does the light powder go to the antinodes?
Savart[117] examined the question, and wrote two papers on
the results of his study.   He believed the powder showed
that "toutes les fois qu'un corps résonne, non-seulement il
est le siége de plusieurs modes de division qui se superposent,
mais encore que parmi tous ces modes de division il en est
toujours deux qui se prononcent plus fortement que tous les
autres."[118]   He thought that the nodal lines of the principal
mode of vibration were also nodal lines of the secondary
mode, but that the secondary mode had other nodal lines in

[114] Edward Neville da Costa Andrade and D. H. Smith, Phys. Soc. Proc.
43, 405 (1931).   This work was done at the University of London, where
Andrade is Professor of Physics.

[115] See Appendix Six.

[116] Lycopodium powder is exceedingly light in weight.   Bulk for bulk it
weighs less than half as much as water.   It consists of the spores of a plant
that belongs to the same genus as ground pine.

[117] Félix Savart, Ann. de chim. et de physique, 36, 187 and 257 (1827).

[118] Faraday (p. 300 in the reference in footnote 119) translates this statement as follows: "Every time a body emits sounds, not only is it the seat
of many modes of division which are superposed, but amongst all these
modes there are always two which are more distinctly established than all
the rest."

addition. He believed that the sand went to the nodal lines of the principal mode, and that the light powder collected largely on the other nodal lines of the secondary mode.

It is not easy to see why the sand and the powder should separate in this way, and other work soon showed that Savart was mistaken. But it is interesting—and comforting —to know that a man who was so clever an experimenter and so eminent a physicist drew this erroneous conclusion from his experiments.

Soon after Savart's papers were published, Faraday [119] carried out a series of experiments which led him to explain the motion of the powder in an entirely different way. He attributed the motion to little currents which the vibration of the plate produces in the air above it. These currents are to be thought of as directed from the nodal lines toward the antinodes, and as carrying with them any light powder that may be on the plate. "So strong and powerful are these currents, that when the vibrations were energetic, the plate might be inclined 5°, 6°, or 8° to the horizon and yet the gathering clouds retain their places."

How might the air currents be produced? Faraday suggested the following explanation. When a part of the plate moves upward the air immediately above it is forced to move upward. When the same part of the plate moves downward it leaves a space into which air flows. Part of this air comes in from above and part from the sides. The part that comes from the sides leads to the establishing of slow currents along the surface of the plate. These currents circulate from the nodal lines toward the antinodes, upward over the antinodes, back at a higher level toward the nodal lines, where they again descend toward the plate.

[119] Michael Faraday (1791-1867), Phil. Trans. 121, 299 (1831). Faraday was an extraordinary experimental genius. Although without much formal education he became assistant to Humphry Davy at the Royal Institution, and later was the director of that laboratory. He is best known in connection with his investigations of electric phenomena.

If particles on the plate are sufficiently heavy they are not greatly affected by the currents, and they wander toward the nodal lines. If the particles are very light they are carried along by the currents, and then dropped where the currents rise near the antinodes.

Is there any test that can be applied to Faraday's explanation? Suppose that the plate could be made to vibrate in a region from which most of the air had been pumped out. Then the air currents could not be important, and the powder ought to move, as the sand does, toward the nodal lines. Faraday succeeded in carrying out this experiment. Under the exhausted receiver of an air pump the powder did move toward the nodal lines. The experiment has recently been repeated by Andrade and Smith [114] with the same result. So it now appears that Faraday's explanation of the motion of the powder, as being produced by these air currents, is correct.

Why does the powder gather in little circular heaps? The powder in the heaps is not at rest. "When a single heap is examined . . . it will be seen that the particles of the heap rise up at the center, overflow, fall down upon all sides, and disappear at the bottom, apparently proceeding inwards; and this evolving and involving motion continues until the vibrations have become very weak." [120] Faraday's explanation of this motion is that when the plate rises it pushes the powder upward; then when it moves downward "it forms a partial vacuum, into which the air, round the heap, enters with more readiness than the heap itself; and as it enters, carries in the powder at the bottom edge of the heap with it. This action is repeated at every vibration, and as they occur in such rapid succession that the eye cannot distinguish them, the centre part of the heap is continually progressing upwards; and as the powder thus accumulates above, whilst the base is continually lessened by

[120] Faraday, p. 316 in reference in footnote 119.

what is swept in underneath, the particles necessarily fall over and roll down on every side." [120]

Faraday's explanation of the motion in the heaps is probably satisfactory after the powder has once collected into heaps. But what makes it collect? To answer this question it is necessary to go back to a principle which was first stated two centuries ago by Daniel Bernoulli.[121] This principle states that in air, water, or any other fluid which is in motion, an increase in speed is accompanied by a decrease in pressure. Of course there may be at the same time other changes in pressure—either increase or decrease—produced in other ways; and in the simple form in which the principle has just been stated it applies to that part of the change which is associated with change in speed. Bernoulli's principle is easily illustrated experimentally, and it has many applications. To see how it applies to the lycopodium powder on a Chladni plate let the circles in Fig. 51 represent two spores of the powder. Although they are very light they are heavier than an equal volume of air. So the air in its vibration swings up and down past the spores. In order to get through the opening between the spores the air has to travel faster than it does at other points. Consequently, in accordance with Bernoulli's principle, the air pressure between the spores is lessened, and so the outside air pressure urges them toward each other. Thus Bernoulli's principle explains the collecting of the powder into little heaps.

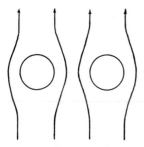

FIG. 51.—Apparent Attraction of Two Spores of Lycopodium.

[121] Daniel Bernoulli (1700-1782), *Hydrodynamica* (1738), pp. 7, 26, 96, 256*ff*. Daniel Bernoulli belonged to a family of illustrious mathematicians. His most important work was this treatise on hydrodynamics, written while he was teaching in St. Petersburg, now Leningrad.

67. Normal Modes of Bells.

—The general shape of a church bell is shown in Fig. 52.[122] One important characteristic of our occidental bells is the thickening which will be

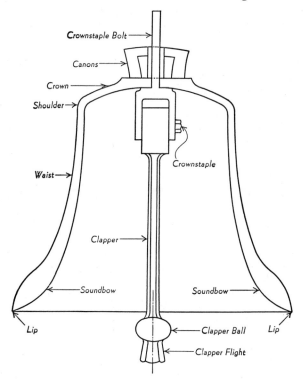

Crownstaple Bolt ⟶

Canons ⟶

Crown ⟶

Shoulder ⟶

Crownstaple

Waist ⟶

Clapper ⟶

⟵ Soundbow   Soundbow ⟶

Lip   ⟵ Clapper Ball   Lip

⟵ Clapper Flight

FIG. 52.—Shape of a Modern Bell [From William Gorham Rice, *Carillon Music and Singing Towers of the Old World and the New,* Dodd, Mead (1930), p. 231. Figure drawn by John Taylor and Company, Loughborough, England.]

noticed in the soundbow, on which the clapper strikes. This thickened ring appears to contribute in an important way to the sound from a bell.[123] The special shape of the bell, and

[122] If the reader will decide how the interior height of the bell in Fig. 52 appears to compare with the diameter of the mouth, and will then measure these distances on the figure, he may discover that he is subject to an interesting optical illusion.

[123] P. J. Blessing, Physikal. Zeitschr. **12,** 597 (1911).

the differing thickness of the material as we pass up from the lip through the soundbow and the waist to the crown, make it exceedingly difficult, if not impossible, to obtain theoretically any good approximation to the frequencies of the various normal modes. For knowledge of these frequencies we must rely upon experiment.

It has been known for a long time that more than one tone can be heard when a church bell is rung. Each simple tone is of course produced by the vibration of the bell in one normal mode, and the blow of the clapper sets the bell to vibrating in a number of its normal modes at the same time. The nodal lines may be divided into two classes, one class running up and down the bell and the other around it. It is customary to speak of these classes as *nodal meridians* and *nodal circles*.

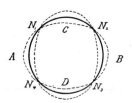

FIG. 53.—Gravest Mode of Vibration of a Bell. We are looking up at the mouth. The dotted lines show the shapes between which the bell vibrates.

Our knowledge of the positions and numbers of the nodal lines has developed only gradually. When any more or less bell-shaped body vibrates in its gravest mode it has been known for many years that there are four equally spaced nodal meridians. To see how a bell vibrates in this case let us imagine ourselves looking up at the mouth of the bell. One diameter, *AB* in Fig. 53, increases in length at the same time that the perpendicular diameter *CD* decreases in length. Then the motion is reversed. The nodal meridians are in the positions marked with *N*'s. It is easy to see that the number of nodal meridians must be even, and that if the vibration is mainly flexural the number cannot be less than four.

Question 168. Suppose that the vibration of a bell is entirely flexural, so that the vibration does not change the perimeter of the mouth. If there were only two nodal meridians how would the bell vibrate? How would it vibrate if there were just three nodal meridians?

A pretty way of demonstrating the existence of the four nodal meridians is to use instead of a bell a large glass goblet—which is somewhat like an inverted bell. If the goblet is half filled with alcohol, and the rim is then stroked radially with a violin bow, the surface of the alcohol is violently agitated except near the nodal lines. Little ripples play on the surface, and drops thrown toward the center form a figure that reminds one of that on a Chladni plate.[124]

One consequence of the mode of vibration shown in Fig. 53 is that the sound is faint along the axis of the bell. At the same time that A and B are approaching each other C and D are receding from each other. Thus the compression that A and B send out along the axis interferes with the rarefaction that C and D send in the same direction.

Question 169. Should you expect a similar interference effect along the axis of a tuning fork?

The material along the nodal meridians in Fig. 53 is not at rest. When the length of the diameter AB is increasing we see that, if the perimeter of the mouth does not change, the material near N_1 must move toward A, and *vice versa*. Although the material near N_1 has very little radial motion it does vibrate in a direction parallel to the surface. So far as radial vibration is concerned N_1, N_2, N_3, and N_4 are nodal lines, but so far as tangential vibration is concerned they are

[124] This pattern appears to have been first observed by Chladni, *Ent-deckungen über die Theorie des Klanges* (1787), p. 25. Chladni used water instead of alcohol. When alcohol is used it was noticed by F. Melde [Pogg. An. **109**, 147 (1860)] that the drops which form the figure may last for two or three seconds—floating on the surface of the rest of the alcohol. The reason why the drops last has doubtless something to do with the nature of the surface. See Osborne Reynolds, Manchester Literary and Philosophical Society, Proc. **21** (1881), or the *Scientific Papers of Osborne Reynolds*, **1** (1900), p. 413.

antinodal lines. We are usually interested in the sound which the bell sets up in the air, and since it is only the transverse motion of the bell that produces compressions and rarefactions in the air, we usually speak of N_1, N_2, N_3, and N_4 as nodal lines.

It has been known for at least three centuries that a vessel like a glass tumbler or finger bowl may be made to sing by drawing a moistened finger along its rim.[125] A part of the reason why this is possible is that the tumbler, like a bell, vibrates in a mode which has nodal meridians, and that the material in these meridians is not at rest, but vibrates back and forth in the direction in which the finger moves.

68. Beats from Bells.—A tone from a bell is often affected with beats, and we shall now see how they are produced. In most vibrating bodies the nodal lines for any given mode have their positions determined by the structure of the body and the boundary conditions. That is, the location of the nodal lines does not depend on how the vibration of the body is produced. But there are exceptions. If a bell is perfectly symmetrical about its axis, and is free except where it is clamped at the middle of the crown, the boundary conditions and the structure of the bell do not determine the location of the nodal meridians. In this case the point which is struck is an antinode, and the nodal meridians are distributed accordingly. If the bell is not perfectly symmetrical its structure does determine the positions of the nodal meridians.

To see what happens let us consider first the vibration

---

[125] This effect is mentioned by Galileo and by Kircher. Reference to it is to be found in Galileo's *Two New Sciences* (1638), English translation by Henry Crew and Alfonso de Salvio, p. 99, and on p. 188 in Kircher's *Phonurgia Nova,* published at Campidone in 1673.

For some time Athanasius Kircher (1601-1680) taught philosophy, mathematics, and Oriental languages at Würzburg, and then for a number of years he taught mathematics in Rome. He was a prolific writer, and in the latter part of his life he gave up teaching and devoted himself to study.

of a teacup. If we tap the cup at various points around the rim we find that at some points it gives one pitch, and at other points another pitch. The lower pitch is given when we tap at the handle, or opposite the handle, or 90° from the handle. The higher pitch comes out when we tap 45° or 135° from the handle. We are dealing with two normal modes of vibration. Each mode has four nodal meridians. In one of the modes the handle is on a nodal meridian, and in the other it is on an antinodal meridian. For the mode which has the handle on a nodal meridian the stiffness and inertia coefficients are almost the same as if there were no handle, but for the mode which has the handle on an antinodal meridian the inertia coefficient is increased by the presence of the handle. When we tap 45° from the handle we bring out the mode which has the handle on a nodal meridian, and the pitch is much the same as if the cup had no handle. When we tap at the handle we bring out the other mode, and the greater inertia makes the pitch lower.

Now let us return to the bell. If the bell is not perfectly symmetrical there are two normal modes like those of the cup. But the lack of symmetry in a bell is much smaller than that which a handle produces in a cup. So the pitches of the two modes in the bell are much closer together. If we tap the bell on a nodal meridian for one of the modes we do not elicit that mode, but we do bring out the other. If the point at which we tap is not on a nodal meridian for either mode we bring out both of them. The beats that we hear are the beats from the two modes of vibration.

It is easy to demonstrate that this explanation of the beats fits the facts. If a hemispherical metal bell is tapped at random it is likely that beats will be heard. If the bell is tapped at one point after another around its circumference certain points are found at which the beats of the fundamental mode vanish, and if the bell is loaded at one of these points with a sufficient wad of wax it is found that the frequency of the beats has been changed.

The first important study of the higher modes of vibration of church bells was carried out by Rayleigh.[126]　To determine the number of nodal meridians he tapped at point after point around the bell, and found the number of positions in which there were no beats from the pitch in question.　To find nodal circles he tapped up and down along one meridian.　When he approached a nodal circle the tone from the component in question grew faint.　With the aid of a Helmholtz resonator to listen to the component that he was examining he was able to make a beginning in our knowledge of the nodal lines for several of the component tones from bells.

Question 170.　An experimenter taps with a mallet at various positions around the circumference of a bell.　He observes that the gravest pitch from the bell is affected with beats.　At how many different azimuths can he tap without observing these beats?

Question 171.　Rayleigh found that the beats from the 2d, 3d, 4th, and 5th partial tones of a bell disappear respectively at 8, 12, 12, and 16 different azimuths.　How many nodal meridians are there for each of these modes?

[126] Lord Rayleigh, Phil. Mag. **29,** 1 (1890).

CHAPTER EIGHT

FORCED VIBRATION AND MAINTAINED VIBRATION

69. Maintenance Requires an External Force.—In Art. 49 on p. 126 we mentioned three bodies which execute forced vibrations: The card used with a Savart wheel, the diaphragm in one type of automobile horn, and the drumskin of the ear. Before taking up questions of forced vibration in more detail let us consider a few additional cases.

Among the exhibits at Independence Hall in Philadelphia is a large "ratchet rattle" that used to be in the Old Court House in Philadelphia, and was used to summon the night watch of the city. The rattle has a toothed wheel that can be turned by a handle, and against the teeth rests a thin strip of wood. The action is like that of a Savart wheel, but the sound produced is much louder. A somewhat similar ratchet rattle can sometimes be bought as a toy. The strip of wood is forced to vibrate, and it vibrates at the frequency with which it drops from one tooth to the next.

A large proportion of the sounds made by insects are the result of forced vibrations produced by "stridulation" —that is, by rubbing one part of the body on another. For instance, the common field cricket has on the under side of each "tegmen" (i.e. "fore wing" or "wing cover") a rib that runs sideways and carries a row of some 130 tiny pointed teeth. On the inner edge of the tegmen is a sharp scraper across which the teeth of the opposite tegmen can be rubbed. This rubbing sets both tegmina into forced vibration.

The diaphragms in telephone receivers and transmitters and in radio loudspeakers also execute forced vibrations. In the receiver and loudspeaker a varying electric current produces a varying magnetic field, and the varying magnetic field leads to the motion of the diaphragm. The diaphragm is forced to vibrate with the frequency that is impressed upon it.

In each of these cases it is to be noticed that the force which produces the vibration is supplied from outside. In this it differs from the restoring force that we have considered in connection with simple harmonic motion. The restoring force is an *internal force* that is involved in the stiffness of the vibrating body itself. But when a vibration is forced the force that controls the vibration is supplied by some outside body. We speak of the force in this case as an *external force* or as an *impressed force*. If a body is to be kept vibrating it must be acted upon by some external force.

70. **Varying Forces.**—The impressed force that maintains a vibration cannot be a steady one that pulls always with the same strength and in the same direction. On a violin it does seem as if the bow pulls the string steadily in one direction, but we shall see later (Art. 80) that the pull is really not steady. If a force is to set up a periodic vibration the force must itself be periodic. It may act always in one direction, the strength of the force becoming periodically greater and smaller; or it may act first in one direction and then in the opposite direction. In either case there must be some change in the force, and this change must occur periodically. When the electric current in a wire experiences periodic changes in the direction it flows we speak of it as an "alternating current." Similarly when a force pulls alternately in one direction and in the opposite direction we may speak of it as an *alternating force*.

We may represent the changing strength of a force by

a curve, like the vibration curve that we have used to represent a vibratory motion. In Fig. 10 on p. 39 the distance of a point above the axis represented the displacement of the chosen particle, and the curve showed how the displacement of the particle changed as time went on. In a similar way we may draw a curve that shows how a force changes with time. If the force acts vertically we may represent its strength when it acts upward by distance above the axis of the curve, and its strength when it acts downward by distance below the axis. If the force acts horizontally we may represent it as we did a horizontal vibration. That is, when the force acts toward the right we may represent its strength by distance above the axis, and when it acts toward the left by distance below the axis.

Since the vibration curve in Fig. 10 shows how the displacement of a particle depends on time we spoke of the vibration curve as a *displacement-time* curve, and in the same way the curve that shows how a force depends on time is called a *force-time* curve. When an alternating force changes in such a way that the force-time curve has the same shape as the displacement-time curve for a simple harmonic motion it is customary to speak of the force as a *simple harmonic force*. We also speak of the frequency with which the impressed force varies as an *impressed frequency,* and the frequency with which the body would vibrate if there were no impressed force as a *free frequency* or a *natural frequency*.

Question 172. Let Fig. 10 on p. 39 represent a simple harmonic force. At what instants—points on the diagram—is the force the greatest? At what instants does the force vanish? At what instants is the force changing most rapidly? At what instants is the force not changing?

Question 173. What is the shape of the force-time curve for a force that pulls steadily in one direction, with no change whatever in its strength?

Question 174. What is the shape of the force-time curve for the blow of a hammer on a nail?

Question 175. The weight in a pile driver strikes blow after blow on a pile. What is the shape of the force-time curve for the series of blows?

Question 176. You stand at one end of a hammock and swing some one in the hammock. What is approximately the shape of your force-time curve?

71. Amplitude and Energy of Forced Vibration.—A free vibration always dies out. There is always some damping force that gradually takes away the energy of vibration and changes it into some other form of energy. If the amplitude of vibration is to continue unchanged it is necessary for some impressed force to supply energy, and to supply it, on the average, at the same rate at which the damping forces take it away. If an impressed force supplies energy more rapidly than the damping forces carry it away the amplitude of the vibration increases, and if the impressed force supplies energy less rapidly than the damping forces carry it away the amplitude of vibration decreases.

It is not difficult to see that a force supplies energy when it urges the body in the direction in which the body is moving, and that it takes energy away when it urges the body in the opposite direction. Think, for instance, of a child in a swing. If you wish to keep him swinging, or to make him go higher, your pushes are in the direction in which he is going, not in the opposite direction.

When a simple harmonic force is producing or maintaining a simple harmonic motion it is possible for the force to urge the body in the direction of motion during part of the cycle, and in the direction opposite to the motion during another part of the cycle. Whether the force on the whole supplies energy or takes it away, and how rapidly it supplies the energy or abstracts it, depends in part on the relative phases of the force and the vibration. The mathematical theory shows that energy is supplied most rapidly when the impressed force is in phase with the velocity.

Question 177. When a simple harmonic force is supplying energy to a simple harmonic motion most rapidly the displacement-time curve and the force-time curve are not in phase with each other. Which is ahead?

Question 178. If we draw the displacement-time curve for a simple harmonic motion, and also the force-time curve for the restoring force, how do the phases of these curves compare? What question in Chapter Three had a similar answer?

The damping forces that act on a vibrating body are less when the amplitude of vibration is small, and they increase as the amplitude increases. When an impressed force is first applied to a body that is free to vibrate it supplies energy more rapidly than the damping forces carry the energy away. But as the amplitude of vibration becomes larger the damping forces carry away the energy more rapidly, and before long a steady state is reached in which the damping forces carry off the energy, on the average, just as fast as the impressed force supplies it. The amplitude of vibration has now become steady, and it remains steady as long as the impressed force continues to act—provided of course that other conditions do not change.

When the amplitude of the forced vibration has become steady this steady amplitude depends on how near the impressed frequency is to a natural frequency. If the forcing frequency differs considerably from that with which the body would vibrate if it were free a mathematical study shows that the velocity is not nearly in phase with the impressed force. It follows that the impressed force does not supply much energy, there is little energy for the damping forces to carry away, and the amplitude of the vibration is small. But if the forcing frequency is very close to a natural frequency the mathematical theory shows that the velocity is nearly in phase with the impressed force. The impressed force now supplies energy rapidly, the damping forces carry it rapidly away, and the amplitude is large. The large response that occurs when the forcing frequency is close to the natural frequency is known as *resonance,* or sometimes as *sympathetic vibration.*

A helpful means of representing the result at which we have arrived is provided by the curves in Fig. 54. The frequency of the impressed force is small at the left side of the figure, and increases as we pass toward the right. At *N* it is close to the natural frequency. The height of any one of the curves at any frequency represents the rate at which the impressed force is supplying energy. It also represents the rate at which the damping forces are carrying energy away. When the natural frequency is in the audible range a considerable part of the damping may be brought about by sound waves that spread out from the vibrating body and bring energy to our ears. In such cases the height of the curve gives an indication of the loudness of the sound. The sound is loudest when the forcing frequency is close to a natural frequency.

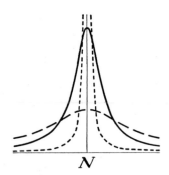

Fig. 54. — Three Resonance Curves. On each curve the resonance is greatest when the frequency of the impressed force is close to the free frequency *N*. The dotted curve is for a case where there is little damping, the dashed curve for one where the damping is large, and the full curve for an intermediate case.

One other fact of importance in this connection is that the precise shape of any curve in Fig. 54 depends on the amount of damping. It can be shown that if the damping is small the curve is tall and narrow, like the dotted curve in the figure, whereas if the damping is greater the curve is lower and wider. Illustrations of this fact will be given in Art. 72.

The material that we have just been considering may seem somewhat abstract, but the conception of resonance at which we have arrived is extremely important. There are many interesting phenomena which depend upon resonance, and there are many technical problems in which an understanding of resonance is essential. Some of these problems have little direct connection with sound, and they concern matters as widely separated as the vibrations set up in machinery and the currents in electric circuits.

72. Various Cases of Resonance.[127] —An excellent mechanical illustration of the large response which may occur at the proper frequency is provided by the apparatus shown in Fig. 55. A piece of board is somewhat beveled, so that it can rock slightly from side to side. From it rise three strips of steel of different lengths, and at the top of each strip is a wooden ball. Each strip of steel with the ball that it carries has its own natural frequency. If the board is placed on a table and rocked slightly at any one of the three natural ·frequencies the corresponding ball

Fig. 55.—Board with Three Springs to Illustrate Resonance.

swings back and forth with a large amplitude, and at the same time the two other balls are not much affected.

Another mechanical case occurs in the vibration of a bridge. Sometimes a bridge has a natural period not far from that of the footsteps of a man who is walking. The successive steps of one man are not likely to produce a vibration of such violence as to damage a bridge, but the foot-

---

[127] This article deals with cases of resonance. There are many cases of forced vibration in which the forcing frequency is not close to a natural frequency, and in which there is consequently no resonance. For a beautifully carried out experimental study of several such cases see Marty, Ann. de physique, **1**, 622 (1934).

falls of many marching men may supply energy at a dangerous rate. This danger was perhaps not recognized as early as 1831, for in that year a suspension bridge at Broughton, near Manchester, England, gave way,[128] and it is supposed that the failure was caused by too violent a forced vibration.

Another interesting illustration of forced vibration may be found in connection with studies of bells. In Art. 67 we have seen that a bell has various normal modes of vibration, each with its own natural frequency. If a properly tuned fork is set vibrating and its stem pressed against a bell the bell may respond to a surprising extent. The mass of the bell may be a thousand, or even ten thousand, times that of the fork, but if the bell has a natural frequency that is very close to that of the fork it responds with a clear, pure tone that is very different from the complex sound produced by a blow from the clapper.

A bell may be excited with the aid of a modern electric oscillator. With such an oscillator it is possible to produce an electric current that varies in a manner which is nearly simple harmonic, and of which the frequency is readily varied. Such a current may be amplified and sent through a small electromagnet. A light strip of iron may be coated with rubber dam and placed between the electromagnet and the bell. The changing electric current causes a changing magnetic field, and so makes the strip of iron through its rubber cushion press against the bell with a varying force. When the frequency of this force is the same as that of one of the normal modes of the bell the bell responds and sings

---

[128] "A party of men belonging to the 60th regiment of rifle corps with their officers, amounting to about eighty in number, had been exercising on Kersal Moor, and were returning to their Barracks in Regent-road, Salford, and when on the bridge, one of the bolts connected with the iron rods which go into the anchorage on that side of the bridge nearest the toll-house, gave way, and one side of the bridge fell into the river, and precipitated nearly all the men with their arms and accoutrements, into the water."

Quoted from the *Manchester Times* for April 16, 1831, through the courtesy of Dr. H. Lowery, Head of the Department of Pure and Applied Physics at the College of Technology, Manchester.

that one tone steadily—provided, of course, that the exciting strip of iron is not on a nodal line of the mode in question. If the frequency of the oscillator is gradually changed it is possible to pick up different natural frequencies of the bell. When the exciting frequency passes through one of the natural frequencies the loudness grows and falls off again in the way that Fig. 54 would lead us to expect. [129]

We know (Art. 60) that the air in a tube has a series of natural pitches. When a vibrating tuning fork is held at the end of a tube the air in the tube responds and the tone swells out if the pitch of the fork is not far from one of the natural pitches of the tube. Since the free vibration of the air in the tube dies out very quickly we know that the damping is large and the resonance curve broad. We therefore expect the air in the tube to respond rather well, even if the pitch of the fork is not very close to a natural pitch of the tube. As a matter of fact, we find that we can change the length of the tube, and consequently its natural pitch, very appreciably and still get a satisfactory response when the tuning fork is brought near.

Question 179. Sound is a form of energy. When a vibrating tuning fork is brought near to the end of a tube of suitable length the sound becomes much louder. Have we here a means of creating energy?

An air resonator is sometimes used under each bar of a xylophone, in order to bring out more strongly the fundamental tone of the bar. A somewhat similar cavity is employed to reinforce the tones from metallic strips that are struck in the organ stop known as a "celestial harp."

[129] This method of investigating the vibration of bells was first described by Franklin G. Tyzzer [Journ. Franklin Inst., 210, 55 (1930)], who greatly extended our knowledge of the normal modes. Further work was carried out with similar equipment by Arthur Taber Jones and George W. Alderman [Journ. Acoust. Soc. 4, 331 (1933)]. The vibrations of Chladni plates have been studied in a similar manner by Andrade and Smith [footnote 114 on p. 177 of this book] and by Robert Cameron Colwell in a whole series of papers beginning in 1931.

The Helmholtz resonators which we considered in Arts. 54 and 63 on pp. 140 and 167 are not very different from the cavities of which we have just been speaking. If a Helmholtz resonator is in a region where the air is vibrating with a frequency near that of its fundamental mode the resonator picks up the sound: The pressure of the air inside of the resonator increases and decreases to a considerably greater extent than it does outside of the resonator, and this varying pressure enables an ear applied to the nipple of the resonator to hear a tone that might otherwise be too faint or too much confused with other sounds for it to be picked up with certainty. This is the purpose for which Helmholtz invented his resonators. Helmholtz resonators are very simple and very important aids in picking out the simple components of a musical sound. The tuning of such a resonator, as already mentioned, is readily accomplished by rolling a finger over its mouth.

Since the free vibration of the air in a Helmholtz resonator dies out very quickly we know that the damping must be large and the range of resonance broad. To show that this really is the case we may use vibrating tuning forks of different pitches. The forks may be brought, one after another, to the mouth of a resonator; or the forks may be held, one after another, a foot or so from the ear, and the resonator alternately applied to the ear and taken away. By either means we find that our conclusion is quite justified: The resonator responds tolerably well to a fair range of frequencies. This fact, of course, limits the usefulness of Helmholtz resonators when we attempt to separate tones that lie fairly close together.

The "murmur of the sea" that is sometimes heard when a shell is held to the ear is another resonance phenomenon. The cavity inside of the shell reinforces various faint noises that are already present in the surrounding air. In some shells the cavity has a shape very different from that of a

Helmholtz resonator, and has a very different series of normal modes. In some shells the first few natural overtones are much closer to the fundamental than they are in a Helmholtz resonator, and such shells may pick up slight noises of these various pitches. For this reason the shell may give a louder murmur than is obtained with a Helmholtz resonator of the same fundamental pitch.

Question 180. Why is the sound heard in a shell likely to be an irregular murmuring noise instead of a definite musical tone?

The passage inward to the drumskin of the ear is also a cavity which has its own natural frequency. If that frequency is present in the external air it is reinforced and made more prominent than would otherwise be the case. When a chorus is singing loudly a person near to the singers may often notice high pitched overtones that are thus reinforced. When attention has once been drawn to these overtones they may at times be very conspicuous and very unpleasant.

Question 181. Helmholtz [*Sensations of Tone,* 4th Eng. ed., p. 116] gives the frequency that the canal of the external ear reinforces as running from about 2640 cycles/sec. to 3168. If the canal is in the neighborhood of 3 cm. long, and may be regarded as a tube which is open at one end and closed at the other, what is the lowest frequency that it can reinforce?

A tuning fork is often mounted on a resonant box.[130] This box is practically a rather wide tube that is open at one end for the lower pitched forks, and for the higher pitched forks is often open at both ends. The stem of the fork

---

[130] The use of the resonant box is attributed to Marloye, a French maker of acoustic apparatus. In the third edition of his catalog (Paris, p. 48, 1851) he pointed out that the loudness of the sound from a tuning fork depends on the body against which the stem of the fork is held, and that this fact has sometimes led to a belief that there is some variation in the pitch. "C'est même parce que plusieurs questions sur ce sujet m'ont été adressées en 1841 quand mon diapason a paru, que j'ai songé à le monter sur une caisse exécutant le même nombre de vibrations que lui, pour dissiper cette illusion."

forces the wooden box to vibrate, and that in turn sets the air inside of it to vibrating. The fundamental of the air in the box has a frequency close to that of the fork, and so this tone is considerably reinforced.

Question 182. When the stem of a vibrating tuning fork is placed on top of a wooden table or other extended wooden surface there is also a reinforcement of the sound. When the tuning fork is mounted on a resonant box perhaps the reinforcement is after all due in large part to the wood. How could you find out whether the air in the box really has much to do with it?

Question 183. By lifting the resonant box to the experimenter's mouth and blowing suddenly across it it is possible to get some idea of the natural pitch of the cavity. This pitch is sometimes found to be somewhat sharper than that of the fork which is mounted on the box. Do you see any reason for this difference?

One well known illustration of resonance is afforded by two tuning forks of the same pitch mounted on similar resonant boxes. If one fork is set to vibrating and is soon afterward stopped, the other may be heard continuing the sound. Sometimes it is even possible for each fork to set the other alternately into vibration. This may be accomplished by setting one fork vibrating and then damping it by a finger laid on it for a moment. The second is heard sounding, and when it is similarly damped the first is heard. In this way the sound may be passed back and forth several times from one fork to the other. In a room where the sound can spread in all directions this experiment works best with the forks fairly near to each other, but in a hard walled tube, where the intensity does not fall off greatly with distance, the effect may be observed with the forks much farther apart. Zahm[131] states that "with two similar tuning forks executing 128 vibrations per second, and placed with

[131] J. A. Zahm, *Sound and Music,* ed. 2 (1900), p. 265. I do not find this statement in Koenig's *Quelques Expériences d'Acoustique,* nor in any article at which I have looked. Perhaps Zahm had the statement directly from Koenig himself.

the open ends of their resonant cases facing the opposite ends of the conduit of St. Michel, in Paris, Dr. Koenig was able, by exciting one, to cause the other to resound very distinctly, although more than a mile distant."

The fact that the vibration of a tuning fork lasts for so long a time shows that the damping must be very small. Consequently we expect that one tuning fork will not set another into appreciable vibration unless their pitches are very nearly the same. This expectation proves to be entirely correct. The addition of a small lump of wax to one of the forks may be sufficient to prevent any audible response, even though the change in pitch is so slight as to be little more than barely perceptible.

Question 184. Two tuning forks of the same pitch are (a) mounted on appropriate resonant boxes that rest on a wooden table, (b) mounted on appropriate resonant boxes that are held by two assistants, (c) not mounted, but held by two assistants. Under these different conditions should you expect much difference in the extent to which one fork responds to the other?

Two well known illustrations of resonance are readily obtained with a piano. The pressing of the damper pedal [132] lifts the dampers away from the strings, and so leaves all the strings free to vibrate. When the damper pedal is held down it is possible to sing into the piano and then hear it singing back. The piano also responds readily to a more complicated sound like a cough. When the damper pedal is not depressed it is possible to free the strings for any given note by pressing the digital for that note. If the digital for g_2 or c_3 is pressed down quietly and then the digital for c_1 is struck and then released, it is very likely that the g_2 or c_3 will be heard singing on.

Question 185. In the experiment just described why do g_2 and c_3 respond to c_1? What other notes would respond to c_1? How

[132] Sometimes called the "loud pedal."

should you expect the temperament of the scale to affect these responses?

The air in a room has certain normal modes of vibration. With regard to church auditoriums Sabine [133] quotes Bishop Conaty as saying "he found it difficult to avoid pitching his voice to that note which the auditorium most prolongs notwithstanding the fact that he found this the worst pitch on which to speak." Rayleigh [134] says, "There is an underground passage in my house in which it is possible, by singing the right note, to excite free vibrations of many seconds' duration, and it often happens that the resonant note is affected with distinct beats. The breadth of the passage is about 4 feet, and the height about 6½ feet."

Rayleigh also writes, [134] "Some of the natural notes of the air contained within a room may generally be detected on singing the scale. Probably it is somewhat in this way that blind people are able to estimate the size of rooms." Erasmus Darwin [135] tells that "the late blind Justice Fielding walked for the first time into my room, when he once visited me, and after speaking a few words said, 'This room is about 22 feet long, 18 wide, and 12 high'; all which he guessed by the ear with great accuracy."

Question 186. Certain of the normal modes of vibration of the air in a rectangular room are the same as those of the air in a tube which has the same length and is closed at both ends. If such a room is 22 ft. [= 6.7 m.] long what are the frequencies of the normal modes that lie near the fundamental pitch of a man's voice? See Art. 60 on p. 153, and Question 79 on p. 82.

73. Absorption of Sound by Resonators.—We have seen that a resonator is often used to make a tone louder. There

[133] Wallace Clement Sabine, Am. Acad. Arts and Sciences, Proc., **42,** 60 (1906); reprinted in Sabine's *Collected Papers on Acoustics,* p. 79.
[134] Lord Rayleigh, *Theory of Sound,* Macmillan, ed. 2, vol. 2 (1896), p. 72.
[135] Erasmus Darwin (1731-1802), *Zoonomia,* ed. 3, vol. 4 (1801), p. 262. Charles Robert Darwin, author of the *Origin of Species* and the *Descent of Man,* was a grandson of Erasmus Darwin.

the time it takes a wave to travel along the string from A to B.

Any disturbance of a small part of the string produces waves that run along the string, are reflected at each end, and travel back and forth until they die out. If a wave started by the fork travels from A to B and back again during any whole number of vibrations of the fork all the waves traveling toward the right are in phase with each other, all the waves traveling toward the left are in phase with each other, and standing waves of considerable amplitude are set up on the string. The vibration is usually so rapid that the eye cannot follow it. The string does not appear to pass from one position to another, but to be in all of its positions all of the time. If the string is white and there is a dark background the nodes and the ventral segments show beautifully.

When the vibration of the string is large it is found that the end A is close to a node. A is not exactly at a node, for it is the motion at A that makes the rest of the string vibrate. To see how the distance from A to a node affects the vibration let us turn to Eq. (11) on p. 136. In that equation l stood for the length of the string, and the string was vibrating in its fundamental mode. That is, l stood not only for the length of the string but also for the distance from one node to the next. Eq. (11) applies to our present case if l stands for the distance from one node to the next, whether that happens to be the same as the length of the string or not. With this meaning for l, (11) shows us that if we increase the weight at C in Fig. 58 we shall increase the length of a ventral segment. The result is shown in Fig. 59. In each of the cases in this figure one end of the string is fastened at B, and the other vibrates between A_1 and A_2. In each diagram there is a node at C, and the ventral segment is widest at D. The tension on the string is least in the top diagram and greatest in the lowest. If the distance A_1A_2 is fixed we see that the width of the segment at D depends on how near C is to A.

Fig. 60 shows a series of photographs of the forced vibration of a rubber cord that had white dots painted on it at regular intervals. The dots appear in the photographs

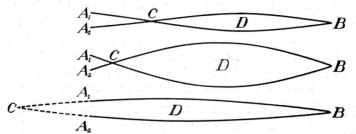

FIG. 59.—Sizes of Vibrating Segments on a String When the Node C Has Different Positions.

as vertical white lines. The cord was not driven by a tuning fork, but by a special apparatus which can be seen at the left. Instead of changing the tension of the cord changes were made in the impressed frequency.

Question 191. In Fig. 60 are the diagrams for the greater frequencies at the top of the page or at the bottom? How do the frequencies compare for photographs 2 and 8?

Question 192. If the photographs in Fig. 60 had all been obtained with the same frequency how would the tension required for photograph 2 compare with that for photograph 8?

Question 193. Melde sometimes used his tuning fork in the "parallel" position shown here. If all other conditions are the same

how should you expect the length of a ventral segment for the parallel position to compare with that for the transverse position?

Question 194. When the fork is in the parallel position the pulley sometimes appears to be turning steadily around.[139] Sometimes

[139] This rotation was discovered independently by several experimenters. The complete theory of the motion has not yet been developed. References to

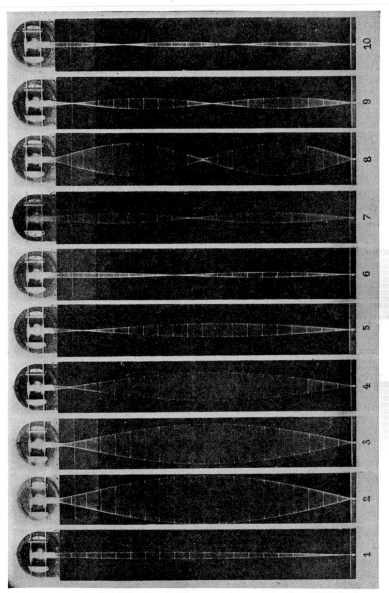

FIG. 60.—Forced Vibration of a Rubber cord [H. J. Oosting, *Physica*, 6, 344 (1926)].

this turning is in one sense and sometimes in the other, but in one sense the rotation is much easier to secure. Can you suggest any explanation for the rotation? In which sense should you expect it easier to secure rotation? Can you devise any simple experimental test of this last matter?

75. The Kundt Tube.—A few years after Melde devised his experiment a young man by the name of Kundt [140] developed a piece of apparatus which is of value in comparing the speeds of sound in different media, and which makes use of the forced vibration of the gas in a tube that is closed at both ends. One form of this apparatus is shown in Fig. 61. *AB* is a glass tube, perhaps a meter long

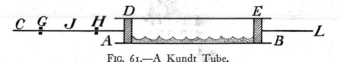

FIG. 61.—A Kundt Tube.

and a few centimeters in diameter, and *CD* is a brass rod, clamped at *G* and *H*. At the end D there is fastened to the rod a cork that fits the glass tube, but fits it rather loosely. Near the other end of the tube is another cork *E* that fits the tube snugly and can be set at a desired position by the handle *L*. Inside of the tube is a small amount of lycopodium spores, cork filings, or some other light powder.

The rod *CD* is stroked at *J* with a piece of chamois skin that has had a little crushed rosin sprinkled on it. This sets the rod into longitudinal vibration, and so makes the cork at *D* vibrate. The cork in turn forces the air in the tube to vibrate. In Melde's experiment we saw that the precise form of response depends on the relation between the period

some of the discoverers and first steps toward the theory are given in a paper by Arthur Taber Jones, Phys. Rev. **27,** 622 (1926). For a number of other cases that are somewhat similar see W. B. Morton and A. McKinstry, Phys. Rev. **29,** 192 (1927).

[140] August Kundt (1839-1894), Pogg. An. **127,** 497 (1866); **128,** 337 (1866); **135,** 337 and 527 (1868). Kundt was at this time Assistant to Professor Heinrich Gustav Magnus in the University at Berlin.

of the fork and the time it takes a wave to travel to the pulley. In a Kundt tube the response depends on the relation between the period of vibration of the cork at D and the time it takes a wave to travel from D to E. Any disturbance inside of the tube is reflected back and forth between the corks until it dies out. If a wave travels from D to E and back again during any whole number of vibrations of the cork at D all the waves that travel to the right are in phase with each other, all the waves that travel toward the left are in phase with each other, and standing waves of considerable amplitude are set up in the tube.

The powder in the tube is Kundt's clever means of finding out where the nodes and antinodes are situated. In Melde's experiment we need only look at the string in order to see the location of the nodes. But in a Kundt tube the air at a node looks no different from that at an antinode. Before the rod CD is stroked the tube may be tapped until the powder has collected in a line along the bottom of the tube. Then the tube may be turned about its axis until the powder is almost ready to fall. Then when the rod is stroked the powder at the nodes is not disturbed, but that between the nodes drops into festoons, somewhat as shown in Fig. 61.

If the tube is not turned on its axis before the rod is stroked the drooping festoons do not form, but the appearance at the nodes is nevertheless quite different from that between them. In fact, there is often a gradual movement of the powder, and there may be a tendency for it to collect in heaps near the positions of the nodes.

Kundt made use of his apparatus to compare the speeds of sound in different media. How may that be done? We know that the frequency of vibration of the air in the tube is the same as the frequency of vibration of the rod. We can measure the distance from node to node in the air, we know the distance from node to node in the brass, and we know that Eq. (7) on p. 79 holds for both the air and the brass. So if we know the speed of sound in air we can find the speed of sound in brass. If we replace the brass by a rod of some other solid material we can find the speed of sound in it. Kundt also modified his apparatus in such a way that he was able to compare the speeds of sound in different gases.

Question 195. When an experimenter is using the Kundt tube shown in Fig. 61 how does he know where to put the cork E?

Question 196. In Fig. 61 is the cork D close to a node or an antinode?

Question 197. In Fig. 61 the rod CD is 100 cm. long. The distance from one node in the tube to the next is 5 cm. What is the speed of sound in the rod?

Question 198. If you wish to determine the speed of sound in a number of different gases what modification of the apparatus shown in Fig. 61 might be desirable?

76. Ripples in a Kundt Tube.—Each festoon in a Kundt tube is crossed by many transverse ridges or ripples, and various other facts have been learned.[141] In some of the recent studies the vibration of the air has been set up by loud speaker units instead of by a cork on the end of a rod. In this way it is possible to keep the air vibrating for as long a time as desired. When the air is thus kept in steady vibration there sometimes forms at each antinode a very thin disk of powder extending clear across the tube.[141] This makes it possible to measure the distance from antinode to antinode with considerable accuracy. In this book we shall consider none of the phenomena except the ripples.

The first explanation [142] for the ripples was that they

[141] Interesting accounts of phenomena observed in Kundt tubes are given by Rolla V. Cook, Science, **72**, 422 (1930); E. Hutchisson and F. B. Morgan, Phys. Rev. **37**, 1155 (1931), and Edward Neville da Costa Andrade, Phil. Trans. A230, 413 (1932).

[142] J. Bourget, Mémoires de la Soc. des Sciences physiques et naturelles de Bordeaux, **9**, 329 (1873).

might be caused in the same way as the heaps at the nodes, but by an overtone of the rod. One objection to this explanation is that the distance from ripple to ripple is so small that the overtone would have to be a very high one, and it would be remarkable if one very high overtone were so much stronger than others as to produce distinct ripples. Moreover it has been found [143] that if the rod is made shorter and shorter the distance from ripple to ripple does not decrease in proportion. In addition recent work shows that the distance from ripple to ripple depends on the loudness of the sound, on the size of the particles, and on the average pressure of the air in the tube. These facts seem fatal to any explanation in terms of an overtone.

A second explanation, developed by W. König,[144] depends on the Bernoulli effect which we have met on p. 180. In Fig. 51 the line that joins the two spores is perpendicular to the general direction in which the air flows, and the spores attract each other. If we draw a similar diagram for the case where the line that joins the spores lies parallel to the air current, we see that in the space between the spores the air is slowed down and therefore has a somewhat increased pressure. This means that when the line joining the spores lies in the direction of the current the spores repel each other. When the line joining the centers is neither parallel to the current nor perpendicular to it König's calculations showed that the spores would tend to move to a position in which the joining line is perpendicular to the current.

Question 199. On the basis of the facts just stated how may we explain the ripples in a Kundt tube? Does this explanation seem to you satisfactory?

A third explanation, suggested by Schweikert,[145] depends

---

[143] F. Neesen, Verh. der physikal. Ges. zu Berlin, **3,** 14 (1884) ; more fully in Wied. An. **30,** 432 (1887).

[144] Walter König, Wied. An., **42,** 353 and 549 (1891).

[145] Gustav Schweikert, An. d. Physik, **52,** 333 (1917).

on the theory of vortices developed by Helmholtz and applied by him to series of parallel cirrus clouds.[146]   Fig. 62 may help us to understand Helmholtz's reasoning.   It represents a region high up in the sky, and the air above AB is traveling to the right faster than that below AB.   Under such conditions the surface AB is unstable.   Suppose, for instance, that at C the surface is humped up a little.   Then in the upper layer the air flows faster between C and D than it does between E and H.   So Bernoulli's principle shows that the pressure which the upper layer exerts at C

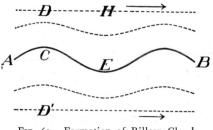

Fig. 62.—Formation of Billow Clouds.

is less than that which it exerts at E.   Similarly in the lower layer the pressure at C is greater than that at E.   Thus the amplitude of the wavy line $ACEB$ grows until the crest of each wave breaks and forms a vortex or eddy in which the air from both layers is mixed.   The temperatures and humidities of the two layers may be such that the mixing leads to condensation and the formation of clouds.   The crests of the waves in the bounding layer AB are somewhat uniformly spaced, and so the clouds that form are also somewhat uniformly spaced.

How are these ideas to be applied to the ripples in a Kundt tube?   In each ventral segment the air swings alternately to the right and to the left.   The air near the floor

[146] Hermann von Helmholtz, *Wiss. Abh.*, 1, 146; 3, 289 and 309.   These papers were presented before the Akad. der Wiss. in Berlin in 1868, 1888, and 1889.

of the tube contains cork filings or other powder. The air above it is not thus loaded, and the two layers may be regarded as meeting at a surface like *AB* in Fig. 62. This surface is unstable, and as the air flows in each direction the surface breaks into a series of vortices that carry the cork filings with them. When the vibration in the tube subsides the vortices drop their cargo, and the particles from each vortex form one ripple.

Question 200. When the rod in a Kundt tube is stroked why do the particles rise from the floor of the tube?

The most recent explanation of the ripples is proposed by Andrade.[141] When the vibration of the air carries it with sufficient rapidity past a small obstacle he finds [147] that the motion of the air is greatly modified. Fig. 63 is one

FIG. 63.—Vortex System Around a Cylindrical Obstacle [Photograph kindly supplied by Professor Andrade]. The cylinder was 2.37 mm. in diameter, was perpendicular to the plane of the page, and was in the position of the white spot near the middle of the figure. The air was swinging back and forth to the right and left. The path of the air was made visible by smoke.

of his photographs. Around the obstacle there is a system of slowly rotating vortices. When there are two or more obstacles, and they are far enough apart, each has its own separate vortex system. If two obstacles are fairly close to each other a single vortex system forms around both of

147 E. N. da C. Andrade, Roy. Soc. Lond. Proc., **A134,** 445 (1931).

them, the two particles are urged toward each other, and they tend to set themselves so that the line joining them is perpendicular to the general direction of the current. If they are far enough apart for each to have its own vortex system they tend to set themselves at such a distance apart that the two systems of vortices just touch each other. It follows that particles which happen to get close to each other will turn so as to set their joining lines across the tube, and that these groups of particles will space themselves along the tube at distances which depend on the size of the vortices. If the vibration becomes stronger it is to be expected that the vortices will be larger and the ripples farther apart. It is found that this really is the case.[141]   The amplitude of vibration in the tube is greatest at the antinodes, and decreases toward the nodes. So it is to be expected that the vortices will be largest at the antinodes, and the ripples farthest apart there. This, too, is found to fit the facts.

Moreover, when there is very little powder in the tube it sometimes happens that there are not more than two or three ripples. In such a case Schweikert's explanation would hardly lead to any ripple formation whatever, and König's explanation would lead to a separation of these few ripples until the repulsive force between them became too small to produce any further movement. At present our best explanation of the ripples appears to be Andrade's—that the ripples depend on the slowly rotating vortices which the particles produce in the air that streams past them.

77. Coupled Systems.—When we have spoken of forced vibrations we have usually been interested in some single body on which the force acted, and we have considered the vibration of that one body. If the reader has had a course in physics he will remember that, according to Newton's third law of motion, every force has an equal and oppositely directed reaction. This is just as true of varying

forces as of steady forces. When a Savart wheel exerts a periodic force on a card the card exerts a periodic reacting force on the wheel. When the tuning fork in Melde's experiment exerts a periodic force on the string the string exerts a periodic reaction on the fork.

The reaction which a card exerts on a Savart wheel has probably very little effect on the wheel, but the reaction which the string in Melde's experiment exerts on the fork is sometimes so vigorous that it stops the vibration of the fork. When a vibrating body or vibrating system consists of two or more parts that could vibrate independently if they were not connected we speak of the whole as a *coupled system*. Many of the bodies with which we are concerned are really coupled systems. A tuning fork and a Helmholtz resonator close to it form a coupled system. A violin string, the wooden body of the violin, and the air inside of the body combine to form a more complicated coupled system. The vocal chords and the resonant cavities in the head form another coupled system.

When one part of a coupled system is set vibrating it exerts a periodic force on another part of the system. This second part executes a forced vibration, and exerts a reacting force on the first part. That reacting force modifies the vibration of the first part. When the force that one part of the system exerts on another is small we say that the *coupling is loose* or that the system is *loosely coupled,* or sometimes that the *coupling is weak.* When the force is large we speak of the coupling as *close,* or occasionally as *tight.* When a tuning fork is at some distance from a Helmholtz resonator the coupling between them is very loose; when the fork is screwed tightly to a resonant box the coupling between the fork and the box is very close.

A coupled system may be forced to vibrate or it may vibrate freely. If any part of the system is subject to a periodic force the whole system executes a forced vibration.

If any part of the system is set vibrating, and the system is then left to itself, the system executes a free vibration, but the coupling adds to our difficulty in understanding just what happens.

A coupled system has its own set of normal modes of vibration, and the frequencies of these modes are usually not the same as those of the component parts of the system. The looser the coupling the more nearly do the frequencies of the normal modes of the system approach the natural frequencies of the components, and the closer the coupling the wider is the departure likely to be. Even in the case where there are only two components and the components are just alike, the system as a whole has usually a normal mode a little sharper, and a normal mode a little flatter, than either of the components.

It is obvious that the theory of coupled systems is of great importance. It is however beyond the limits set for this book, and we shall simply consider a few illustrations.

78. Illustrations of Coupled Systems.—As one illustration of the free vibration of a coupled system consider the

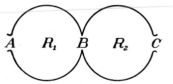

double resonator shown in Fig. 64. Let the volumes of the component resonators be the same, and let the mouths, A and C, be of the same shape and size. If there were no communication at B there would be two separate resonators. If the opening at B is small the coupling is loose, and if the opening is large the coupling is closer.

FIG. 64.—Double Resonator. This resonator consists of two simple resonators, R_1 and R_2, joined by the opening B.

This system has two normal modes of vibration. In one mode the air swings inward at the same time at both A and C, and the vibration is the same as if there were no opening at B. In this mode the pressures in R_1 and R_2 are in phase with each other. In the other mode the air swings inward at A at the same time that it swings outward at C and to the left at B. In this mode the pressure rises in R_1 at the same time that it falls in R_2. That is, in this mode the phases of the pressures in R_1 and R_2 are opposite.

Question 201. Of the two modes of vibration that have just been described which has the higher pitch?

Question 202. Do the frequencies of the two normal modes of the resonator shown in Fig. 64 differ more widely when the opening at B is large or small?

In Chapter Eleven we shall see that the cavity in the human mouth is often a double resonator in which the amount of coupling is determined by the position of the tongue.

An illustration of the maintained vibration of a coupled system is afforded by an organ pipe and a Helmholtz resonator. If the pipe is sounding steadily, and the resonator has a natural pitch a little lower than that of the pipe, it is found that as the resonator approaches the mouth of the pipe the pitch that is heard rises somewhat. If the natural pitch of the resonator is a little higher than that of the pipe it is found that as the resonator approaches the pipe the pitch falls a little. The effect is large enough to be detected easily by ear. However, if there is any doubt as to whether the effect is real all that is necessary is to have a tuning fork of nearly the same pitch vibrating not far from the pipe. As the resonator approaches the pipe the frequency of the beats changes, and it changes in the direction that fits the statement just made.

Question 203. A tuning fork slightly flatter than an organ pipe is beating with the pipe. A resonator slightly flatter than the pipe is brought toward the mouth of the pipe. Does the frequency of the beats increase or decrease?

79. Periodic Forces which are Not Simple Harmonic.

—The periodic forces with which we have been dealing are simple harmonic. Most actual forces, even when they are periodic, are not so simple. The tramp of marching feet gives rise to a periodic force on the floor or pavement, but it is obvious that this force is not simple harmonic. The teeth of a Savart wheel exert a periodic force on the card, but it is clear that this force is not simple harmonic. The rhythmic pulling of a crew is periodic, but neither the separate pulls nor their resultant is simple harmonic.

We know (Art. 70) that a changing force may be represented by a curve. A periodic force is represented by a periodic curve. Now when any curve is periodic there is a most remarkable theorem that tells how the curve might have been built up. We owe this theorem to Fourier.[148]   It states that when a curve is periodic it may be regarded as made up by combining simple harmonic curves in the way shown in Fig. 11 on p. 41; it states that for each periodic curve there is just one definite set of simple harmonic curves that will combine to produce it; and it states that the wave lengths of the component simple harmonic curves are in the ratio $1 : \frac{1}{2} : \frac{1}{3} : \frac{1}{4} : \frac{1}{5} \cdots$.   When the curve represents a periodic force Fourier's theorem tells us that the force may be regarded as the resultant of a number of simple harmonic forces, all acting at the same time, and having frequencies in the ratios $1 : 2 : 3 : 4 : 5 \cdots$.   It is partly for this reason that the importance of a harmonic series of frequencies is so great.

When a periodic force acts on a body or system that has a number of normal modes of vibration it may be that some of the component frequencies of the force are close to the frequencies of certain normal modes.   In each case

---

[148] Jean Baptiste Joseph Fourier (1768-1830), famous French mathematician. Fourier stated this theorem and made various applications of it in his book, *La Théorie Analytique de la Chaleur* (1822).

where this happens there is resonance, and the force may cause a considerable vibration in that particular normal mode. Now when a periodic force is resolved into its simple harmonic components it is usually found that the components with the lower frequencies are the strongest, and that the high frequency ones are very weak. It follows that if the low frequency components of the force have frequencies close to those of normal modes of the system on which the force is acting, those modes will be brought out with especial prominence.

We shall see later (Arts. 122 and 135-139) that the facts stated in this article have an important bearing on the qualities of organ pipes and on the differences between the sounds of different vowels.

80. Maintained Vibration of Violin Strings.—We turn now to a few cases of maintained vibration. Let us consider first how a bow can set up and maintain the vibration of a violin string. There is a certain amount of friction between the bow and the string, so that when the bow is drawn steadily across the string the latter is drawn aside somewhat from its original position of equilibrium. But if the pull of the bow is steady it would seem that the string ought to take up a new position of equilibrium—much as if we were to take hold of the string with a finger, draw it slightly aside, and hold it there. There is no obvious reason why a steady force should set the string vibrating. How does the bow produce and maintain the vibration?

The answer is found in the fact that the pull of the bow is not steady. To understand why the pull is not steady it is necessary to have in mind certain facts about friction. If a book is lying on a table it is possible to press horizontally against the book without causing it to move. This is because the friction between the book and the table balances the push. If the push is more gentle the friction becomes smaller, if the push is harder the friction becomes greater. So long as the book does not move, the friction changes in such a way as always to balance the push.

But if the push becomes sufficiently strong the book does slip. That is, under given circumstances there is a largest value that the friction can have, and if the push becomes greater than that largest value it is no longer possible for friction to balance the push, and the book slips. This largest value that the friction can have without any slip occurring may be called the *maximum static friction* between the book and the table—that is, the maximum under the given circumstances.

As soon as the book begins to slip it is found that the friction decreases somewhat, and that the amount of friction remains nearly the same so long as the book slips, provided it does not slide very rapidly. The friction which occurs while the book slides is called the *kinetic friction* between the book and the table. We are now prepared to state briefly that under given circumstances kinetic friction is less than maximum static friction.

How does this apply to a violin string? The farther the string is drawn aside from its original equilibrium position the larger is the force that is needed to hold it displaced. This displacing force is provided by friction between the string and the bow. As the bow draws the string farther aside the friction between them increases, and this increase goes on until the maximum static friction is reached. Then the string slips backward along the bow, the static friction is replaced by kinetic friction, and, in spite of the forward motion of the bow, the string swings backward and then starts forward again. As soon as the string is moving forward at the same rate as the bow the friction becomes static friction, and the string moves with the bow until the maximum static friction is again reached. The maintenance occurs because the forward pull on the string just before it begins to slip is greater than the forward pull just after it begins to slip.

It is conceivable that a condition might be reached in which the kinetic friction just balanced the restoring force, so that the bow might hold the string steady in a displaced position instead of causing it to vibrate. But if such a condition were reached any slight variation in bowing pressure, or in the roughness of the bow, would start a little vibration of the string, and the vibration would be likely to grow and be maintained.

Question 204. In Art. 110 we shall consider the vibration curves for different points on a violin string. On the basis of the statements just made what should you expect the vibration curve for the point under the bow to look like?

Question 205. A part of the energy put into a violin comes out as sound. Making use of the ideas in Arts. 71 and 80 what do you suppose would be the shape of the curve that shows how the rate at which the bow supplies energy to the string depends on the time?

Question 206. The squeaking of a door or of machinery is brought about in somewhat the same manner as the vibration of a violin string. How are the ideas in Art. 80 to be applied to the squeaking of a door?

81. Electrically Maintained Tuning Fork.—There are several means by which the vibration of a tuning fork may be maintained. One of the well known methods is shown in Fig. 65. Between the prongs of the fork is an electromagnet. If the electric current through the coil of this magnet grows stronger it makes the magnet stronger, so that the magnet pulls harder on the prongs. If the current grows weaker the magnet pulls on the prongs less strongly. Instead of employing the rest of the apparatus in Fig. 65 suppose for the moment that we have some means of making the current in the electromagnet increase and decrease periodically. The fork then executes a forced vibration, and its frequency is that of the periodic force. If this frequency is very close to the natural frequency of the fork there is resonance and the vibration of the fork may be vigorous.

Now return to the arrangement shown in Fig. 65. If the plate H is just in contact with the wire J the electric current flows and the magnet M draws the prongs of the fork toward each other. This pulls J away from H, the current stops flowing, the magnetism in M weakens, the stiffness of the prongs swings them apart, and J touches H again. Then the process begins once more. Thus the current alternately flows and is interrupted, the frequency of the changing force on the prongs is close to the natural frequency of the fork, and the vibration is maintained.

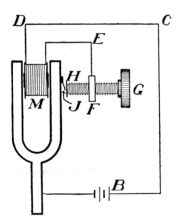

FIG. 65.—Electrically Maintained Tuning Fork. B is an electric battery, from which the current flows through the wire CD to the electromagnet M. From M it flows through the wire E to the brass block F and the thumb screw G. When G is screwed forward it brings the plate H into contact with the wire J, and the current can then flow on through the tuning fork and back to the battery.

When we examine the situation more carefully it seems as if maintenance in this way would be impossible. Fig. 66 is the vibration curve for the right-hand prong of the fork. Time runs downward in this figure instead of to the right. The dotted line shows the position of the prong when the spring J in Fig. 65 makes contact with the plate H. That is, the electric current flows during the time when the vibration curve lies to the right of the dotted line in Fig. 66. It follows that the magnetic force urges the prongs inward during the last part of their excursion outward, and during an equal part of the excursion inward. The energy taken away from the prongs on their journey outward appears to be equal to that given them on their journey inward. There appears to be no resultant transfer of energy to the prongs. So it seems that damping must soon stop the fork, and that the clever idea of Fig. 65 cannot be practical. In spite of this argument the method of maintenance shown in Fig. 65 does work, and it works well. There is a fallacy in the argument, and a reader who has had a course in physics ought to be able to find it.

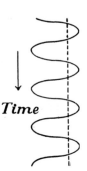

FIG. 66. — Vibration Curve for One Prong of a Maintained Tuning Fork.

Question 207. What is the fallacy in the argument just presented?

Question 208. If the electric current from the apparatus shown in Fig. 65 is run through an electromagnet between the prongs of another fork of the same frequency both forks can be maintained in vibration. Can a second fork be maintained if its natural pitch is an octave higher than that of the fork which interrupts the current? If it is an octave lower?

82. Singing Flames. Early Explanations. — Another illustration of maintained vibration is afforded by the phenomena connected with "singing flames." These flames are of interest in themselves, and they also afford so excellent an illustration of some of the difficulties that are often met in the attempt to formulate a satisfactory physical theory that it will be worth while to devote some space to them and to see something as to how the knowledge of these flames and the ideas about them have developed.

The effect itself seems to have been first observed by Higgins [149] more than a century and a half ago. He introduced a flame of burning hydrogen into a vertical glass tube, and found that under favorable conditions it gave out a musical sound.

[149] See Appendix Six.

The early explanations were neither very clear nor very satisfactory. Perhaps the water vapor formed by the burning of the hydrogen is rather suddenly condensed by the colder air around it, and so causes the air to strike the glass wall and set it vibrating [Hermbstädt]; perhaps there is alternately too much fuel and then too much oxygen from the surrounding air [William Nicholson, Editor of Nicholson's Journal]; perhaps there is a rapid formation of water vapor and then a sudden condensation of it, thus setting the air in the tube to vibrating like that in an organ pipe [De Luc]; perhaps the water vapor is cooled by contact with the air that enters the bottom of the tube, thus contracting and permitting new air to press nearer to the flame and so forming more water vapor [Delarive].

It soon became clear that the vibration is not primarily that of the glass tube, but is a vibration of the contained air. Chladni gave two reasons for this point of view: First, the tube can be taken hold of at any point without affecting the note; and second, the pitch is nearly that obtained by blowing across the end of the tube. But Chladni made no suggestion as to how the tone is produced.

83. Faraday's Explanation.—Before many years Faraday[149] showed that any explanation which depends on water vapor produced by the burning of the hydrogen cannot be correct. Faraday was able to get a flame to sing when the whole tube was so hot that no water vapor could condense inside of it, and he was also able to get a flame to sing when he burned a jet of carbon monoxide, which does not produce any water vapor.

Faraday's explanation[150] is that the sound arises from a series of explosions, and that the tube regulates the rate at

[150] F. Auerbach [in Winkelmann, *Handbuch der Physik,* ed. 2, vol. 2 (1909), p. 478] says that this explanation was suggested by Count Puschkin and developed by Faraday. Faraday makes no mention of Puschkin, and gives the explanation as if it were his own. I have not found Puschkin's paper.

which the explosions occur. By sweeping the eyes rapidly past the tube while the flame is singing it is not difficult to see that the flame is not steady, and by the use of a rotating mirror Wheatstone [151] showed clearly that the flame really is hopping up and down while it sings.

Is the hopping up and down of the flame produced, as Faraday thought, by a series of explosions? After nearly half a century this question was examined by Töpler.[152] Töpler's results were obtained in two entirely different ways— with a "stroboscope" and with his "Schlieren method," the latter of which we shall not discuss in this book.

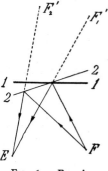

FIG. 67.—Rotating Mirror.

The stroboscope takes v a r i o u s forms,[153] but the underlying idea is not a difficult one. Suppose that the vibrating body is in a darkened room, and that by some means, say by a regular series of electric sparks, we can see the vibrating body only at certain instants. If the frequency of the sparks is precisely the same as that of the vibration we shall always see the body in the same position, and it will appear to be at rest in that position. If the time from one spark to the next is a trifle greater than the period of vibration it is clear that in the interval between sparks the body must make one vibration and an additional fraction of a vibration. So at each spark the body is seen a little

[151] Sir Charles Wheatstone, Phil. Trans., 124, 586 (1834) ; or *Wheatstone's Scientific Papers*, p. 88. Wheatstone's rotating mirror has come into very general use. Fig. 67 shows why it is so valuable. The mirror is vertical and we are looking down upon it. F represents the flame, or other object being viewed, and E the observing eye. When the mirror is in the position 11 the image of the flame is at F'₁, and when the mirror has turned to 22 the image has moved to F'₂. Thus successive images of the flame are seen in different positions in space, and it is possible to observe the changes that occur in the flame.

[152] August Töpler, Pogg. An., 128, 108 and 126 (1866).

[153] As to who first made use of the stroboscopic principle see Appendix Six.

farther along in its path. If the period of the sparks is only slightly greater than that of the vibration the body appears to move slowly through cycle after cycle of its vibration.

Instead of illuminating the body by a series of sparks there are other ways in which we may arrange to get momentary glimpses of it at regular intervals. One of these ways is to use a circular disk that has near its outer edge a uniform series of narrow radial slits. If the disk spins steadily in its own plane, and the vibrating body is viewed through it, the body is seen each time that a slit comes in front of the eye.

By the methods which Töpler employed he was able to show that in most cases, if not in all, the flame does not go out. Faraday's explanation has usually been regarded as meaning that each explosion drives the gas in the nozzle momentarily backward, and so puts out the flame until the flow of gas has been reestablished and a fresh explosive mixture is ignited by the heat that still remains. Töpler found that the flame does not go out. There is a little flame left burning, so that the usual interpretation of Faraday's "explosions" cannot be regarded as correct.

Question 209. A singing flame is observed through the slits in a spinning stroboscopic disk. In one case the frequency with which the slits pass the eye is a trifle greater than the frequency of the vibration, and in another case it is a trifle less. How does the apparent motion in the two cases differ?

Question 210. In Melde's experiment the damping of the string is very appreciable. The energy which keeps up the vibration of any given ventral segment comes from the tuning fork and has to travel through all the nodes that lie between the fork and the segment in question. It follows that at the nodes the string cannot be absolutely at rest, but must execute a small vibration of some sort. In an interesting study of this small motion Raman [154] observed the string when it was illuminated by electric sparks that occurred with a frequency nearly

[154] Sir Chandrasekhar Venkataram Raman, Phys. Rev., 32, 309 (1911).

twice that of the string. What is seen when a vibrating body is viewed stroboscopically at a frequency nearly twice that of the vibration? What if the viewing frequency is close to half that of the vibration?

84. Attempt at a Theory.—We have found that the pitch given by a singing flame is a natural pitch of the air in the surrounding tube, and that the flame is hopping up and down. With these facts in mind let us attempt an explanation of the singing. In Fig. 68 *AB* is the "singing tube" in which the vibration of the air is maintained, and *CD* is the "supply tube" for the gas. Suppose that the air in *AB* has been started to vibrating slightly in its fundamental mode. Then the pressure is varying slightly, and is doing so periodically. At the phase when the pressure around the flame is small it would seem that the gas should flow rapidly from the nozzle, the flame should be large, and heat should be given rapidly to the surrounding air, thus producing considerable increase in pressure. Similarly, when the pressure is large the flame should be small, and should produce only a small increase in pressure.

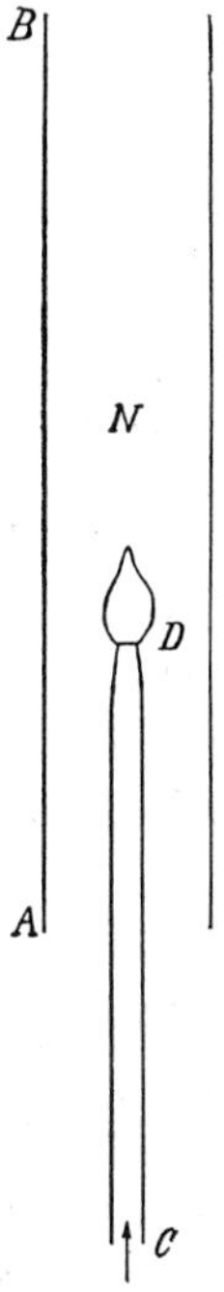

Does this change in the rate at which heat is developed occur in such a way that it can increase and maintain the vibration of the air? The sound that travels out from the tube carries energy with it, and so damps the vibration in the tube. If nothing maintains the vibration the largest pressure in one cycle is not quite as large as that in the preceding cycle, and the smallest pressure in any cycle is not quite small as that in the preceding cycle. If the vibration is to be maintained it must be by some agent that increases the pressure when it is large, or decreases it when

Fig. 68.— A Singing Flame.

it is small. This is not the phase relationship which our reasoning has led us to expect in the case shown in Fig. 68. In fact, our reasoning would lead us to expect the flame to aid in damping any vibration in the tube rather than to maintain it. But the flame does maintain the vibration. Obviously something is the matter.

Question 211. Do you find in the last two paragraphs any flaw in the reasoning that might account for the difficulty in which we are involved?

85. Further Studies.—Probably we are in need of further experimental facts. An important contribution to our knowledge of singing flames was made by Sondhauss.[155] From the time when Sondhauss first began to study physics he was fascinated by singing flames, and at various times during the succeeding years he experimented with them. The gas that he burned was usually hydrogen, his burner was often, like that in Fig. 68, simply a small hole at the top of a slender piece of glass tubing, and the lower end of this gas supply tube was in a flask in which the hydrogen was generated.

Sondhauss found that if he pushed a cotton plug up into the gas supply tube the gas might work its way through the plug, and the flame look just the same as if there were no plug, but the flame would not sing. Moreover, the relative lengths of supply tube and singing tube seemed to be important. For a given supply tube there were certain lengths of singing tube for which the flame would sing readily, and others for which he could not coax it to sing. These facts seemed to mean that in order for the flame to maintain the vibration of the air in the singing tube it was necessary that there should also be a vibration of the gas in the supply tube.

[155] Carl Friedrich Julius Sondhauss (1815-1886), Pogg. An., **109**, 1 and 426 (1860). Sondhauss was Director of the Realschule at Neisse, in eastern Germany.

Sondhauss proposed no clear explanation of the sing-ing.[156] The first approach to a satisfactory explanation ap-pears to have been given by Rayleigh [157] in a Friday eve-ning lecture at the Royal Institution. Rayleigh assumes that there is vibration, not only of the air in the singing tube, but also of the gas in the supply tube; that the vibra-tions in the two tubes have the same frequency; and that the pressure inside of the nozzle at the top of the supply tube does not differ greatly from the pressure just outside of it. These assumptions seem entirely reasonable, and we shall find that they resolve the difficulty which we met in the last paragraph in Art. 84.

In Fig. 68 suppose that the length of the supply tube CD is less than quarter of a wave length for sound of the given frequency in the gas that is in CD. Let us suppose further that the supply tube is fed at C from a pipe of con-siderably larger bore or from a flask. Then in the stand-ing waves which are superposed on the steady upward flow of gas in CD there must be an antinode not far from C, and if CD were long enough there would be a node a quar-ter of a wave length above this antinode. Although no such node exists the vibration in CD is the same as if the tube did extend farther upward.

At some instant the pressure at the node N in the large tube is at its maximum. Let us consider the state of affairs at an instant a quarter of a period earlier. At this instant the pressure of the air is practically the same at all points in AB, and in its vibration the air has its most rapid motion.

[156] His explanation is contained in a single sentence in which he suggests that the high temperature of the flame causes the vibration in the gas supply tube, and that this in turn gives rise to the vibration in the singing tube. "Nach meiner Ansicht ist die durch die Gasflamme bewirkte bedeutende Temperatur-Erhöhung die Ursache der primitiven Schwingungen der Gas-säule, welche dann die Luftsäule der Klangröhre in tönende Schwingungen versetzen." Page 466 in the reference given in footnote 155.

[157] Lord Rayleigh, Roy. Inst. Proc., 8, 536 (1878); or Nature, 18, 319 (1878); or *Theory of Sound*, ed. 2, vol. 2, art. 322h.

In the lower half of AB the air is swinging upward, and in the upper half downward, and the pressure at any chosen point is increasing rapidly. Since the pressure just outside of the nozzle D is increasing rapidly the pressure just inside of the nozzle is also increasing rapidly. When the pressure at any point is increasing we know that the gas near that point is swinging toward the nearest node, and away from the nearest antinode. At the instant in question the vibration of the gas in CD is therefore carrying it rapidly upward, and the flame is large. Since the burning of the gas and the communication of heat to the neighboring air are not instantaneous we see that the most rapid supply of heat occurs shortly after the instant that we have been considering. That is, the most rapid supply of heat occurs when the pressure is greater than the average. If our present reasoning is correct we were in error when we assumed that the gas came from the nozzle most rapidly when the pressure in the air near the nozzle was least. Our present reasoning leads to a greatest supply of heat near the instant when the pressure is greatest, and therefore explains how a flame can increase a slight vibration, and can then maintain it.

Question 212. What is the state of affairs a quarter of a period after the instant when the pressure at N in Fig. 68 is a maximum?

Question 213. If the length of the supply tube CD in Fig. 68 is three eighths of a wave length, to what conclusion does Rayleigh's reasoning lead?

Rayleigh's reasoning has led us to expect the flame at D in Fig. 68 to be largest at an instant near that at which the pressure at N is greatest. In order to find out whether this is really the case Richardson [158] made use of a manometric capsule.

[158] Edward Gick Richardson, Phys. Soc. Lond. Proc., 35, 47 (1922-1923).

The manometric capsule was invented by Koenig,[159] and consists essentially of a thin box, *AB* in Fig. 69, divided into two compartments by a very light and flexible membrane *M*. Illuminating gas passes through one compartment and burns in a small flame. The membrane keeps the gas from passing into the other compartment, but yields readily under changes in pressure. In the figure the sound comes in from the left. When a compression enters the capsule the flame burns higher, and when a rarefaction comes it burns lower. Since the changes of pressure in audible sounds occur so rapidly that the eye cannot follow the corresponding changes in the flame, Koenig usually observed with the aid of a rotating mirror, like that described in footnote 151 on p. 225.

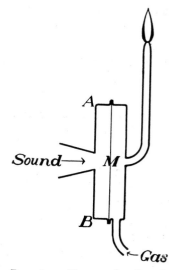

FIG. 69. — Manometric Capsule. The shape of the box or capsule *AB* is often that of a flat round pill box. The box is here tipped up and viewed from the side, so that the round top and bottom are at the left and right in the diagram.

Richardson's singing tube was made of brass and had two holes cut in it at the level of the flame. One hole was in the front, and was covered by a glass window through which the singing flame could be observed. The other hole was in the side of the tube, and was covered with the membrane of a manometric capsule. The part of the capsule to the left of the membrane in Fig. 69 was not used, and the changing pressure in the singing tube acted directly on the membrane. The flame from the mano-

[159] Rudolph Koenig, Pogg. An., **122**, 242 (1864); **146**, 161 (1872); or *Quelques Expériences d'Acoustique,* p. 47.

metric capsule was brought around to the front of the singing tube and fixed near the bottom of the glass window, so that both flames could be observed at the same time. For examining the flames a stroboscopic disk proved more satisfactory than a rotating mirror, and when Richardson viewed the flames through the stroboscopic disk he could see that as the two flames rose and fell they were almost in phase with each other. This means that the singing flame really is largest at an instant near that at which the pressure in the singing tube is greatest, and this is precisely what Rayleigh's reasoning had led us to expect. The result is highly satisfactory.

An extension of the answer to Question 213 leads us to expect that the flame will sing when the length of the supply tube is less than quarter of a wave length of the sound in the gas, or between two quarters and three quarters of a wave length, or between four quarters and five quarters, etc.; and that the flame will not sing when the supply tube has other lengths. It has been found,[160] however, that, although the flame cannot be coaxed to sing for all lengths of supply tube, it will sing when the supply tube has lengths that are not included among those for which Rayleigh's theory accounts. Perhaps some modification of Rayleigh's theory will lead to a more complete understanding of the phenomena.

Question 214. In the paper referred to in footnote 158 Richardson suggests an explanation for the singing when the supply tube has lengths for which Rayleigh's theory would lead us to expect no singing. After reading Richardson's suggestion what is your judgment of it?

86. The Rijke Tube.—Another way in which heat may be used to produce vibration of the air in a tube was dis-

---

[160] Mildred Burnette Porter, M.A., thesis (1920), deposited in the library at Smith College but not published. Also Richardson in footnote 158.

covered by Rijke.[161]   In his first experiments he used a tube
80 cm. long and about 3.5 cm. in diameter.   Inside of the
tube was a horizontal piece of wire gauze.   The edges of
the gauze were bent so that it could be pushed to a position about a quarter of the way up the tube, and would
then stay there.   To make such a tube sing it is held vertical and the gauze is heated by a flame until it begins to
glow.   The flame is removed, and while the gauze is cooling it is likely that the tube will sing.   The pitch is that
natural to the heated air in the tube.   With a large tube
the effect may be very powerful, and if the gauze is heated
electrically instead of by a flame the sound may be maintained for as long a time as desired.

The sound from a Rijke tube and that maintained in
the same tube by a flame are much alike, but the means by
which they are maintained are apparently different.   In both
cases there is a vibration of the air in the tube, and in both
cases there is also a draft up the tube as the heated air
rises in it.   When the maintenance is by a flame it may be
that the draft is not important.   At any rate, Rayleigh [162]
was able to get a flame to sing in the neck of a glass globe
which had no other opening.   In the Rijke tube, on the
contrary, the draft appears to be essential.

In the Rijke tube the production and maintenance of the
sound were explained by Rijke as follows: "As to the explanation of the phaenomenon, that, I think, is not hard to
find.   In warming the wire-gauze, the temperature of the
sides of the tube is raised also.   If the lamp be then with-
drawn, an ascending current of air is established, which,
passing through the meshes of the wire-gauze, is necessarily
heated, and in consequence dilates.   To this dilatation immediately succeeds a contraction, due to the cooling effect

161 Pieter Leonhard Rijke (1812-1899), Phil. Mag., 17, 419 (1859); or
Pogg. An., 107, 339 (1859).   Rijke was Professor of Natural Philosophy in the
University at Leiden.
162 See footnote 157 on p. 229.

of the sides of the tube. It is to these successive dilatations and contractions, in my opinion, that we must attribute the production of the sounds."

A more satisfactory explanation was suggested by Rayleigh.[163] The rate at which the air near the gauze is heated depends on the difference between the temperatures of gauze and air. The cooler the air the more rapidly does the gauze impart heat to it. At what phase in the vibration is the air near the gauze the coolest? Let the tube be speaking its fundamental, so that there is a node at the middle, and let the gauze be in the lower half of the tube. When the vibration of the air is superposed on the through draft we see that in each cycle the air moves farther upward than it does downward, so that the coolest air comes to the gauze near the end of the upward swing, and, under the conditions assumed, this is at the time when the pressure is greatest. This is precisely what is needed for maintenance.

Similar reasoning shows that if the gauze is in the upper half of the tube it damps the vibration instead of maintaining it. It is interesting to turn a Rijke tube upside down while it is singing. This brings the gauze into the upper half of the tube, and the sound dies out very quickly. If the tube is then turned right side up again the gauze may still be warm enough to make the sound revive. It is sometimes possible in this way to repeat the inverting of the tube, and to hear the sound die out and revive more than once.

Question 215. What objection is there to Rijke's explanation of the maintenance in his tube?

Question 216. What is the line of reasoning which shows that maintenance is not to be expected when the gauze is in the upper half of the tube?

---

[163] Lord Rayleigh, *Theory of Sound,* ed. 2, vol. 2, art. 322*j*; or references in footnote 157.

Question 217. Does it seem likely that the through draft considered in Art. 86 may help to clear up the difficulty met at the end of Art. 85? Do you see any means of testing this suggestion experimentally?

87. Another Singing Tube.—It has been known for a long time that when a bulb is blown at the end of a narrow glass tube the tube sometimes sings while the bulb is cooling off. The pitch of the sound is that of the free vibration of the air in the bulb and tube. Who first discovered the effect is not known. Perhaps the first publication about it was by a Dr. Castberg, who had seen in the shop of a glass blower in Vienna a musical instrument built from such tubes. Very likely the singing had been observed by glass blowers in still earlier years. At any rate, the effect has several times been rediscovered, and a number of notes have been published telling of the discovery.[164]

The first to give a satisfactory explanation of the effect appears to have been Rayleigh.[165] The bulb and the tube close to it are much hotter than the part of the tube a little farther from the bulb. A quarter of a period before the instant of greatest compression the air in the tube is moving inward most rapidly. As it passes from cooler to warmer parts of the tube it picks up heat from the walls. The transfer of heat is not instantaneous, and the greatest heating occurs near the instant when the pressure is greatest. This, as we have already learned, is the phase relationship that is needed for maintenance of the sound.

Knipp [166] has devised a form of this tube which serves

[164] Castberg, Gilbert's An. der Physik, **17,** 482 (1804). For other articles on the same subject see Carl Michael Marx, Jahrbuch der Chemie and Physik, **19,** 132 (1827) and Journal für praktische Chemie, **22,** 129 (1841); August Pinaud, l'Institut, **3,** 366 (1835), or Pogg. An., **42,** 610 (1837); F. L. Robeson, Science, **73,** 265 (1931); William R. Cole, Science, **74,** 461 (1931); and the references in footnote 166.

[165] See the references in footnote 157 on p. 229.

[166] Charles Tobias Knipp, Phys. Rev., **12,** 491 (1918); **15,** 155, 245, 336 (1920). Floyd Rowe Watson, Science, **53,** 393 (1921). Both Knipp and Watson are at the University of Illinois.

as a convenient source of sound. One of his tubes is shown in Fig. 70. It is made of pyrex, so that there is no danger of cracking by quick heating. The heat is supplied by a ring burner at A, and the sound comes out at B. The pitch can be lowered by attaching additional pieces of tubing to the right of B. Smaller changes of pitch can be made by raising or lowering the water level at C.

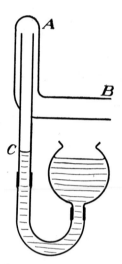

FIG. 70.—One Form of Knipp Tube.

Question 218. Quick compression of air heats it, and quick rarefaction cools it. What bearing does this fact have on Rayleigh's explanation of the singing?

88. Sensitive Flames.—In connection with singing flames and singing tubes we shall consider very briefly the subject of "sensitive" flames. These flames become shorter when a sound of sufficient intensity and suitable pitch falls upon them. The first scientific paper about a flame that burned in the open and was sensitive to sound appears to have been written by Le Conte.[167] During a private musical entertainment he noticed that one of the gas lights was under a pressure nearly sufficient to make it flare. Soon after the music began he observed that the flame from this light went up and down in time with the music. "A deaf man might have seen the harmony."

In the years since Le Conte's discovery a number of sensitive flames have been devised. One of the best known is Tyndall's "vowel flame," [168] which burns to a height of a

[167] John Le Conte (1818-1891), Amer. Journ. Science, 25, 62 (1858); or Phil. Mag., 15, 235 (1858). Le Conte was Professor of Natural Philosophy in South Carolina College.

[168] John Tyndall, Phil. Mag., 33, 92 and 375 (1867); or Sound, ed. 3 (1876), pp. 257-273.

couple of feet, and responds differently to different vowels. The pressure required to produce this flame is considerably higher than that in the gas mains, but for a number of the sensitive flames that have been developed the pressure in the mains is sufficient.

Many of these flames respond best to pitches that are rather high. Tyndall found that the seat of the sensitiveness is at the orifice from which the flame burns, and Tyndall and his assistant, Mr. Barrett, found that jets of smoke may also be sensitive to sounds. Rayleigh [169] observed that when a sensitive flame is moved through a region in which there are standing waves the response is greatest at the antinodes, and that sensitive jets of smoke do not alternately bulge and grow slender, but bend from side to side. These last two facts show that the response depends on the motion of the air and not on changes in its pressure.

Of the many other studies of sensitive flames [170] we shall mention only two. One is a recent piece of work by Zickendraht,[171] who finds that when the opening from which the gas issues is an accurately made circular cylinder the flame is not sensitive, but that it may become very sensitive if a piece of platinum wire or some other obstacle is brought to the edge of the flame at its base. It may also be sensitive if the opening from which the gas issues converges rapidly to a circular orifice with a sharp edge.

If a flame is perfectly symmetrical about its vertical axis, so that a horizontal section is a circle, Zickendraht finds that it is not sensitive. When the horizontal section is more or less elliptical the sensitiveness depends on the direction from which the sound comes. The flame is most sensitive when the sound comes toward one of its wider sides. The

[169] Lord Rayleigh, Phil. Mag., **7**, 153 (1879) ; **17**, 188 (1884).

[170] For a bibliography which will give some idea of the large amount of study that has been devoted to sensitive flames see Appendix Seven.

[171] Hans Zickendraht, Helvetica Physica Acta, **5**, 317 (1932). Zickendraht is Professor of Physics at Basel, in Switzerland.

upward paths of the gas in different parts of the flame are not parallel to each other—they spread apart and then bend in toward each other again. If they approach at a sufficiently large angle they cause the upper part of the flame to be rather short and flat and spread out in a plane perpendicular to that of the lower part. According to Zickendraht the effect of the sound is to increase the difference in flow of the different parts of the gas from the orifice, thus increasing the angle at which the component streams approach each other a short distance above the orifice, and thus in turn shortening the upper part of the flame.

The other work that we shall mention was done by Brown.[172] He employed flames and also jets of air impregnated with smoke, and he examined the latter stroboscopically. As a result of his studies he has suggested that the sensitiveness of a flame is brought about in the following way. The stream of burning gas is rather sharply separated from the more quiet air through which it flows. The surface between the two is unstable (Compare Fig. 62 on p. 212) and tends to break into vortices which travel upward along the boundary of the flame. When sound waves of a suitable frequency are swinging the flame slightly from side to side they aid the growth of these vortices. Each vortex as it whirls around mixes some of the more quiet air from outside the flame with the more rapidly moving gas that is coming from the nozzle. This mixture with air from outside makes the gas burn faster and so makes the flame shorter.

89. The Trevelyan Rocker.—As a last illustration of maintained vibration we turn very briefly to the Trevelyan rocker. A common form of this instrument is shown in the upper part of Fig. 71, and a cross-section of the block *B* in the lower part of the figure.

[172] G. Burniston Brown, Phil. Mag., **13**, 161 (1932); Phys. Soc. Proc., **47**, 703 (1935). Brown is Lecturer in Physics at University College, London.

If the rocker is laid in a nearly horizontal position, with the ridges *C* and *D* resting on some hard support *S*, and if the rocker is then tipped a little and released, it will rock back and forth several times, the ridges alternating their blows on the support. If the block *B* is heated sufficiently, and the rocker is again placed in position and the rocking started, it may soon settle down to a rapid rocking of small amplitude, accompanied by a sound of moderate pitch. To make the experiment work well brass is often used for the block *B*, and clean lead for the support *S*.

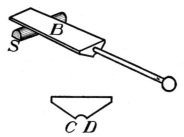

FIG. 71.—Trevelyan Rocker.

The effect was discovered in 1805 by Schwartz,[173] an inspector in one of the smelting works in Saxony, and then independently, about a quarter of a century later, by Trevelyan.[174] The first important explanation of it was given by Leslie,[175] who suggested that when one ridge of the rocker rests on the cold lead heat flows into the lead and makes it expand. The little hump thus produced gives an upward push to the rocker. Meantime the other side of the rocker is falling. It soon reaches the lead and is pushed upward by a hump that grows underneath it. While this goes on the first hump disappears because the heat spreads from it into other parts of the lead. The alternate upward pushes on the two ridges are regarded as maintaining the vibration.

The conduction of heat seemed to Forbes[176] too slow a

[173] Reported by Ludwig Wilhelm Gilbert, An. der Physik., 22, 323 (1806).

[174] Arthur Trevelyan, Roy. Soc. Edinb. Trans., 12, 137 (1831, pub. 1834); Phil. Mag., 3, 321 (1833); 6, 85 (1835).

[175] Sir John Leslie. I have not found any publication on the subject by Leslie, but in Trevelyan's 1833 paper he says that the explanation by the expansion of the lead was suggested by "the late Professor Leslie."

[176] James David Forbes (1809-1868), Phil. Mag., 4, 15, 182 (1834); or Roy. Soc. Edinb. Trans., 12, 429 (1834). Forbes was elected to the Royal

process to maintain the vibration of the rocker, and he suggested another explanation. But Davis [177] showed that when the heat does not have to travel farther than the small distances involved in the Trevelyan rocker it is entirely possible for the expansion and contraction to occur with sufficient rapidity, and Rayleigh [178] pointed out that the phase of the expansion is such as to make maintenance possible. Then after more than forty years Chuckerbutti [179] found that the frequency of the sound differed rather widely from that calculated on the basis of Leslie's hypothesis, and also that a twisting of the handle seemed to be important. There appears however to have been an error in the work of Chuckerbutti, and results obtained by Bhargava and Ghosh [180] and by Richardson [181] show that the frequency of the rocker does agree fairly well with that predicted from Leslie's hypothesis.

Various other interesting facts about the Trevelyan rocker have been brought to light by various investigators, but we shall leave the further study of them to the student who is interested in looking up some of the literature to which references are given in Appendix Seven.

Question 219. How can you show that the phase of the expansion suggested by Leslie is such as to maintain the vibration of a Trevelyan rocker?

Question 220. In addition to the vertical forces involved in Leslie's explanation of the Trevelyan effect Faraday suggested that the maintenance may be aided by horizontal forces. His idea was that the growing and dying out of each lead hump is affected by heat from

Society of Edinburgh when he was only nineteen years old. He succeeded Sir John Leslie as Professor of Natural Philosophy in the University at Edinburgh. Later he became Principal of the College of St. Andrews.

[177] A. S. Davis, Phil. Mag., **45**, 296 (1873).

[178] Lord Rayleigh, refs. in footnote 157 on p. 229.

[179] B. N. Chuckerbutti, Ind. Assoc. Cult. Sci., Proc., **6**, 143 (1921).

[180] S. Bhargava and R. N. Ghosh, Phys. Rev., **22**, 517 (1923).

[181] E. G. Richardson, Phil. Mag., **45**, 976 (1923).

the hump under the other ridge, so that the growth and dying out is not simply an up and down process, but the top of the hump has also a sideways motion. Toward which side should you expect the resulting horizontal force on the rocker to act? Would the phase relationship between this force and the vibration of the rocker be such as to aid the rocking or to hinder it?

CHAPTER NINE

HEARING

90. Introduction.—Our ears pick up changing compressions and rarefactions in the air about us, and from these changes we learn something about pitch and loudness, something about the voice or other instrument that produces the sound, something about the direction from which the sound reaches us. It is even through spoken words, picked up from the air by our ears, that many of our ideas come to us. How is it that changes in the pressure of the air can give all this information? What processes go on in the ear as it sends its messages to the brain? What processes are they that go on in the brain itself?

This last question we shall not attempt to discuss. As to such questions as the others it is obvious that if we are to find answers we shall need information from the fields of anatomy and psychology as well as physics, and that when answers have been found they will not only be of general interest, but will also be of importance to the acoustic engineer who is designing equipment that affects the ear, and to the otologist who deals with ears that are not functioning satisfactorily.

Many problems connected with the process of hearing have not yet been solved. But a fair amount of information about the ear has been collected, and in this chapter we shall consider briefly some of the facts of audition, then a little about the anatomy of the ear, and lastly the theories which attempt to explain the facts.

91. Frequency Limits of Audition.—We shall begin our study of the facts of audition with certain matters that have to do with simple tones. It is well known that we can-not hear tones of all frequencies. If a hand is moved back and forth at the rate of one or two cycles per second we do not hear any tone of that frequency. The high shrill notes from certain insects are annoying to some persons while at the same time they are not heard by others. There are vibrations of still higher frequency which affect a sensitive flame but cannot be heard by any human ear. How high a pitch and how low a pitch can be heard by a normal ear?

The pitches obtained in the earlier studies varied con-siderably. Savart,[182] working with apparatus which he had devised, found that many observers could detect a tone that had a frequency of only 7 or 8 cycles/sec., whereas Helm-holtz [183] found the lower limit at about 30 cycles/sec. It is difficult to obtain a vibration that is really simple and does not contain overtones, and Helmholtz suggested that with the apparatus used by Savart it is probable that an overtone was heard and not the fundamental.

Values obtained for the upper limit of audible frequency have also varied considerably. Wien [184] drew attention to the fact that both the lower and the upper limits depend in an important way on the intensity of the sound. The earlier experimenters may not have been fully aware of this fact, and they had in any case no satisfactory means of measuring the intensities. In Art. 93 we shall see that when sounds are sufficiently loud the lower limit of audible fre-quency is in the neighborhood of 16 or 20 cycles/sec, and the upper limit in the neighborhood of 20,000 cycles/sec.

Question 221. If the lower limit of audible frequency is taken as 16 cycles/sec. and the upper limit as 20,000 cycles/sec., how many octaves are included in the audible range? How many if the lower limit is taken as 20 cycles/sec.?

[182] Félix Savart, Ann. de chim. et de phys., **47,** 69 (1831).
[183] Hermann von Helmholtz, *Sensations of Tone,* 4th Eng. ed., p. 176.
[184] Max Wien, pp. 2, **30,** in the second article cited in footnote 188 on p. 248.

92. Loudness.—In Art. 33 the intensity of any train of waves was defined as the amount of energy that the waves carry through unit area in unit time, and in the same article it was stated that in many cases a louder sound corresponds to a more intense train of waves. It is found, however, that the loudness of a sound does not increase in proportion to its intensity. If one sound is 100 times as intense as another it does not sound 100 times as loud.

When dealing with pitch we have found that frequency ratios are of great importance. We know that if one note is an octave above another its frequency is twice as great. In musical intervals we are not concerned with frequency differences but with frequency ratios. Similarly it has been thought that the ratio of two intensities might serve as a measure of the difference in loudness. Thus if sound A is 100 times as intense as sound B, and B is 100 times as intense as C, it has been thought that perhaps A would sound as much louder than B as B sounds louder than C.

Although this suggestion does not turn out to be entirely correct, it does nevertheless often prove convenient to deal with a quantity that depends on the ratio of the intensities. And just as we found that musical intervals might be measured by using the logarithms of frequency ratios instead of the frequency ratios themselves, so here it proves convenient to employ the logarithm of the intensity ratio instead of the ratio itself. The quantity thus obtained is called the difference between the *intensity levels* of the two sounds.

If the intensity of sound A is ten times that of B the logarithm of the intensity ratio is 1. In this case the intensity level of A is said to be one *bel* [185] higher than that of B. If the intensity of A is 100 times that of B the logarithm of the intensity ratio is 2, and the intensity level of A is said

[185] The word *bel* has been chosen in honor of Alexander Graham Bell (1847-1922), the inventor of the electromagnetic telephone.

to be two bels higher than that of *B*.   Instead of using the
bel itself it is customary to express differences in intensity
levels in terms of *decibels*,[186] i.e., tenths of a bel, and for
this unit the abbreviation "db" has come into general use.
Thus if sound *A* is ten times as intense as *B* its intensity
level is 10 db higher, and if the intensity of *A* is 100 times
that of *B* the difference in their intensity levels is 20 db.

A change of 1 db is so small as to be scarcely perceptible.
The range from the faintest sound that can be heard in a
quiet room to a sound so loud as to begin to be painful may
be as much as 130 or 140 db.   Some idea as to the significance of different numbers of decibels may be obtained from
Table Three.

TABLE THREE—APPROXIMATE INTENSITY LEVELS OF VARIOUS NOISES

The values given are intensity levels above an intensity of 10^{-16} watts per
square centimeter.

Number	Noise	Level, db
1	Airplane, nearby....................................	120
2	Subway station. Noise on platform when train is passing	100
3	Subway train. Inside express car......................	100
4	Noisiest spot at Niagara Falls..........................	95
5	Riveter, as ordinarily heard from street.................	85
6	Street noises. Fifth Ave. and 42d St., New York........	75
7	Ordinary conversation.................................	70
8	Horse trotting on asphalt pavement....................	65
9	Information booth in large railway station...............	60
10	One typewriter in small office.........................	40
11	Turning page of newspaper...........................	30
12	Purring cat..	25
13	Rustle of leaves in gentle breeze......................	20
14	Threshold of hearing.................................	0

Question 222.   If one sound brings us energy a million times
as rapidly as another, how many decibels higher is it?

[186] Some German authors are using the word *phon* with the same meaning that *decibel* has in English speaking countries.

Question 223. If I_1 and I_2 stand for intensities of two sounds, and b for the number of decibels by which the intensity level of the first is higher than the second, what equation connects these quantities?

Question 224. One author has said that "twins crying together are only three decibels louder than one crying alone." If he means that the intensity level from the two twins is three decibels higher than that from one alone, how should you decide whether his statement is correct?

Question 225. In Table Three noise No. 2 is how many times as intense as noise No 7? No. 10 is how many times as intense as No. 13?

Studies have been made to find out whether the loudness of a sound increases in proportion to the rise in its intensity level.[187] It is to be noticed that an intensity level can be measured physically, whereas loudness is simply a matter of judgment. We wonder whether an observer gives the same judgment at different times, and whether different observers agree in their judgments of relative loudness. In neither case is the agreement found to be remarkably good, but in both cases it proves to be fair.

For moderate intensities it is found that if one sound is half as loud as another its intensity level is approximately 10 db lower. From Fig. 72 more general conclusions can be drawn. In this figure the number on each curve indicates the initial intensity level above a certain standard of intensity, the numbers plotted horizontally indicate the amounts by which the intensity of the sound was reduced, and the numbers plotted vertically indicate the fractions by which the loudness was judged to have been decreased.

[187] L. F. Richardson and J. S. Ross, Journ. Gen. Psychol., **3**, 288 (1930).
Donald A. Laird, Emery Taylor, and Herman H. Wille, Jr., Journ. Acoust. Soc., **3**, 393 (1932).
Lloyd B. Ham and John S. Parkinson, Journ. Acoust Soc., **3**, 511 (1932).
R. R. Riesz, Journ. Acoust. Soc., **4**, 211 (1933).
P. H. Geiger and F. A. Firestone, Journ. Acoust. Soc, **5**, 25 (1933).
Harvey Fletcher and W. A. Munson, Journ. Acoust. Soc., **5**, 82 (1933).

Question 226. The intensity of a sound is reduced from 80 db to 60 db. Does the reduction in loudness obtained from Fig. 72 agree with the rough statement at the beginning of the above paragraph?

Question 227. In Fig. 72 curves for higher initial intensity levels lie to the right of those for lower initial levels. What conclusion may be drawn?

93. The Auditory Diagram.—We have now learned something about the ranges of pitch and intensity level that the ear can appreciate. Al-

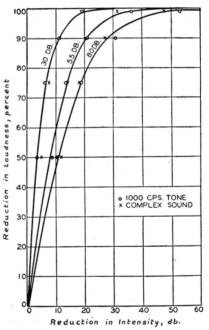

though we have said nothing about the actual amounts of energy involved, the fact that it is possible for a speaker to address a large audience shows that the energy needed for hearing and understanding m u s t b e very minute. Even a very energetic speaker sends out sound at a rate that is a very small part of a horsepower, so that the amount of energy which streams from his mouth in each second must be small. And of that small amount each auditor receives only a much reduced fraction. When we consider the enormous range of inten-

Fig. 72.—Relation between Intensity Level and Loudness [Geiger and Firestone].

sity between the faintest sounds that can be heard and the level at which the auditor hears the words, we see that at the threshold of hearing the flux of energy must be exceed-

ingly minute. How large is it? Does it differ at different
frequencies?

Two of the first important studies of such questions were
carried out by Wien.[188] He made use of an important relation between the intensity of a simple sound and the changes
of pressure that occur as the waves go past. This relation
may be stated by the equation

$$I = \frac{p^2}{2\rho c}, \tag{13}$$

where I stands for the intensity of the sound, p for the amplitude of the simple harmonic change in pressure, ρ for
the density of the air, and c for the speed of sound in air.
Since ρ and c are known, a measurement of p provides a
means of determining I. Wien succeeded in measuring the
extremely minute pressure amplitude, and in this way found
the threshold intensity—that is, the intensity of the faintest sound that can be heard. He illustrates the extraordinarily minute amount of energy to which the ear is sensitive by calculating that if the energy used by a blade of
grass in raising itself from the ground as it grows could be
turned into sound it would be a sound of moderate loudness.[189]

Wien's first study of the threshold intensity was carried
out at three pitches—at 220, 337, and 440 cycles/sec. At
these pitches his results showed that the threshold intensity
was lower at the higher pitches. That is, at the higher
pitches he found the ear more sensitive. His second study
was made at a number of pitches in the range from 50

[188] Max Wien, Wied. An., 36, 834 (1889); Archiv für die gesammte
Physiologie, 97, 1 (1903). Wien began this work at Berlin, where he was
studying under Helmholtz and Kundt.

[189] Page 850 in the first paper cited in footnote 188. Using more modern
values and assuming that a blade of grass may grow 7 cm. in a week, and
that this new growth has a mass of about 30 mg., I find that if the energy
were turned into sound at the frequency of middle c, it would be about 27 db
above the threshold. If the pitch were an octave or two higher the level
would be about 40 db above the threshold.

cycles/sec. to 12,000 cycles/sec., and revealed enormous differences in the threshold intensity at different pitches. The smallest threshold intensity was reached at about 2000 cycles/sec., and at 50 cycles/sec. he found it more than a hundred million times as great as at 2000 cycles/sec.

With the development of modern electric devices the measurement of simple harmonic pressures that are extremely minute has become less difficult, and studies of the

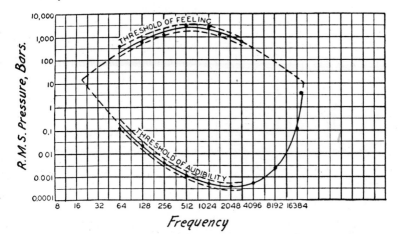

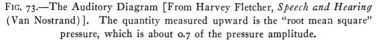

FIG. 73.—The Auditory Diagram [From Harvey Fletcher, *Speech and Hearing* (Van Nostrand)]. The quantity measured upward is the "root mean square" pressure, which is about 0.7 of the pressure amplitude.

threshold intensity have been made for many ears and at various frequencies. The results for different ears differ considerably.[190] The curves in Fig. 73 are drawn from averages for a number of "normal" ears.

We know that when the intensity of a tone gradually increases, without any change in frequency, the tone grows louder and louder. When the intensity is sufficient the ear begins to experience a tickling sensation, and if the sound

[190] See an excellent article by Harvey Fletcher, Journ. Franklin Inst., **196**, 289 (1923). This article contains a bibliography of 93 papers. See also Fletcher's book, *Speech and Hearing* (1929), pp. 132-144.

is brought to a finger or some other part of the body it can

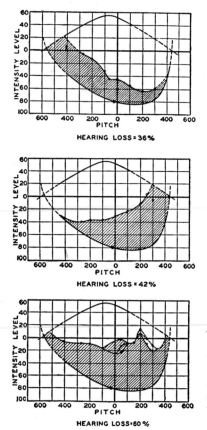

HEARING LOSS = 36%

HEARING LOSS = 42%

HEARING LOSS = 60%

FIG. 74.—Auditory Diagrams for Three Persons Who Were Hard of Hearing [From Harvey Fletcher, *Speech and Hearing* (Van Nostrand)]. The outer curves give the auditory diagram for a normal ear. In each diagram the upper curve and the middle curve give the diagram for the person in question.

be felt. If the intensity is still further increased the effect on the ear becomes painful. The intensity at which the ear begins to experience the tickling sensation Fletcher calls the *threshold of feeling.*

Both the threshold of audibility and the threshold of feeling depend on the frequency. In Fig. 73 the lower curve gives the threshold of audibility, and the upper curve the threshold of feeling. These curves are averages for many persons whose hearing is regarded as normal. The curves for individual ears are much more irregular. Fig. 74 shows the auditory diagrams for three persons who were hard of hearing. The threshold of audibility for each of these persons is at the top of the region that is cross-hatched.

Question 228. One simple tone has a frequency of 256 cycles/sec. Another is an octave higher. If the intensities of the tones are the same how do the amplitudes of their pressure changes compare?

Question 229. In one simple tone the amplitude of the pressure change is 100 times that in another. What is the difference in their intensity levels?

Question 230. At what frequency does Fig. 73 indicate that the ear is most sensitive to sound? to feeling?

Question 231. In a normal ear and at 64 cycles/sec. how does the threshold intensity for audibility compare with that at 128 cycles/sec.?

Question 232. In a normal ear and at 64 cycles/sec. what is the difference between the intensity levels at the threshold of feeling and at the threshold of audibility?

Question 233. What differences are there in the hearing of the persons whose auditory diagrams are given in Fig. 74?

94. Discrimination of Pitch and Loudness.—How much can we change either the pitch or the loudness of a tone without the ear detecting the change? For a time it was thought [191] that if the smallest perceptible change in frequency were divided by the frequency itself the quotient would be the same at all frequencies, and that if the smallest perceptible change in intensity were divided by the intensity itself this quotient, too, would be the same at all intensities. We now know that both of these statements hold fairly well, but that neither of them is exactly correct.

We shall take up first the sensitiveness of the ear to small changes in frequency, and passing over the earlier investigators we turn briefly to two of the more recent studies.

Knudsen [192] has examined the sensitiveness of the ear to small changes in pitch. At a level of 40 db above the

[191] Students who have some knowledge of psychology will recognize here the law that is connected with the names of Weber and Fechner.

[192] Vern Oliver Knudsen, Phys. Rev., 21, 84 (1923). This work was done while Knudsen was a student and assistant at the University of Chicago. He is now in the University of California at Los Angeles. He has been President of the Acoustical Society of America, and he received the 1934 award of $1000 for an important paper presented before the meetings of the American Association for the Advancement of Science.

threshold of audibility he found that as the pitch rises from
50 cycles/sec. to 600 the ear can detect smaller and smaller
fractional changes in frequency, and that from 600 to 3200
the barely perceptible fractional change stays about the
same.   At 50 cycles/sec. the frequency must change by about

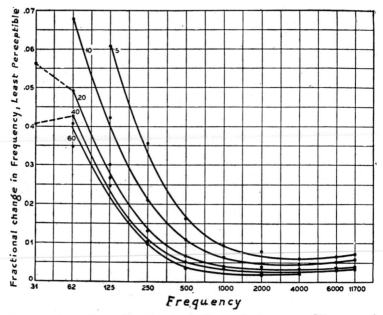

FIG. 75.—Least Perceptible Fractional Change in Frequency [Shower and
Biddulph].   The number at the upper end of each curve gives the intensity
level above the threshold of audibility.

one per cent before the ear can detect any change.   Above
600 cycles/sec. a change of a third of this amount is sufficient.   Knudsen's work has been extended by Shower and
Biddulph,[193] and Fig. 75 shows their results at five levels.

Question 234.   Does the 40 db curve in Fig. 75 agree fairly
well with the results found by Knudsen?

[193] E. G. Shower and R. Biddulph (Bell Telephone Laboratories), Journ.
Acoust. Soc., 3, 275 (1931).

Question 235. From Fig. 75 do you find that the ear can detect a smaller change in pitch when the tone is loud or when it is faint?

Question 236. At a level of 60 db and a frequency of 2000 cycles/sec. how small a fractional change in frequency does Fig. 75 show that the ear can detect? How many cents are there in the corresponding musical interval?

Question 237. At what frequency can the ear just detect a change in pitch of 70 cents when the sound is 60 db above the threshold? When it is 5 db above the threshold?

The ear is not nearly as sensitive to changes in intensity as to changes in pitch. Under favorable circumstances it is possible to detect a change in frequency of a fifth of a per cent, but a change in the intensity cannot be detected unless it is at least five per cent. At very low intensity levels and very low frequencies it is necessary for the intensity of a sound to be increased tenfold before any change is detected in the loudness, but as the intensity rises and the frequency increases it is found that the ear becomes more sensitive. When the intensity level is 30 db and the frequency 100 cycles/sec. a 50 per cent increase in intensity can be detected, and with further rise in intensity and with increase in frequency to about 2500 cycles/sec. there is a continued increase in the sensitiveness of the ear to changes in intensity.[194]

An interesting question has to do with the number of simple tones that a normal ear can distinguish as being different, either in pitch or in loudness. At any given intensity we can start with the lowest pitch that we can hear, find how much the frequency must rise for the ear to detect a change in pitch, then how much further rise is necessary before the ear can detect a further change in pitch, and so on. In this way we can find how many steps of frequency the ear can detect at the given intensity, and we can then carry out the same experiment at each of many intensities. We

[194] R. R. Riesz (Bell Telephone Laboratories), Phys. Rev., **31**, 867 (1928).

may also carry out a similar study in which we keep the frequency the same, and see how many steps of loudness can be detected.

In this way we can divide up the whole auditory diagram into a large number of regions of such size that a change of either frequency or intensity cannot be detected unless it is sufficient to carry us as far as from the middle of one of these regions to the middle of another. The total number of these regions may then be taken as the total number of simple tones that the ear can distinguish as being different, either in pitch or in loudness. At the intensity where the auditory diagram is widest there are about 2000 perceptible steps in frequency, and at the frequency at which the diagram has the greatest height there are about 370 perceptible steps in loudness. The total number of simple tones that can be distinguished as different in either pitch or loudness is more than half a million.

If the ear can distinguish this large number of simple tones how vast must be the number of distinguishable complex tones! A consideration of these numbers may help us to appreciate the amazing ability of the ear to discriminate among the multitudinous sounds that reach it.

95. Masking.—It is well known that one sound may make it difficult to hear some other sound. The hissing of an air valve on a steam radiator may drown out the ticking of a watch. The roar of a subway train makes conversation difficult. Are there any general statements that can be made about this effect? Or is it simply a case where one sound does not stand out sufficiently above the general noise?

A very interesting study of this matter was made by Mayer.[195] His conclusion was that a loud enough sound may "obliterate" or "mask" a sound of higher pitch, but that no sound, however loud, can mask a tone of lower

---

[195] Alfred Marshall Mayer (1836-1897), Phil. Mag., 2, 500 (1876). Mayer was Professor of Physics at Stevens Institute of Technology.

pitch. Mayer's discovery was an important one, but his simple and remarkable conclusion proves to be entirely too sweeping.

Wegel and Lane [196] have made a careful study of the masking of one simple tone by another. Fig. 76 shows some of their results. The masking tone had a frequency of 1200 cycles/sec. For the lowest curve it was about 45 db

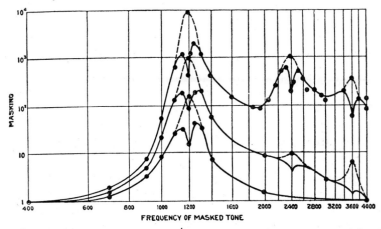

Fig. 76.—Masking of Various Tones [Wegel and Lane]. The horizontal lines cross the diagram at levels of 0, 20, 40, 60, and 80 db above the threshold of audibility.

above the threshold of audibility; for the middle one, 60 db; and for the highest, 80 db. When a second tone had a frequency and intensity level that are represented by a point on one of the curves, that tone was just masked by the corresponding 1200 cycle tone.

Question 238. Will a 1200 cycle tone at 45 db above the threshold of audibility mask an 800 cycle tone at 20 db? Will it mask a 1600 cycle tone at 20 db?

Question 239. What would the answers to question 238 be if the 1200 cycle tone were 60 db above the threshold of audibility? 80 db above the threshold?

196 R. L. Wegel and C. E. Lane, Phys. Rev, 23, 266 (1924).

Question 240. What do you suppose is the explanation of the dips in the curves at 1200 cycles/sec.?

96. Combination Tones.—When two simple tones reach the ear at the same time it is sometimes possible to hear along with them a third tone. This effect was probably first detected by the Italian violinist Tartini [197] more than two centuries ago. In honor of him the tones have sometimes been called *Tartini tones,* although Tartini himself called them *terzi suoni* (third sounds).

The frequency of the combination tone that was first discovered is the difference between the frequencies of the generating tones, and for that reason, following Helmholtz, it is now often called a *difference tone.* For instance, if c_4 and g_4 are played together it is sometimes possible to hear along with them a very soft c_3, and if c_4 and f_4 are played together it is often possible to hear with them a soft f_2.

Question 241. Do you find that the frequencies of the two combination tones just mentioned really are the differences between the frequencies of the generating tones? What is the simplest way you find to make the necessary calculation?

Question 242. Is the difference tone from c_4 and e_4 sharper on an instrument which is tuned to the just scale or to equal temperament? By how many cents does it differ?

Question 243. The pipes for some of the lowest notes that are desired in an organ would be so large as to take up considerable space and use considerable wind. So these notes are sometimes produced as difference tones from higher pitched pipes. If the c that has a frequency of about 16 cycles/sec. is to be produced in this way what pipes would probably be used to produce it? If the note were obtained from a single open pipe instead of as a difference tone, how long would the pipe have to be?

[197] The discovery of these tones is sometimes attributed to Giuseppi Tartini, sometimes to the German organist Georg Andreas Sorge, and sometimes to the French Jean-Baptiste Romieu. For statements which these three men themselves made about the discovery see Arthur Taber Jones, The American Physics Teacher, **3,** 49 (1935).

The combination tones just mentioned are *difference tones of the first order*. A first order difference tone may combine with one of the generating tones to give a *difference tone of the second order*, a second order difference tone may combine with one of the generating tones or one of the first order difference tones to give a *difference tone of the third order*, and so on. Difference tones are not the only kind of combination tones. Helmholtz [198] discovered that there are also *summation tones*, in which the frequency is the sum of the frequencies of the generators.

Question 244. Two tones have frequencies $7N$ and $10N$. What are the frequencies of the difference tones of the first five orders? Why are you asked to examine the first five orders rather than four or six or some other number?

97. First Explanation.—The first explanation of difference tones was a simple one. It was known that when the frequencies of two tones are nearly the same there are beats. The frequency of the beats is the difference between the frequencies of the tones. If the frequencies of the tones are made to differ to a greater and greater extent the beats become more and more rapid. So it was natural to think that when the beats are sufficiently rapid they blend to form the soft difference tone—much as the successive puffs through the holes in a siren blend to form a tone. This explanation is simple, and it gives the correct pitch.[199]

One objection to this explanation is based on Ohm's law. If we are to hear a simple tone the changing pressure of the air must contain a simple harmonic component that has

---

[198] Hermann von Helmholtz, Pogg. An., **99**, 497 (1856).

[199] Tartini gave the pitches of many of his third sounds an octave too high. It was not long, however, until the correct pitch was learned.

An error of an octave in judging pitch is very easy to make, especially with tones that are fairly simple. The reader may convince himself of this difficulty by attempting to whistle the same note that he plays on a piano. Without the use of a resonator he may find it difficult to be sure whether he is whistling the right note or is off by an octave or two.

the given frequency. Now when two simple tones are beating it is true that the pressure rises and falls to a greater
extent during the loud part of a beat than during the weak
part. But if we consider the average pressure during the
loud part and the average pressure during the weak part
we do not find a difference in these averages. That is, we
do not find that the average pressure rises and falls with
the frequency of the beats. So it becomes difficult to see
how beats can blend into a tone. Moreover, Ellis [200] found
that in some cases he could hear a difference tone and at the
same time "the rattle of the beats." If beats and tone can
be heard at the same time it is difficult to see how the beats
can have blended to produce the tone.

98. **More Recent Explanation.**—In view of the first of
the difficulties just mentioned Helmholtz [201] advanced an
explanation which is entirely different and is also less easy
to understand. It depends on a "non linear" character of
the restoring force. When a body is executing a free simple
harmonic motion the restoring force is proportional to the
displacement (Art. 51), and the curve which shows how the
restoring force depends on the displacement is therefore a
straight line. If the restoring force is not exactly proportional to the displacement the curve bends instead of being
straight, and we say that the restoring force is "not a linear
function" of the displacement.

Question 245. When the restoring force is proportional to the
displacement how do you see that the curve just mentioned is a
straight line?

When the restoring force is not a linear function of the
displacement neither a free vibration nor the vibration produced by a simple harmonic force is precisely simple harmonic, but it may be regarded (Art. 79) as the resultant of

[200] Helmholtz, *Sensations of Tone,* 4th Eng. ed., p. 153.
[201] Hermann von Helmholtz, Pogg. An., **99**, 497 (1856), or *Sensations of Tone,* 4th Eng. ed., pp. 156, 411.

a number of simple harmonic motions. Moreover, when two simple harmonic forces act on such a system it can be shown that the resulting vibration consists in part of simple harmonic components with the frequencies of the impressed forces, and in part of simple harmonic components with other frequencies. Among these other frequencies one is the difference between the impressed frequencies and another is their sum.

In the application of these ideas to combination tones it is to be noticed that in the vibrating mechanism in the ear (Art. 103) the restoring force is not a linear function of the displacement. Consequently when two simple harmonic forces act on the ear at the same time it is entirely possible that something in the ear may be forced to vibrate with the frequencies of the impressed pressures and also with frequencies which are the difference and the sum of the impressed frequencies.

Mathematical analysis led Helmholtz to conclude that difference tones and summation tones would be faint—very likely so faint that they would not be noticed except when the generating tones are loud. A difference tone is often lower in pitch than either of the generating tones, but a summation tone is always higher. So the generating tones are more likely to mask summation tones than they are to mask difference tones, and this might account for the fact that difference tones were discovered before summation tones, and are easier to hear.

Difference tones are not, however, always as faint as Helmholtz's analysis suggests, and a great deal of study has been devoted to the manner in which they really are produced. The suggestion which Helmholtz made involved not only a restoring force which is not a linear function of the displacement, but also a restoring force which is *asymmetric*. That is, the body on which the simple harmonic forces act may be so constituted that the restoring force called into play by a displacement in one direction is larger than that called into play by an equal displacement in the opposite direction. This is the case in the mechanism of the ear.

Question 246. Can you devise some simple apparatus to illustrate clearly a restoring force which is asymmetric?

An important study of such asymmetric vibrators has been made by Waetzmann.[202] He used a light rubber membrane about 5 cm. in diameter, mounted vertically, and loaded on one side. The load was sometimes of wax and sometimes had a piece of metal added to the wax.

Question 247. With a loaded membrane like that just described why is the restoring force asymmetric?

Fig. 77 is one of Waetzmann's vibration curves. Two simple harmonic pressures of nearly the same frequency

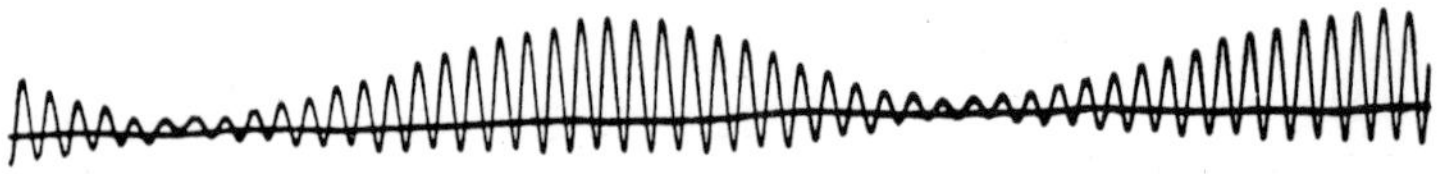

FIG. 77.—Vibration of an Asymmetric Membrane [Waetzmann]. In this case the membrane is subject to two simple harmonic pressures of nearly the same frequency.

were acting on the membrane, and we see that if a curve were drawn to represent the average displacement the curve would not be a straight line but would go up and down with the frequency of the beats. That is, this asymmetric membrane does execute a real vibration that has the same frequency as the beats. When the difference between the generating frequencies was greater, and the beats consequently more rapid, Waetzmann was able to obtain a vibration that had a frequency equal to the difference between the frequencies of the generators, and had an amplitude

[202] E. Waetzmann, An. der Physik, 62, 371 (1920) ; Zeitschr. für Physik, 1, 271 and 416 (1920).

several times as great as that of either of the generating frequencies! It appears that some lack of symmetry is an important factor in the production of difference tones.

99. The Quality of Musical Sounds.—We are familiar with the fact that a note played on one musical instrument may sound quite different from the same note played on another instrument—even when the two notes have the same pitch and are equally loud. The difference in the sound may arise in part from slight noises that accompany the musical sound, or from differences in the way the note is attacked, or from differences in the way the loudness changes while the note is sounding. But in addition to all these incidental factors there may be a very real difference in the steady sounds themselves. It is this difference to which the word *quality* is usually applied. Instead of *quality* use is sometimes made of the French word *timbre,* or of the expression *tone color*—the latter being a translation of the German term *Klangfarbe.*

Upon what does the difference in the qualities of two notes depend? When we deal with simple tones we know that the vibration curves all have the same shape—differing only in wave length and in amplitude. Now differences in wave length correspond closely to differences in pitch, and differences in amplitude are related to differences in loudness. Moreover, unless they are too loud all simple tones sound much alike except for differences in pitch and loudness. These facts suggest that the quality of a musical sound may be related to the shape of the vibration curve. When a vibration curve is periodic we know (Art. 79) that it may be built up by adding certain simple harmonic curves. Since these simple curves represent simple tones it is reasonable to suppose that the quality of a musical sound depends on the simple tones which form it.

The above reasoning seems perfectly straightforward, and in a general way it is no doubt correct. But the question arose as to whether the relative phases of the component simple tones have any effect on the quality of the sound. If we add the two curves shown in Fig. 78 the resultant is the upper curve in Fig. 79. If the lower curve in Fig. 78 is advanced half a wave length before the curves are added the resultant is the lower curve in Fig. 79. Obviously the two curves in Fig. 79 differ in shape. If they are vibra-

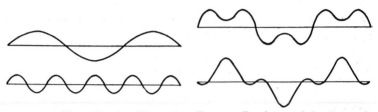

FIG. 78. — Two Simple Harmonic Curves which are to be Added.

FIG. 79.—Resultants of the Curves in Fig. 78 with Different Initial Phases.

tion curves for musical sounds do the musical sounds differ in quality?

Since quality is judged by the ear, the only way to answer this question is to listen to the sounds that correspond to the two curves. It proves to be a matter of great difficulty to make sure that the sounds which an experimenter produces are really represented by curves which do not differ except in the phases of their components, and a large amount of experimental skill has been devoted to the solution of this problem.[203] Helmholtz came to the conclusion that the relative phases of the component tones does not affect the quality of the resultant. Koenig, on the contrary, found a definitely observable effect. Lloyd and Agnew,

[203] See, for instance, the following important papers.

Hermann von Helmholtz, Pogg. An., 108, 280 (1859), or *Sensations of Tone,* 4th Eng. ed., pp. 119-126.

Rudolph Koenig, Wied. An., 14, 369 (1881), or *Quelques Exp. d'Acoustique,* p. 218.

M. G. Lloyd and P. G. Agnew, Elec. Rev. and Western Electrician, 55, 487 (1909).

E. K. Chapin and F. A. Firestone, Journ. Acoust. Soc., 5, 173 (1934).

with equipment that was available at the United States Bureau of Standards, found no certain effect. Chapin and Firestone have found that some effect can be detected when the sound is loud.

It is probably safe to say that the relative phases of the components of a musical sound have little effect on the quality, and that what effect they do have is not observable except when the sounds are loud. In fact, we usually say that the quality is determined by the relative frequencies and intensities of the component simple tones.[204] It is now customary to represent the components of a musical sound as forming a "spectrum" in which the frequencies and amplitudes—or intensities—of the components are shown but no attention is paid to their relative phases. Examples of such spectra will be found in Figs. 98, 107, 110 on pp. 304, 320, and 323.

Question 248. In a certain musical sound there are various simple tones with various intensities. If the loudness of the sound is increased in such a way that the intensities of all the simple components are increased in the same ratio it is possible that there might be a change in the quality. Why?

100. **Volume and Brightness.**—It may be well to mention two further characteristics of sound. We have spoken of pitch, of loudness, and of quality. Psychologists sometimes speak of the "volume" of a sound and of its "brightness."

"Low notes from an organ have a certain voluminousness, a certain spaciousness, however quiet they may be; whereas a very high pitched note lacks this spaciousness. Hence volume varies with frequency. . . . There is much evidence to show . . . that the volume of a sound is the result of indeterminateness of localization. High-pitched sounds are small, it is said, because their localization is much

---

[204] For some modification of this simple statement see Arts. 135-139.

more exact and precise. This is due, chiefly, to their shorter wave-length, in consequence of which their waves do not travel round obstacles with the same facility as those of longer wave-length. The opposite is the case with tones of low pitch: they are much more difficult to localize because the sound-waves come from all directions at the same time. In consequence, it is maintained, a tone of low pitch will be judged to be more voluminous." [205]

As to brightness, "some psychologists think that tones vary in brightness and dullness independently of their changes in pitch and other qualitative aspects, but it is much more probable that 'brightness' is simply a better descriptive term for the high pitches, and 'dullness' for the low pitches." [206]

101. **Sense of Direction. Difference of Intensity.**—It is often easy to get some idea as to the direction from which a sound comes to us. By what means do we become aware of the direction?

Perhaps the first answer that suggests itself is that the sound is louder at the ear which happens to be turned toward the source, and that we have become accustomed to judging the direction by means of this difference in loudness. Let us consider this suggestion. Unless the source is rather close to the observer its distance from one ear is so nearly the same as its distance from the other ear that no appreciable difference in loudness would be produced by the difference in distance. Nevertheless it is quite possible that the head might shield the farther ear to such an extent that a difference in loudness could be detected. Any such shielding could hardly be important at low pitches, for if the pitch is low the distance around the head is only a small fraction of a wave length, and the variations in pressure are

[205] H. Banister, in *Discussion on Audition* (1931), The Physical Society (London), p. 106.
[206] Edwin G. Boring, *The Physical Dimensions of Consciousness,* D. Appleton-Century Co. (1933), p. 25.

then much the same at both ears. When the pitch is higher the wave length is shorter, and for these higher pitches it is entirely possible that differences in intensity at the two ears might be detected.

More than half a century ago Rayleigh [207] made calculations which indicated that for pitches as low as middle c the difference in intensity produced by the shielding of one ear would be too small to detect. His calculations dealt with the intensity of the sound on opposite sides of a rigid sphere, and he assumed that differences in intensity on opposite sides of the human head would be similar. For three ratios between circumference of sphere and wave length of sound he found the intensity on the farther side of the sphere cut down to the following fractions of the intensity on the near side.

Circumference of sphere divided by wave length	2	1	0.5
Intensity on farther side divided by intensity on near side	0.46	0.57	0.88
Corresponding reduction in db	3.4	2.5	0.5

Question 249. The three cases in the above table correspond approximately to what pitches?

These results suggest that differences in intensity at the two ears may help in determining the direction from which sounds arrive when the sounds are of moderately high pitch, or contain components that have moderately high pitches, but that difference of intensity cannot be of importance when the sounds are simple and of low pitch. Nevertheless it is found that the direction can be determined as easily when the pitch is low as when it is high. Moreover, More and Fry [208] have pointed out that "A sound coming from a considerable distance to a horse must affect each of his ears

[207] Lord Rayleigh, Nature, 14, 32 (1876).
[208] L. T. More and H. S. Fry, Phil. Mag., 13, 452 (1907).

with the same intensity. Yet a horse, or any other of the
animals tried, had no difficulty in locating the direction of a
noise. . . . If a person stations himself behind and somewhat to the *right* of an animal and then whistles, the animal
invariably moves his head or ears to the *right* and continues
the motion until pointing directly to the person, although he
may be hidden. . . . The results are quite certain, that such
animals locate sounds accurately and yet have no means of
doing this by comparing the intensity of the sounds in the
two ears."

102. **Difference in Phase or Time.**—Another possible
explanation of the ability to determine the direction from
which a sound comes lies in a difference of phase. Even if
differences of phase do not affect the quality of a musical
sound it is conceivable that they may nevertheless aid in
determining direction. If the wave fronts reach one ear
a little before they reach the other they arrive at the two
ears in different phases. Does a difference in phase give a
sense of direction?

This question has been examined by various experimenters.[209] One method used is to lead to each ear the
sound from a tuning fork. The pitches of the two forks
are so nearly the same that the beats are extremely slow
—sometimes as slow as one beat in a minute. The experimental arrangements are such that the sound which reaches
one ear comes from one of the forks, and the sound that
reaches the other ear comes from the other fork. The sound
is usually heard as that of a single fork, but instead of the
alternating increase and decrease in loudness which generally characterizes beats there is observed an apparent movement of the source. The phase difference is slowly changing, and when the sound that reaches the right ear has a
phase a little in advance of that which reaches the left ear

[209] See Appendix Seven.

the sound appears to come from a point that lies somewhat toward the right, and *vice versa*.

After describing his experimental arrangements Rayleigh says,[209] "At the very first trial on July 31, the period of the cycle being 5 seconds, Lady Rayleigh and I at once experienced a distinct right and left effect, the sound appearing to transfer itself alternately from the one side to the other." Other studies have on the whole given results in agreement with Rayleigh's conclusion that for sounds of the lower pitches a difference in phase gives information regarding direction.

If we use sharp clicks instead of musical sounds, bringing one click to each ear, it is found[210] that when the interval between the clicks is greater than some 0.02 sec. both clicks are heard. But when the interval is less than this only one click is heard, and the direction from which this click seems to come depends on which ear receives the click first. In the case of a simple musical tone it seems also to be true that the apparent direction is not determined by the phase difference itself, but rather by the difference between the times at which the same phase reaches the ears.[211]

Question 250. A middle *c* tuning fork is held to the right of an observer. If the flow of sound were not distorted by the observer's head what would be the approximate difference in phase at the two ears? the approximate difference in the times at which the same phase would reach the two ears? What would the answers to these questions be if the tuning fork were an octave lower?

Why is it that although changes in phase have very little effect on judgments of musical quality, they do nevertheless affect judgments of direction? When we are dealing with direction we must remember that the two factors which we have considered—intensity and phase or time—require

[210] Johann Wittmann, Archiv für die gesamte Psychol., **51**, 21 (1925).

[211] H. Banister, in *Discussion on Audition* (1931), The Physical Society (London), p. 104.

E. M. von Hornbostel, *ibid.*, p. 120.

two ears for the formation of any judgment, whereas judgments of quality can be made with only one ear. Stefanini [209] draws attention to the fact that when there is a difference in phase at the two ears the two drum membranes —and other moving parts—are not in phase with each other. It is entirely possible that this difference in phase of motion in the two ears might lead to a judgment of direction. Banister [211] has pointed out that "the sensory impulses which underlie all sensation are, according to present-day psychological theory, discrete. If we may assume . . . that these nerve-impulses are initiated by the sound-waves when the displacement from the mean position has a certain value and when the movement is in a certain direction, we can see that the time-difference between the arrival of sound-waves at the two ears will be followed by a similar time-difference in the initiation of the sensory nerve-impulses in the two ears. So there will be a stream of impulses in the nerve fibres of the two ears, with a certain time-difference between them. In other words a difference in phase, or in the times of arrival of the waves, at the ears, will result in clues being available for lateral localization."

Inside of a room judgments of the direction of a source of sound are complicated by reflection. And whether indoors or out, our judgments in any case are not entirely dependent on differences in intensity and differences in the time at which a given phase arrives. We may see the person who speaks, or we may know where he is. It is by the use of extra-auditory factors that the ventriloquist accomplishes his illusions.

Question 251. What objection is there to supposing that a difference in the time at which a certain phase reaches the ears may be an important clue in determining direction when the pitch is moderately high?

Question 252. By what means may we know from what direction a sound comes when the sound is complex?

103. The Ear.—The ear is usually regarded as consisting of three parts: The outer ear, the middle ear, and the inner ear. Fig. 80 is a diagrammatic section, with the inner ear much enlarged. The outer ear lies to the left of the membrane T, and the inner ear to the right of O and r. The

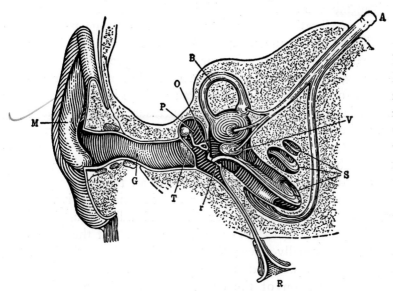

Fig. 80.—Diagrammatic Section Through Right Ear [From Kimber and Gray, *Textbook of Anatomy and Physiology,* Macmillan (1933)].

middle ear is so small that if it contained water it would hold only five or six drops.

The outer ear and the middle ear contain air. The inner ear contains watery fluids. Most of the inner ear is encased in bone except for two small openings into the middle ear. One of these openings is round, and is known as the "round window" r. The other is more or less oval, and is called the "oval window" O. Both windows are covered with membranes which prevent the escape of the fluids from the inner ear and which are capable of vibrating.

Between the outer ear and the middle ear is the "drum-

skin" or "drum membrane" or "tympanic membrane" *T*.
When sound waves arrive at the ear the compressions and
rarefactions enter the outer ear freely, but do not readily
reach the middle ear except by way of the drum membrane.
It is the resulting difference in pressure on the two sides of
this membrane that forces it to vibrate.

This vibration occurs best when the average pressure
of the air in the outer ear is about the same as that in the
middle ear. When we go up or down in an elevator in a tall
building, or when we drive on a road that ascends or de-
scends for some considerable distance, there is often a very
appreciable change in the average pressure of the air near
us, and consequently of that in the outer ear. The average
pressure in the middle ear is usually kept nearly the same as
that in the outer ear by a slight movement of the air in the
proper direction through the "eustachian tube" *R*, which
runs from the middle ear to the rear of the nasal cavity. If
the pressure in the middle ear does not readily adjust itself
there is a feeling of pressure in the ears, and the act of
swallowing usually opens the eustachian tube and allows
the pressures inside and outside to equalize.

The vibration of the drum membrane is transmitted
through the middle ear by means of three small bones which
are often called the "hammer," the "anvil," and the "stirrup." The drum membrane and the three bones are represented in a very diagrammatic way in Fig. 81. The handle
of the hammer is fastened to the drum membrane at *B* and
holds that membrane drawn inward, so that it is an asymmetric vibrator. Under the action of ordinary sound waves
the hammer and anvil move together, much as if they were
a single body. The foot of the stirrup is covered by the
membrane in the oval window and fastened to that membrane, and the foot of the stirrup is almost as large as the
window. At *G* the stirrup is so close to the edge of the
window that it can hardly move. When *B* swings to the

right the stirrup moves almost as if it were rocking around *G*, with *F* swinging toward the right.

The longer dimension of the oval window is about 3 mm. The drum membrane has an area fifteen or twenty times that of the oval window, and the leverage of the three middle ear bones is such as to make the force in the middle of *FG* approximately three times that at *B*. As a result, the changes in pressure that the stirrup exerts on the liquid in the inner ear are some fifty or sixty times as great as the pressure changes in the outer ear.

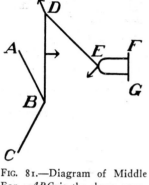

FIG. 81.—Diagram of Middle Ear. *ABC* is the drum membrane, *BD* the hammer, *DE* the anvil, and *EFG* the stirrup. The arrow at *D* represents a supporting ligament, and the two other arrows represent muscles.

The inner ear is very complicated. It consists of three parts: The "vestibule," the "semicircular canals," and the "cochlea." The vestibule, as its name implies, is an entrance to the semicircular canals and to the cochlea. The semicircular canals lie approximately in three perpendicular planes, and are of service in keeping our bodies balanced rather than in hearing. The cochlea has the shape of a tiny snail shell, and is only 6 mm or 7 mm in diameter at its widest part. Yet inside of this small organ is contained the apparatus by which the motion of the stirrup in the middle ear makes us aware of all the manifold sounds that come to us—all the commingling instruments and qualities of sound from a symphony orchestra, all the varied sounds of field and forest and waterfall, all the knowledge and changes of mood that are brought by the voices of our friends.

The inner ear is lined with a membrane, and inside of it are the fluids, some other membranes, nerve terminals, and so on. The human cochlea is a coil of about two and a half turns. In Fig. 82 it is represented as uncoiled and straightened out to its full length of some 30 to 35 mm. At *o* is the oval window, to the membrane of which the foot of the stirrup is fastened, and at *r* is the round window. Since the liquids in the inner ear are only slightly compressible, and the walls fairly rigid, the membrane in the round window yields when the stirrup urges the liquid inward or outward at the oval window.

The space inside of the cochlea is separated into two parts by membranes and related structures, as indicated by

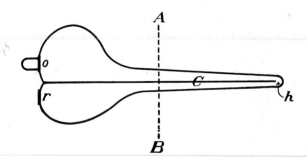

FIG. 82.—Diagram of Uncoiled Human Cochlea.

the horizontal line in Fig. 82. These structures do not extend quite to the farther end of the cochlea, but leave there a tiny opening *h* which is known as the *helicotrema*.

If we take a section across the cochlea, like *AB* in Fig. 82, we can get some idea of the structures that separate its two principal canals. Fig. 83 shows such a section, and Fig. 84 is an enlargement of part of the section. It will be seen that part of the separating structure is the bony *laminis spiralis ossea,* and another part is the flexible *membrana basilaris* or *basilar membrane*. The width of the basilar membrane is least (perhaps 0.2 mm) at the end near to the round and oval windows, and is greatest (about 0.5 mm) close to the helicotrema.

Arranged along the basilar membrane from one end to the other are two rows of rods discovered in 1851 by Alfonso Corti and known by his name. Each row contains some 4000 to 6000 rods, and the two rows meet and form arches like the one near the middle of Fig. 84. Like the basilar membrane, these arches are smaller toward the windows and larger toward the helicotrema.

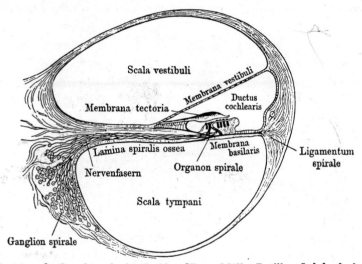

FIG. 83.—Section through the Cochlea [From Müller-Pouillet, *Lehrbuch der Physik,* Vieweg (1929)].

One end of a Corti arch is at the edge of the basilar membrane, and the other end is farther out on the membrane. So any vibration of the membrane causes a rocking of the arch. And if the arch rocks it disturbs the hair cells that may be seen in Fig. 84 projecting up to the tectorial membrane. These hair cells in turn are connected with fibers of the auditory nerve.

104. **Theories of Hearing.**[212]—The best known theories

[212] For further treatments of theories of hearing see Journ. Acoust. Soc., 1, 295-356 (1930); *Report of a Discussion on Audition,* published by the Physical Society of London (1931); George Wilkinson and Albert A. Gray, *The Mechanism of the Cochlea* (1924).

of hearing are resonance theories. More than two and a half centuries ago it was suggested that the cochlea may contain some sort of a mechanism that is similar to a musical instrument. The mechanism was thought to act by resonance, different parts of it responding to different frequencies. Some three quarters of a century ago this idea was much further developed by Helmholtz, and resonance theories of hearing are now often connected with his name.

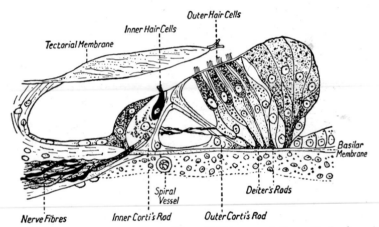

FIG. 84.—Enlarged Part of Fig. 83 [From Wilkinson and Gray, *Mechanism of the Cochlea*, Macmillan (1924), p. 69].

Suggestions have differed as to what structure it is that acts as a resonator. An early suggestion was the *laminis spiralis ossea*. Helmholtz thought at first that it might be the organ formed by the rods of Corti, but after it was found that the ears of amphibia and birds do not contain Corti rods he turned to the basilar membrane. Recently it has been suggested as more likely that the resonating structure may be the tectorial membrane.

For the present let us suppose that the resonating structure is the basilar membrane. The whole cochlea is so small that any change of pressure in the contained liquid

distributes itself almost immediately throughout the cochlea.   That is, at any given instant we may think of the
pressure as being the same at all points in the cochlea.   Now
look again at Fig. 82.   When the oval window moves inward the round window moves outward, and *vice versa*.   At
any instant the pressure on both sides of the basilar membrane is practically the same.   When the vibration of the
oval window is very slow the liquid in the cochlea moves
through the helicotrema.

When the frequency is greater it seems likely that some
part of the basilar membrane might vibrate.   In Fig. 82
suppose that a small part of the membrane in the neighborhood of C vibrates, and that the rest of the membrane
remains practically at rest.   When o moves inward the membrane at C moves downward and r moves outward.   The
liquid that moves is principally that to the left of C.   The
inertia that is involved in the vibration is principally the
inertia of this part of the liquid.   The nearer C is to the
windows the smaller is the inertia, and the farther C is from
the windows the greater is the inertia.   So there is a considerable difference in the inertia coefficients for vibrations
of different parts of the membrane.   The stiffness coefficient depends principally on the stiffness of the small part of
the membrane itself, and on the stiffness at o and r, and so
does not differ greatly for different parts of the membrane.
It follows that different parts of the membrane, together
with the associated liquid, have different natural frequencies.   When the frequency of an impressed vibration is that
of one of these natural frequencies, that part of the membrane responds much more vigorously than other parts.
Thus certain tones are picked up by certain parts of the
membrane, and other tones by other parts.

Question 253.   If the above theory of hearing is correct which
end of the basilar membrane responds to high pitched tones?

Question 254. On p. 272 it is stated that the basilar membrane is wider at one end than at the other. On the above theory of hearing does this difference make the range of audible pitches greater or less than it would be if the membrane had the same width throughout?

Question 255. On the above theory of hearing how are we to explain the ability of the ear to analyze a complex tone into its simple components? How are we to explain difference tones? beats? the limits to audible frequencies?

Question 256. There are means by which it is possible to remove from a sound certain chosen frequency components. When a musical instrument is giving a steady sound, and from this sound the fundamental and several of the lower pitched components are removed, Fletcher [213] finds that the ear still hears the fundamental. How can this be explained?

Among experiments which support the above theory of hearing there is one that has been carried out on guinea pigs. [214] When a guinea pig hears any tone that lies within its auditory compass it responds by a twitch of the ear. By means of a tiny drill only 0.1 mm in diameter it has been possible to bore a minute hole through the bony wall of the cochlea of a guinea pig in such a way as to break a few threads of the ligament that keeps the basilar membrane stretched. This loosens a very narrow region of the basilar membrane. After such an operation it was found that the animal was deaf to tones that covered a small range of pitch, and that the deafness was for fairly high pitches when the loosening of the basilar membrane was near the window end of the membrane. Various objections have been raised to such theories of hearing as that given above. According to these theories different pitches are recognized as different because they produce their greatest response at different positions in the

213 Harvey Fletcher, Phys. Rev., **23**, 427 (1924).
214 H. Held and F. Kleinknecht, Pflüger's Archiv, **216**, 1 (1927).

cochlea. Now the normal discrimination of pitch is so keen that if such theories are correct it must be possible to distinguish different frequencies when the resonant mechanisms involved in the basilar membrane are only a fiftieth of a millimeter apart. It has been suggested that so fine a discrimination would be extremely remarkable.[215] However, it may be answered that this minuteness of discrimination is similar to that which we know is possible in the retina of the eye.

Another objection to such theories is that the basilar membrane contains blood vessels, and that these vessels must dilate and contract as all blood vessels do. It has been suggested that any such change in the load carried by the membrane would shift the position of maximum response for a given frequency. As a result a given frequency would not always be heard at precisely the same pitch.[216]

It has also been possible to introduce extra pressure on the round window. It was thought that the pressure would put an additional load on the window, and would therefore change the position of maximum response in the basilar membrane. If the position of maximum response were shifted it would seem that the pitch of the tone perceived ought to be different, but no change in pitch was observed.[217]

Attention has also been called [218] to "the accuracy of the adjustments, whatever they are and wherever they are, by which various frequencies are differentiated" and to the permanence of the adjustment. "A mechanism which is to meet the requirements of sound analysis as well as our ears do, must have a frequency range of about ten octaves, must be very accurate in adjustment and must be essentially permanent in adjustment over a period of at least fifty years. This

[215] Leonard T. Troland, p. 305 in the first reference in footnote 212.
[216] G. E. Shambaugh, p. 297 in the first reference in footnote 212.
[217] Augustus G. Pohlman, p. 350 in the first reference in footnote 212.
[218] F. W. Kranz, p. 354 in the first reference in footnote 212.

certainly seems rather difficult to achieve in the limited volume of the inner ear and having as the sole materials of construction, the rather soft tissues which are found therein."

What other theories of hearing are there? May it not be that frequencies are perceived more directly than is assumed in resonance theories? Why should not frequencies themselves be picked up by the nerves and carried to the brain? It is found that when a nerve fiber is sufficiently stimulated an impulse passes along it. The impulse is followed for a short time by a "refractory phase," during which no stimulus will affect the nerve fiber.[219] In fact, it is found that a nerve fiber cannot transmit more than some 700 to 1000 impulses in a second. So for frequencies higher than this any direct transmission of frequency by a nerve fiber seems out of the question. It has been suggested, however, that this frequency limitation applies only to a single fiber, and not to a group of fibers. It is possible that the group of fibers which form a nerve might cooperate in such a way as to transmit higher frequencies.[220]

Various other theories have been suggested. The only one which we shall mention here is a combination [221] of a resonance theory and a theory of direct transmission of frequencies. On this theory the pitch that is heard depends partly on the position of maximum stimulation of the basilar membrane, and partly on a "time pattern" carried to the brain by the nerves. For the lower pitches the latter is regarded as more important, and for the higher pitches the former.

The discussion in this article has not led to any certain conclusion. At the present time it is probable that some form of resonance theory fits the facts—at any rate for the

[219] E. D. Adrian, *The Basis of Sensation* (1928), p. 25.
[220] Leonard T. Troland, p. 304 in the first reference in footnote 212.
[221] Harvey Fletcher, p. 311 in the first reference in footnote 212.

higher frequencies—as well as any other that has been proposed.

Question 257. On a resonance theory of hearing can you account for the fact that pressure on the round window does not change the pitch that is heard?

Question 258. In the above discussion of theories of hearing nothing has been said about loudness. Can you develop any hypothesis to account for differences in loudness?

CHAPTER TEN

MUSICAL INSTRUMENTS

105. Introduction.—In Chapters Seven and Eight we have considered the free vibration and the forced vibration of various systems. In this chapter we shall discuss more fully the free vibration and the forced vibration of certain systems which are employed for the purposes of music. Most vibrating systems are not suited to the production of music, and there are two reasons why they are not thus suited. In the first place, the normal modes of vibration are in most cases inharmonic, and in the second place, the damping is often so great that the tones die out rather quickly, so that unless means are employed for maintaining the vibrations no music with sustained chords is possible.

"The sound producing parts of a musical instrument, in general, perform two distinct functions. Certain parts are designed for the production of musical vibrations. The vibrations in their original form may be almost inaudible, though vigorous, because they do not set up waves in the air, as is illustrated by the vibrations of the string of a violin without the body of the instrument; or the vibrations may produce a very undesirable tone quality because they are not properly controlled, as in the case of the reed of a clarinet without the body tube. Other parts of the instrument receive these vibrations, and by operation on a larger quantity of air and by selective control, cause the instrument to send out into the air the sounds which we ordinarily hear. These parts, which may be referred to as *generator* and *resonator,* are illustrated by the following combinations: a tuning-fork generator and its box resonator; the strings and soundboard of a piano; the reed and body tube of a clarinet; the mouth and body tube of an organ pipe; the vocal cords and mouth cavities of the voice. . . .

"The resonator cannot give out any tones except those received from the generator, and it may not give out all of these. The generator must therefore be capable of producing the components which we wish to hear, and these must in turn be emitted in the desired proportion by the resonator. If the generator produces partial tones which are undesirable, the resonator should be designed so that it will not reproduce them; if the generator produces tones which are of musical value but which the resonator does not reproduce, we do not hear them, and it is as though they were not produced at all. It follows that we can hear from a given instrument nothing except what is produced by the generator, and further we can hear nothing except what is also reproduced by the resonator." [222]

Our most important musical instruments are largely restricted to those which make use of the vibrations of stretched strings and of the air in fairly narrow tubes. In neither of these cases do the normal modes of vibration deviate widely from a harmonic series. In both cases there are means by which the tones can be maintained at pleasure, and when the vibration is free the tones from stretched strings may last for a sufficient length of time to make them available for music. There are other instruments—like the human voice and the reed organ—which do not use either stretched strings or narrow tubes. But in these the vibration may be steadily maintained, and when this is done the components are forced to be harmonic (Art. 79). Instruments which do not use stretched strings or fairly narrow air columns, and in which the vibration is not maintained,

[222] Dayton Clarence Miller, *The Science of Musical Sounds,* Macmillan (1926), p. 175.

have their place in producing special effects, but most of them are not suited for use without other instruments or when successions of sustained chords are desired. Consequently most of this chapter is concerned with strings and wind instruments.

A string is so slender that the air slips readily around it. The compressions and rarefactions produced by the vibration of a string alone are very small, and it is easy to show experimentally that the sound produced is faint. If the vibration of a string is to be loud enough for the purposes of music it is necessary for the intensity of the sound to be considerably amplified in some way. This amplification is the purpose of a soundboard. Near one or both of its ends a string passes over a "bridge" which rests on the soundboard. Thus the string and the soundboard are coupled by the bridge, and each reacts on the other. The area of the soundboard is so much greater than that of the string that the vibration of the soundboard produces compressions and rarefactions much greater than would be set up by the string alone, and thus the intensity of the sound is sufficiently amplified to be satisfactory for music. The effect on the energy is similar to that of putting a tuning fork on a resonant box (cf. Question 179): There is no creation of energy, but a more rapid use of it.

In wind instruments an opening to the external air is not stretched out in a long narrow line like a string, but is spread over an area which is more extended, even though much shorter. So a wind instrument affects the external air directly and needs nothing that corresponds at all closely to bridge and soundboard.

Most string instruments belong to one of three general classes: The strings may be (a) plucked or (b) bowed or (c) struck. Most wind instruments belong to one of four general classes: (a) The fundamental pitch may be largely determined by a metal reed, (b) the vibration may be maintained by one or two light reeds made of reed or cane, (c) the vibration may be maintained by the lips of the player, or (d) the vibration may be maintained by a thin sheet of wind.

The actual forms of various musical instruments, the details of their construction, and the manner in which they are used, are often more readily understood by examining the instruments themselves than by reading about them. In this book it is assumed that the reader already possesses some knowledge of the general form and manner of use of the more common musical instruments.[223]

The questions which are here discussed have to do with the shapes assumed by vibrating strings, the forces which these strings exert on the soundboard, the means by which the vibration of the air in an organ pipe is maintained, and other questions of similar type.

106. Plucked Strings.—In various instruments the strings are plucked. This is the case of course in the harp, the violin when played *pizzicato,* in the guitar, the mandolin, the banjo, the zither, the ukulele, etc. Among the plucked instruments which are now not so well known are the harpsichord, the spinet, the virginal, the lute, the lyre, and the psaltery.

The first question that we are raising in connection with plucked strings has to do with the successive shapes assumed by the string. The string in Fig. 85 is fastened at A and B. If it is drawn aside at C and then released will it at some instant be in its equilibrium position in the straight line from A to B? And when it comes momentarily to rest below AB will it lie in some such curve as ADB, or will the form consist of two straight lines like AEB, or will it have some other form?

---

[223] A considerable amount of information about the forms of various musical instruments may be found on pp. 226-274 in Müller-Pouillet, *Lehrbuch der Physik,* ed. 11, vol. 1, part 3 (1929); in Barton, *A Text-Book on Sound* (1908), Chap. 8; and in the *Dictionary of Applied Physics,* vol. 4, art. Sound.

Let us first examine these questions theoretically. That is, let us see what answers seem reasonable. We notice that *A* and *B* remain at rest. Perhaps the motion of the string may be regarded as a vibration in which *A* and *B* are nodes. If the string were very long and were not fastened at *A* and

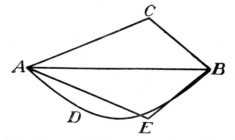

Fig. 85.—A Question as to the Shapes Assumed by a Plucked String.

B it would be possible to set up on it standing waves in which *A* and *B* would be nodes. So it is entirely possible that the part *AB* of the very long string might vibrate in the same way that the real string *AB* vibrates.

Now to produce standing waves there must be two trains of waves traveling in opposite directions (Art. 30). At the

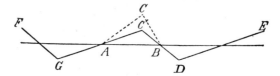

Fig. 86.—Standing Waves which Produce the Vibration of a Stretched String.

instant when the real string is released suppose that the imaginary very long string has on it two trains of waves which are in the same position and are represented in Fig. 86 by the same broken line *FGAC'BDE*. The resultant of the two is twice as high, and in the region between *A* and *B* the resultant is *ACB*. This dotted resultant represents the real string. After a very short time one of the trains has moved a short distance to the right, and the other an equal distance to the left. If the reader will draw the two trains in their new positions, and then obtain their resultant, he will find that the left part of AC and the right part of CB still form part of the resultant, but that near C the shape has changed. If this process is followed, step by step, it will be found that the standing waves between A and B take the shapes shown in Fig. 87 by $AH_1H_1'B$, $AH_2H_2'B$, etc. After half a period the string is momentarily at rest in the

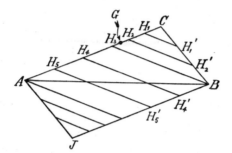

Fig. 87.—Some of the Successive Shapes Assumed by a Plucked String.

position AJB, and then it returns through the same intermediate shapes to ACB.

The use of the two trains of waves on the very long string may at first seem somewhat artificial. But if there are waves traveling toward the left on the real string they are of course reflected at A, and if there are waves traveling toward the right they are reflected at B. So the use of the standing waves on the long string does not seem so artificial after all.

Question 259. If the above reasoning applies to the real string, what are the answers to the questions raised in the second paragraph of this article? What is the shape of the string a quarter of a period after it is released?

If the results at which we have arrived are correct we are prepared to raise other questions: If we select some small part of the string what is the shape of its vibration curve? Are the vibration curves the same for different parts of the string?

We see that any small part of either AC or BC does not move so long as it is on a straight part of the string—that is, until a corner has come down to it from C. This seems perfectly reasonable. Consider, for instance, a small part of the string near H_2. Call this particle G. So long as the string on one side of G pulls it in one direction just as hard as the string on the opposite side pulls it in precisely the opposite direction there is no resultant force to start it moving. When the corner arrives G is suddenly set into motion.

Question 260. What paragraph in Art. 59 deals with a similar situation?

After the particle G has been set moving it continues for a short time on a straight part of the string, like H_4H_4'.

FIG. 88.—Vibration Curve for Particle G in Fig. 87.

So there is again no resultant force acting to change its motion, and it moves steadily and uniformly downward. This downward motion continues until a corner on the line JB reaches the particle and brings it suddenly to rest. We see that the particle G remains for a time at rest on the line AC, then moves steadily downward until it reaches the line JB, remains again at rest for a short time, and then moves steadily upward until it comes to rest on the line AC. Its vibration curve is shown in Fig. 88.

Question 261. If the particle considered were to the right of C how would it move? How if it were to the left of J?

Question 262. If vibration curves are obtained for various particles of the string, how do these curves compare?

Question 263. If the string is plucked in the middle how is Fig. 87 changed? How are the vibration curves changed? What are the answers if the string is plucked very close to one end?

107. Experimental Test.—Our theoretical reasoning has led to a definite picture of the motion of the string. Do real strings behave in this way? One important study of this question was carried out in the University at Berlin by Krigar-Menzel and Raps.[224] Fig. 89 is a diagram of their

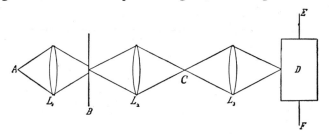

FIG. 89.—Apparatus used by Krigar-Menzel and Raps.

apparatus. A is an electric arc. L_1, L_2, and L_3 are lenses. D is a drum which turns about the axis EF and is driven by clockwork. At B is a screen, perpendicular to the plane of the diagram, and containing a narrow slit that is parallel to EF. This slit is brightly illuminated by the arc A and the lens L_1. The lens L_2 brings the light from the slit at B to a focus at C, so that if there were a screen at C L_2 would produce upon it a bright image of the slit. There is no screen at C, but it is here that the string is stretched, in a position perpendicular to the plane of the diagram. So if there were a screen just beyond C there would appear upon it a bright image of the slit, crossed near its middle by a shadow of the string. And if the string were in vibration the shadow would swing rapidly up and down along the

[224] Otto Krigar-Menzel and August Raps, Wied. An., 50, 444 (1893). The apparatus is described in an earlier paper, Wied. An., 44, 623 (1891).

image of the slit. The bright image of the slit with the string crossing it is projected by the lens L_3 upon photographic paper on the drum D. If the drum were at rest and the string vibrating, there would be simply a blur across the image of the slit. But if the drum is turning then the shadow of the string draws a line on the photographic paper, and when the paper is developed there is upon it the vibration curve for the point of the string that was at C. Fig. 90 gives copies of a few of the curves.

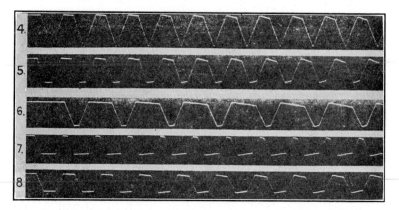

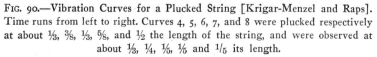

FIG. 90.—Vibration Curves for a Plucked String [Krigar-Menzel and Raps]. Time runs from left to right. Curves 4, 5, 6, 7, and 8 were plucked respectively at about ⅓, ⅜, ⅓, ⅝, and ½ the length of the string, and were observed at about ⅓, ¼, ⅕, ⅕ and 1/5 its length.

Question 264. Are the curves in Fig. 90 approximately what you should expect from the answers to questions 262 and 263?

On examining these curves we notice that in a general way they bear out our anticipations very well. There is however at least one feature that we did not anticipate. The parts that we expected to see horizontal slope somewhat, and they slope to a greater extent after a greater number of cycles. What is the reason? We have assumed that the ends of the string are absolutely at rest. Actually the ends of the string pass over bridges that transmit the vibration to something else. That is, the string is coupled to other parts of the instrument, and the reaction of those other parts affects the motion of the string. Krigar-Menzel and Raps were able to show that when the theoretical reasoning is corrected by taking this reaction into account it leads to the type of vibration curve that is really found.

108. **Force-Time Curve.**—Now that we know something about the vibration of a plucked string we can investigate the changing force that the string exerts on each of the bridges. Will the shape of the force-time curve be similar to any of the vibration curves?

To answer this question let us return to Fig. 87 on p. 285, and let us examine the force-time curve on the bridge at A. In Fig. 91 the triangle represents the bridge, P a pin to which the end of the string is fastened, and AC and AJ

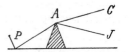

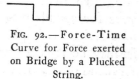

FIG. 91.—Bridge and Adjacent Parts of String.

FIG. 92.—Force-Time Curve for Force exerted on Bridge by a Plucked String.

the same directions as AC and AJ in Fig. 87. When the string has the direction AC the force on the bridge is the resultant of the pull in the part AP of the string and the pull in the part AC. These pulls are partly in opposite directions, but partly they both urge the bridge downward. When the string has the direction AJ the resultant downward push on the bridge is greater than when the string has the direction AC.

We have seen that the string near A maintains the direction AC during a certain fraction of a cycle, and then suddenly shifts to the direction AJ. It maintains the direction AJ during another fraction of the cycle, and again shifts abruptly back to the direction AC. It follows that the force-time curve for the force which the string exerts on the bridge has the shape shown in Fig. 92, where a greater force downward is represented by a lower position of the curve.

Question 265. How does the force-time curve for the force exerted by the string on bridge B in Fig. 87 compare with that for the force exerted on A?

Question 266. After drawing the force-time curves for several positions of plucking how should you say that the shape of the force-time curve depends on the position of plucking?

Question 267. How is the shape of the force-time curve affected by the deviation of the vibration curves in Fig. 90 from the ideal forms?

109. Component Simple Tones.—The vibration curves and the force-time curves that we have obtained for plucked strings are far from being simple harmonic. Surprise has sometimes been expressed that curves which appear no more complicated than that in Fig. 88 should be the vibration curves for sounds which are apprehended by the ear as a whole series of simple tones. However surprising this result may be it is nevertheless a fact that the ear does so apprehend them. In the ideal case where the bridges do not yield, and where the string is perfectly flexible, the curves are periodic. It follows (Art. 79) that each of them may be regarded as the sum of a Fourier series of simple harmonic curves.

To each of these simple curves corresponds a simple tone, and it can be shown that among these simple tones there are none which would be produced by a vibration of the string with a node at the point plucked. Before Fourier series were known Young [225] had pointed out this fact. If a string is plucked at a third of its length those components that have frequencies 3, 6, 9, · · · · · times that of the fundamental are not present; if it is plucked at a quarter of the length the components that have frequencies 4, 8, 12, · · · · times that of the fundamental are not present.

[225] Thomas Young, Phil. Trans., 90, 137 (1800).

Moreover if a vibrating string is touched gently—with a feather, small brush, or the tip of a finger—any mode of vibration which has a node at the point touched is hardly at all affected, while other modes are damped out. What then is the effect of plucking a string, let us say, at a third of its length and then touching it at the same point? The plucking elicits those normal modes of vibration that do not have a node at the point plucked, and touching the string damps out precisely the same normal modes. That is, if the string is damped at the point at which it was plucked it ceases to sound, but it may continue to sound if it is damped at some other point.

Question 268. Helmholtz (*Sensations of Tone,* 4th Eng. ed., p. 53) describes an interesting experiment which is essentially as follows. A stretched string is plucked alternately at a third of its length and a quarter of its length. With a little attention a simple melody may be heard—one note when the string is plucked at a third, and another when it is plucked at a quarter. How is this melody to be explained?

110. Bowed Strings.—Bowed strings, it is well known, are used on all instruments of the violin family. Shall we expect a bowed string to pass through shapes similar to those assumed by a plucked string, or will the forms turn out to be quite different? Are the vibration curves likely to be similar to those of a plucked string, or will they be quite different?

Instead of attempting any theoretical prediction, as we did for plucked strings, let us turn at once to experiment. The first important study of the manner in which a bowed string vibrates was made by Helmholtz.[226] He made use of an instrument which was devised by Lissajous, and which

---

[226] Hermann von Helmholtz, Philosoph. Soc. Glasgow, Proc. **5,** 17 (1860); reprinted in Phil. Mag., **21,** 393 (1861). Or see *Sensations of Tone,* 4th Eng. ed., p. 80.

Helmholtz called a "vibration microscope." In order to understand its action let a black dot be made on a white card that lies on a table, and let an observer look down at the dot through a reading glass or other lens. If the lens is moved slightly sideways, without any change in its distance from the table, the dot appears to move. If the lens is given a slight back and forth motion along a line parallel to the table the dot appears to move back and forth along the same line. If the lens is held at rest while the card is moved back and forth on the table there is a similar movement of the dot. If the back and forth movements of the lens and card occur at the same time, and in perpendicular directions, the two apparent motions of the dot combine and describe a curve similar to one of the Lissajous figures that we met in Arts. 15 and 50.

In the application to a bowed string Helmholtz replaced the dot on the card by a bright spot on the string, and the lens was a small one fastened to one prong of an electrically driven tuning fork. To get a bright spot on the violin string a small part of the string was first blackened with ink, and then rubbed over with wax and powdered with starch. A few grains of starch remained sticking to the string, and one of these was chosen for observation. The image formed by the lens was observed through a magnifying lens, so that the two lenses really formed a low power microscope. When the string was bowed it carried the grain of starch back and forth in one direction, and the tuning fork was so placed that it carried its lens back and forth in a perpendicular direction.

If the frequency of vibration of the starch grain were exactly 1, 2, 3, or 4 times that of the tuning fork the figure seen in the microscope would be steady. When the frequency ratio is close to one of these numbers the figure gradually changes. The motion of the lens carried by the tuning fork was practically simple harmonic, and since

Helmholtz knew the frequencies of both fork and string he could determine what the appearance of the figure would be if the motion of the starch grain were also simple harmonic. The figure showed that the starch grain did not execute a simple harmonic motion, but from the shape of the figure it was possible to obtain the vibration curve for the starch grain.

The vibration curve was often a two-step zigzag like that shown in Fig. 93. It will be seen that this is entirely different from the vibration curves in Figs. 88 and 90 for plucked strings. On a good violin, and with the bow biting well, Helmholtz found that the vibration curve for any given particle of the string is "tolerably independent of the place of bow-ing." This is quite different from a plucked string, where the shape

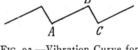

FIG. 93.—Vibration Curve for Particle in a Violin String.

of the curve depends decidedly on the point at which the string is plucked. When the vibration curves for different particles on a bowed string are considered it is found that the curves for different particles are different—as they are on a plucked string. In the vibration curve for the particle at the middle of the bowed string the parts AB and BC in Fig. 93 are of equal length, and slope to equal extents. As the point under observation moves farther from the middle the steps AB and BC differ more and more both in length and in slope. Close to one end of the string most of the time is spent on the step AB, and the step BC is covered quickly. Near the other end of the string it is AB that slopes rapidly and BC that has the gradual slope.

Question 269. No part of the curve in Fig. 93 is horizontal. What does this mean?

Question 270. Every part of the curve in Fig. 93 is straight. What does this mean?

When we examined the plucked string we obtained the vibration curve in Fig. 88 from the successive shapes in Fig. 87. In the case of the bowed string Helmholtz reversed this procedure. From the vibration curves for the various particles of the string he found that the string goes through the shapes suggested by Fig. 94. The bow is being drawn downward near the right-hand end of the string, as shown by the arrow with the tail. At certain instants the shape is the one straight line AB. But during most of the vibration it consists of two straight lines like AC and

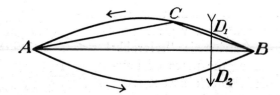

FIG. 94.—Shapes Assumed by a Bowed String. The arrow with a tail shows the position and direction of bowing.

CB. The corner C follows the curved lines around the path indicated by the arrows without tails. It moves steadily along the upper curve from B around to A and then steadily back along the lower curve to B again.

Consider the motion of the particle under the bow. When the corner C is to the left of the bow the particle is on the line CB, and when C is to the right of the bow the particle is on the line AC. When C is at D_1 the particle is at D_1. Then as C moves to the left the line CB grows longer and turns downward, with one end always at B. This motion continues while C moves over to A and then back along the lower curve to D_2. During all this time the particle in question has been moving downward from D_1 to D_2. Then while C moves from D_2 to B and on up to D_1 the line AC turns upward and the particle moves upward from D_2 to D_1. Since it takes C considerably longer to travel from

D_1 to A and back to D_2 than it does to travel from D_2 to B and up to D_1 it follows that the particle moves downward slowly and upward quickly. That is, the motion agrees with the vibration curve in Fig. 93.

Helmholtz found, however, that the vibration curve is not always precisely this two step zigzag. "There are certain observable differences of the vibrational figure which depend upon the bowing point. Little crumples are usually perceived on the lines of the vibrational figure." Helmholtz's study of these crumples was extended by Krigar-

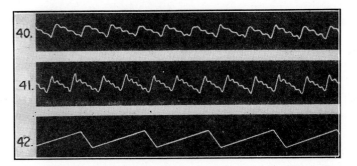

Fig. 95.—Vibration Curves for a Bowed String [Krigar-Menzel and Raps]. In curve 40 the string was bowed a little less than $\frac{1}{9}$ of its length from one end and was observed at $\frac{1}{15}$ of the length from the end. In 41 the point of observation was the same, but the point of bowing was a little more than $\frac{1}{9}$ instead of a little less. In 42 the string was bowed at $\frac{1}{6}$ of its length and observed at the same distance.

Menzel and Raps,[227] and Fig. 95 shows three of their curves. We shall not take the space here to discuss them.

Question 271. If the bow is applied as in Fig. 94 is the vibration curve in Fig. 93 for a particle near the right or the left end of the string? What would the answer be if the bow were applied downward near the left end of the string? If it were applied upward near the right end of the string?

[227] See the second reference in footnote 224.

Question 272. The curve in Fig. 92 shows how the force exerted on one of the bridges by a plucked string changes with time. What is the shape of the corresponding curve for a bowed string?

111. **Relative Motion of Bow and String.**—From Fig. 94 we have seen that the particles under the bow move slowly in the direction of motion of the bow and then rapidly in the opposite direction. This suggests that perhaps the bow catches the string and carries it with it until the pull of the displaced string becomes sufficient to tear it from the bow and cause it to swing rapidly in the opposite direction. This is what we assumed in Art. 80.

During the slower stage of its motion does the part of the string immediately under the bow really move with the speed of the bow? This question was investigated by Raman and then by Kar and by Mitra.[228] In Raman's method, which was followed by Kar and by Mitra, a narrow vertical slit was arranged just behind a horizontal string, and an electric arc was set up in front of the string. So the shadow of a very short length of string fell through the slit upon a photographic plate behind it. The plate ran between horizontal guides and was drawn along while the string was being bowed, thus producing on the photographic plate a vibration curve for the point of the string that was in front of the slit. In order to get a simultaneous curve that would show the speed of the bow Raman fixed a pin so that it projected horizontally from the middle of the bow. The string was bowed as close to the slit as possible. So the pin moved with the bow along the slit at the same time that the string was vibrating along it. If the string in front of the slit moved with the same speed as the bow the slope of the shadow of the string should be the same as the slope of the shadow of the pin. Fig. 96 is copied from one of

[228] C. V. Raman, Indian Assn. Cult. Sci. Bulletin No. 11, p. 43 (1914). K. C. Kar, Phys. Rev., 20, 148 (1922). Manindra Nath Mitra, Indian Journ. Physics, 1, 311 (1926-1927).

Raman's plates. It is seen that the agreement of the two speeds is excellent.

112. The Wolf Note.—"On all stringed instruments of the violin type a certain pitch can be found which it is difficult and often impossible to produce by bowing. . . . At this pitch . . . the bow refuses to 'bite,' and a soft pure tone is almost impossible to obtain; if the pressure of the bow on the string is increased the tone resulting is usually of an unsteady nature with considerable fluctuations in intensity." [229] This note is known as a "wolf." "The more

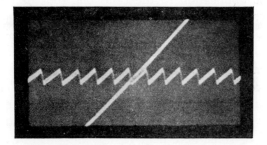

Fig. 96.—Speed of Point Under Bow Compared with Speed of Bow [Raman].

sonorous and brilliant the general tone, the more obtrusive it becomes; if the tone be forced, a disagreeable jar is produced. Hence it is idle to attempt to play the wolf down: the player must humor the troublesome note. It is commonly believed that there is a wolf somewhere in all fiddles, and it is certain that it exists in some of the finest." [230]

Although the existence of the wolf has been known for a long time no important study of it seems to have been made until fairly recently. In instruments of the violin type the vibration of the string is transmitted by the bridge to the wooden body of the instrument. The body incloses an air cavity which communicates with the external air through the

[229] G. W. White, Camb. Phil. Soc. Proc., **18**, 85 (1915).
[230] Edward John Payne, in Grove's *Dictionary of Music and Musicians,* Macmillan, ed. 3 (1928), vol. 5, p. 748.

f-holes. So each string is coupled to the body, and through it to the air cavity.

To examine the vibration of the wooden body of a cello White [229] used an optical lever. This lever is well known in physical laboratories. It consists of a small mirror mounted on a light framework that has three feet. Two feet rest on some fixed support, and the third on the object to be examined. A beam of light reflected from the mirror serves as a long and delicate pointer. Thus minute movements of the object investigated are greatly magnified.

In the application to the cello one foot of the optical lever rests on some part of the belly, and the motion of that particular part is examined. On playing pitch after pitch, each a quarter step higher than the preceding, White found that "as the note approaches the 'wolf-note' the curve becomes exceedingly simple and *a considerable increase in amplitude occurs.* . . . The increased amplitude of the belly at the 'wolf-note' led one to the conclusion that this note, or some note near it, was the pitch of best resonance of the instrument." • This view was confirmed by eliciting these belly vibrations in response to the same note blown on a cornet with its bell near the belly of the cello. Moreover, when the trace was received on a photographic film some couple of feet long, the fluctuations of intensity were shown to correspond to a waxing and waning in the vibration of the belly. White concluded that "the fluctuations in intensity are due to beats which accompany the forced vibration impressed on the resonator and which by reacting on the string may interfere with even bowing."

Raman [231] has pointed out that White's explanation is not adequate. When a simple harmonic force acts on a system that has a natural frequency near to that of the force it is entirely possible for the resultant vibration to contain

[231] C. V. Raman, Phys. Rev., **32**, 391 (1916).

both the free frequency and the forcing frequency, and therefore to give rise to beats. But the free frequency dies out very soon, and with it the beats disappear. A steadily alternating periodic force does not give rise to beats that continue as the wolf note does.

Raman has proposed another explanation. When a violin string is vibrating in the usual manner the work of Helmholtz shows that the lowest partials carry the most energy —the first partial more than any one above it, the second more than any above it, and so on. Raman's theoretical work led to the conclusion that the maintenance of the usual type of vibration requires a certain minimum bowing pressure, and that the more rapidly the energy is being carried away from the string the greater is the minimum bowing pressure that is necessary.

These results combine as follows. The pitch of the wolf is that of a natural frequency of the belly and associated parts. If that note is played the amplitude of vibration of the belly increases, and as it increases it takes energy from the string more and more rapidly. When the amplitude is small the pressure on the bow is sufficient to maintain the usual vibration of the string. With increase in amplitude a point is reached at which the belly takes energy from the string faster than the bow can supply it without an increase in bowing pressure. Consequently the type of vibration of the string changes: The string jumps to the octave, for the maintenance of which the bowing pressure is sufficient. The natural frequencies of the belly are not harmonic, and the octave of the string is not a natural pitch of the belly. So the vibration of the belly dies rapidly, and the drain of energy from the string decreases. When the loss of energy has fallen to a point at which the bow can maintain the usual type of vibration, with the fundamental prominent, the string again takes up that type. Thus the predominant pitch of the string is alternately the fundamental and the octave. It is this alternation, according to Raman's view, that gives the wolf its unpleasant effect.

To test these ideas Raman obtained on the same photograph two vibration curves, one for the belly and one for the string. Fig. 97 shows what he found. It will be seen that at first—that is at the left of the figure—the frequencies shown by the two curves are the same, but that when the amplitude of the belly grows large the string jumps to its octave; and that when the amplitude of the belly de-

Belly

String

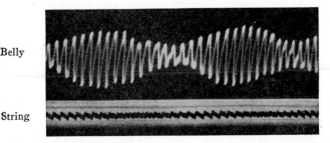

Fig. 97.—Simultaneous Vibration Curves for Belly and String of a Violoncello at the Wolf-Note Pitch [Raman]. Time increases toward the right.

creases sufficiently the string gives its fundamental again. So Raman's explanation appears to be correct.

Raman also pointed out that the above reasoning would lead us to expect the pitch of the wolf to be somewhat lower when there is a mute on the bridge. This, too, he found is the case.

Question 273. Why should the use of a mute lower the pitch of a wolf?

Question 274. If the frequency of the wolf note in Fig. 97 is 176 cycles/sec. what is the frequency of the wolf note cycle?

113. Struck Strings.—The most important modern instrument that employs strings which are struck is of course the piano. Struck strings were also used in the clavichord and the dulcimer.

It may be expected that the vibration of strings when struck may be more complicated than when they are either plucked or bowed. When a string is struck the hammer pushes aside a part of the string, and the displacement of that part causes waves to run from it in both directions along the string. After these waves have been reflected at the bridges they may arrive at the striking position before the hammer has left the string, or they may not arrive until after the stroke is completed. If the hammer is soft, or the blow somewhat gradual, the string is not pushed aside as abruptly as when the hammer is harder or the blow more sudden. It is clear that the type of vibration depends on a number of factors, and that it may be more difficult to understand than the vibration of strings that are plucked or bowed. In this book we shall treat the struck string very briefly.

Half a century ago Wead [232] measured the length of time during which a hammer on a grand piano remained in contact with the string. To do this he glued a strip of gold foil to the face of the hammer, arranged an electric circuit in such a way that when the gold on the hammer was in contact with the string an electric current would flow, and then by means of a piece of physical apparatus known as a ballistic galvanometer he measured the time during which there was a current.

He found that on the lower notes the hammer remained in contact for a longer time than on the high notes, but that on the lower notes the time was a smaller fraction of the period of the string. For c_0, with a frequency of 34 cycles/sec., the hammer remained in contact for some fifth

[232] Charles Kasson Wead (1848-1925), Am. Journ. Sci., 32, 366 (1886). This work was done at Malone, New York, where Wead was born. For the eight years from 1877 to 1885 he was Acting Professor of Physics in the University of Michigan. For twenty years, from 1892 to 1921, he served in the United States Patent Office, where he examined applications for patents on musical instruments.

or sixth of the period, whereas for c_5, with a frequency of 1082 cycles/sec., the hammer was in contact for more than a whole period. On the c_0 string he found that the contact was somewhat briefer when the blow was hard than when it was soft.

Another well known study of struck strings was carried out by Kaufmann.[233] By the method of Krigar-Menzel and Raps (Art. 107) he obtained vibration curves for the strings. He examined the effect of changing the mass of the hammer, of using hard hammers and soft hammers, of different strengths of blow, and of having the hammers strike at different positions along the string.

As to the position of striking, Helmholtz[234] had pointed out that in the middle region of a piano the builder usually arranges to have each hammer strike at a distance from the end of its string which is about a seventh to a ninth of the length of the string. He suggested that this choice might have been gradually adopted because it would make the seventh and ninth partials weak. The first six harmonic partials include only octaves, fifths, and a major third, whereas the seventh and ninth are less consonant.

This reason for the striking point seemed to Kaufmann very questionable. He found that the second partial disappears when the string is struck rather accurately at half of its length, but is strong when the striking point is not far from the half-way position; the third partial disappears when the string is struck rather accurately at a third of the length, but is strong when the striking point is not far from a third of the length. Probably the same is true of the seventh partial and the ninth. Kaufmann examined three grand pianos of standard makes and new construction, and found that the striking point lay between an eighth and

[233] Walter Kaufmann, Wied. An., **54**, 675 (1895). This work was done in Berlin, where Kaufmann was a student under Kundt.
[234] Hermann von Helmholtz, *Sensations of Tone,* 4th Eng. ed., p. 77.

a ninth—usually rather close to an eighth of the length. So it seemed to him that there must be some other reason for the choice of the striking point.

Kaufmann moved his hammer successively to different positions along the string, and he found that the fundamental had its largest amplitude when the hammer was in positions from a seventh to a ninth of the length. With this striking position the sound from the string was strong and full, and Kaufmann concluded that the reason for the choice of the striking position is probably to be found in the prominence which it gives to the fundamental.

Various other studies of struck strings have been made, but in this book we shall not take the space to do more than call attention to the three spectra shown in Fig. 98.[235] When the digital was struck gently some dozen components were detected, and when it was struck vigorously the number was doubled. One interesting feature of the diagram is the "continuous spectrum" shown by the curved line in the lower region of each spectrum. This is attributed to noises which occur at the instant when the string is struck.

Before leaving struck strings we turn for a moment to the question of "touch" on the piano. After the hammer hits the string it rebounds from it, and there is no longer any direct connection between the digital and the string. Is there then any means by which it is possible for the performer to affect the sound after the digital has been depressed? He may of course raise the dampers by means of the damper pedal, and so permit the sound to continue and certain other strings to respond. He may lower the dampers and so destroy the response. On a grand piano he has also the use of a "sostenuto" pedal, which prevents the dampers from acting on strings associated with the digitals

[235] Copied from Erwin Meyer and Gerhard Buchmann, of the Heinrich Hertz Institut für Schwingungsforschung in Berlin, Preus. Akad. Wiss., Physikal.-Math. Klasse, Sitzungsber., p. 735 (1931).

that he is holding down.   He might conceivably touch certain parts of the soundboard, and so produce some effect. But the frame of a modern piano is so strong and massive that any manipulation of the digital itself after it has once been depressed can scarcely change the sound in any way. The effects which a performer obtains on a piano appear

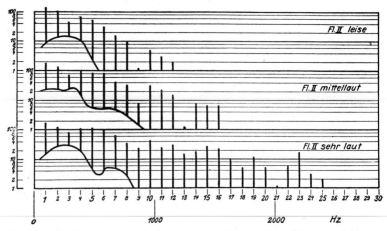

FIG. 98.—Three Spectra of the Sound from a Grand Piano [Meyer and Buchmann]. In the first spectrum the digital was struck gently, so that the sound was soft; in the second it was of moderate intensity; and in the third it was very loud. The loudness is indicated at the left by the scale of amplitudes. The upper row of numbers at the bottom of the diagram represents harmonic components, and the lower row frequencies. The frequency of the fundamental was 96 cycles/sec.

to depend on the speeds with which the digitals are depressed and on the precise times at which they are depressed. By securing the times of depression and the speeds of depression that he wishes, it is possible for the pianist to produce effects that far transcend anything which so simple a description would seem to make possible.

114. Aeolian Tones.—Aeolian tones are often produced when the wind blows over telegraph wires or other slender

obstacles—like the needles on a pine tree—or when a slender rod or a whip is swung rapidly through the air. It makes no difference whether the wind blows past the wire or the wire moves through the air. When such tones were first observed nobody knows. There is a tradition that David hung his harp above his couch, and that the north wind played it at midnight. There is another tradition that in the tenth century St. Dunstan of Canterbury hung his harp where the wind passed through its strings, and that because the harp was played by invisible fingers St. Dunstan was accused of sorcery.

In the course of time there was developed a musical instrument that is played by the wind, and is known as an *aeolian harp*. It often takes the form of a wooden box perhaps five inches from side to side and three inches deep, and long enough to fit in a window opening. The top of the box may have two sound holes, and near the ends of the box are low bridges. Over the bridges pass some dozen gut strings, not stretched very tightly, and all tuned to the same pitch. Somewhat above the strings and parallel to the top of the box is another light piece of wood. Between this upper piece and the top of the box the zephyrs blow across the strings, and may awaken a primitive melody.

115. Strouhal's Investigation.—The first important study of aeolian tones was carried out by Strouhal.[236] His apparatus was very simple, and is shown in Fig. 99. The wooden column C carried two arms AA which could be set at different distances apart. Between these arms was the wire or other object W which was to produce the tone. The whole apparatus could turn about the axis XX, and to cause it to turn there was fastened to it the wooden pulley P. P

---

[236] Vincent Strouhal, Wied. An., **5**, 216 (1878). This work was done in the university at Würzburg at the suggestion and under the direction of Professor Friedrich Wilhelm Georg Kohlrausch.

was driven by a belt from another wheel that was turned by hand.

The pitch that was heard was compared with that on a sonometer—a well known piece of apparatus consisting of a box much like that of an aeolian harp, with one or two wires stretched over it. The pitch of each wire on the sonometer may be adjusted by changing its tension, or more easily by means of a third bridge that can be moved along under the wire.

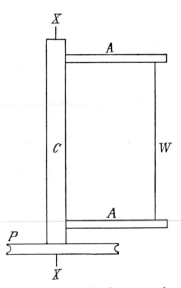

FIG. 99.—Strouhal's Apparatus for the Study of Aeolian Tones.

Some of the results that Strouhal obtained were rather startling. He found that the pitch of an aeolian tone does not depend on how tightly the wire is stretched. Neither does it depend on the length of the wire, nor on the material of which the wire is made. These results are quite contrary to what we know is the case when a wire is plucked or bowed or struck.

He soon found that the pitch does depend on how fast the wire moves. By measuring the distance of the wire from the axis about which it was rotating, and also determining how rapidly the apparatus was rotating, he could calculate the speed of the wire. With a given wire he found that the frequency was nearly proportional to the speed. He also found that for the same speed the frequency was not far from inversely proportional to the diameter of the wire.[237] If N stands for the fre-

---

[237] This last fact had already been discovered by Mr. Herman Smith. "In 1870 he had made a series of rods about 5 ft. long, the sides of each

quency obtained, V for the speed of the wire, and D for its diameter, we may therefore write

$$N = C \frac{V}{D}, \qquad (14)$$

where C is some quantity that is nearly independent of the speed of the wire or its diameter.

Strouhal found further that the frequency depends to some extent on the temperature: The higher the temperature the lower the pitch. If the speed of the wire is slowly and gradually increased there is a gradual rise in pitch, and Strouhal noticed that at certain pitches the sound was louder than at others. The pitches at which the louder sounds were obtained were the pitches given by the normal modes of tranverse vibration of the wire.

116. Strouhal's Explanation.—How are these tones produced? If they were due to the well-known modes of vibration of a wire the frequency would depend on the tension, the length, and the material of the wire. Perhaps they are due in some way to the motion of the air around the wire. If there were a vibration of the air back and forth around the wire it is not difficult to calculate that the pitch obtained must be several octaves higher than observed. So any such vibration seems to provide no explanation.

Question 275. In one of Strouhal's experiments a wire about 0.5 mm. in diameter, moving at a speed of 217 cm./sec., gave a frequency of 620 cycles/sec. If the air were vibrating back and forth around the wire in such a way as to form a compression on one side of the wire at the same time that it formed a rarefaction on the

having [the] same smoothness and of the uniform width of $1\frac{1}{4}$ inches, with a V-shaped or triangular section, and these he swept swiftly through the air like swords, sharp edge first. He found that, although the friction surface was similar on each, they developed different notes, which he discovered to be according to the thickness of the back, the pitches being inversely as the thickness." Quoted from Alexander J. Ellis in his translation of Helmholtz, *Sensations of Tone,* Longmans Green and Company, 4th Eng. ed., p. 554.

other, and if the motion was equivalent to that in a circle with a radius twice that of the wire, what do you obtain for the calculated frequency of the vibration? How many octaves is this above the observed frequency?

Question 276. If æolian tones were due to a vibration of the air back and forth around the wire should you expect the frequency to be greater at higher or at lower temperatures? Does this agree with Strouhal's result?

Question 277. If you use the values given in Question 275 what do you find for the value of the C in Eq. (14)?

Strouhal hit on an explanation that seemed to fit his results very well. It depends on the property of fluids which we have met in Art. 44 under the name of *viscosity*. When any solid body moves through the air, or through any other fluid, in a direction more or less parallel to its own surface it drags with it the air which is in contact with it. That air slips past the layer just beyond it, but not without exerting a small drag. That next layer in turn slips over the layer just beyond it, but again exerts a small drag. It occurred to Strouhal that this viscous drag of one layer on another would make it possible for the air just ahead of the moving wire to pile up a little before it slipped around the wire and escaped.

As the wire moves steadily forward perhaps the pressure ahead of the wire increases, and that behind it decreases, until a certain difference in pressure is reached. Then a small mass of air slips away from in front of the wire and tends to equalize the pressure. Then another mass of air collects in front of the wire, only to slip around when its turn comes. In this way there acts upon the front of the wire an alternating pressure that sets the wire into forced vibration.

Question 278. How does the above explanation account, in a general way, for the various facts that Strouhal discovered?

If the ideas advanced by Strouhal are correct the vibration of the wire must be in a plane parallel to the direction in which the wind blows or the wire moves. If it should turn out that the wire vibrates across the wind instead of parallel to it some other explanation would have to be sought.

An investigation of the direction in which the wire vibrates was carried out by Rayleigh [238] with extremely simple apparatus. The motion of the air past the wire was obtained by the draft in a chimney. "A fireplace was fitted with a structure of wood and paper, which could prevent all access of air to the chimney, except through an elongated horizontal aperture in the front (vertical) wall. The length of the aperture was 26 inches, and the width 4 inches; and along its middle a gut string was stretched over bridges. The strength of the draught could be regulated by slightly withdrawing the framework from the fireplace, so as to allow the passage of air to the chimney otherwise than through the slit.

"A fine point of light was obtained from a fragment of a silvered bead attached to the string with wax, and illuminated by a suitably placed candle, and was observed in the direction of the length of the string through an extemporized telescope." If the vibration of the wire is back and forth in the direction of the wind the bright spot of light seen in the telescope would be drawn out into a horizontal line. If the vibration is across the wind the line would be vertical. "The path of the point of light was seen to be nearly rectilinear and *vertical,* showing that the vibration is *across* the wind." This result is fatal to Strouhal's explanation.

117. **Explanation in Terms of Vortices.**—Investigations of an entirely different subject have suggested another explanation. It is well known that when a boat moves through

[238] Lord Rayleigh, Phil. Mag., **7,** 161 (1879).

the water it encounters a resistance, even though no wind or current opposes it. What causes this resistance? Instead of a boat consider a long cylindrical rod moving sideways. Theoretical studies have shown that if there were a fluid which had no viscosity, i.e., no internal friction, and the rod were moving steadily sideways through this fluid, it would experience no resistance. Although the water, air, or other fluid that the rod had to push out of the way would press backward against it this fluid would slip around to the back and there push forward on the rod with a force that would

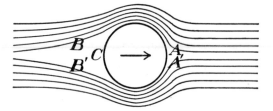

FIG. 100.—Stream Lines in a Fluid when a Cylinder Moves through it.

balance the backward push. There would be no resultant resistance to the motion.

If the fluid has any viscosity at all this result no longer holds. And since all actual fluids do have some viscosity we are interested in knowing how the result is modified. Because of its viscosity and its inertia the fluid that slips around the sides of the rod does not close up immediately behind it. The fluid "cuts the corner" and unites at a little distance behind the rod, as shown by the lines AB and $A'B'$ in Fig. 100. This leaves just behind the rod a small amount of fluid, C, that the rod drags with it. The fluid C is urged backward by the neighboring fluid and forward by the rod. In this way two small whirls or eddies or *vortices* are produced, as shown in Fig. 101. If the speed of the rod becomes sufficient the vortices are torn from the rod and left whirling behind it, while new ones are continually being formed and torn away in their turn. We have met similar vortices in connection with the ripples in a Kundt tube (Art. 76) and in connection with sensitive flames (Art. 88). Other illustrations are found in the turbulent motion in the wake of a boat, and in the swirling of water past a pile or a rock in a river.

When the rod, or other obstacle, moves slowly a considerable part of the resistance to its motion arises from the viscosity of the fluid that slips around it from front to rear. When the body moves rapidly enough to leave be-

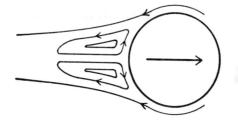

FIG. 101.—Vortices at the Rear of a Moving Cylinder.

hind it a wake of vortices there is an added resistance which arises from the work done in continually setting up new vortices. If the rear part of the body has its shape changed so as to "tail off" and largely fill the space C in Fig. 100 there is less vortex formation and less resistance to the motion. This is the purpose of the "stream lining" of boats and automobiles and airplanes.

In 1912 Kármán [239] showed theoretically that there is just one stable arrangement of the vortices behind a steadily moving cylinder. In that arrangement the vortices on the two sides of the "street" or "avenue" are not opposite each

[239] Theodor von Kármán, Nachrichten von der königl. Ges. der Wiss. zu Göttingen, Math.-Phys. Klasse, p. 547 (1912); or more fully in a joint paper with H. Rubach in Physikal. Zeitschr., 13, 49 (1912). This work was done at Göttingen. Kármán is now Director of the Guggenheim Aeronautical Laboratory at the California Institute of Technology.

other but are staggered as shown in Fig. 102, and the distances h and l are connected by the relation [240] $h = 0.283l$. Moreover the whole avenue of vortices moves forward in the direction of the cylinder, and at a speed which is a defi-

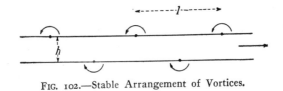

FIG. 102.—Stable Arrangement of Vortices.

nite fraction of that with which the cylinder moves. The theory was tested by sprinkling lycopodium powder on the surface of water and then taking a picture while an obstacle was being drawn through the water. One of the photographs so obtained is reproduced in Fig. 103. In this case

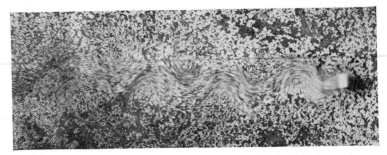

FIG. 103.—Vortices Obtained Experimentally Behind a Moving Body
[Kármán and Rubach].

the moving body was not a cylinder, but the photograph shows the two files of vortices and the sinuous motion of the fluid between them.

What does all this have to do with aeolian tones? Be-

[240] Kármán's equation is really $\cosh\dfrac{h\pi}{l} = \sqrt{2}$. This is equivalent to the equation given above, with the curious factor 0.283.

hind the strings of the aeolian harp there are avenues of vortices. As these vortices pass us they give rise to changes in the pressure of the air, and these changes are perceived as the aeolian tone. The pitch of the tone depends on the number of vortices that pass in a second, and that number depends on the distance from one vortex to the next and the speed at which they travel. The spacing of the vortices bears a definite ratio to the diameter of the wire—if one wire has twice the diameter of another the avenue of vortices is twice as wide, and the vortices on each side of the avenue are twice as far apart. So for a given speed the vortices behind a wire of double diameter are twice as far apart, and the frequency of the aeolian tone is therefore half as great—just as Strouhal found that it approximately is.

If we change the speed at which a given wire moves we do not affect the spacing of the vortices. If we double the speed of the wire we also double the·speed with which the vortices travel. It follows that the pitch of the aeolian tone is an octave higher. This again is approximately what Strouhal found.

When a vortex system like that in Fig. 102 is once established it causes the new vortices to leave the cylinder alternately—first from one side of it and then from the other. The formation and release of these vortices is accompanied by an alternating force which acts sideways on the cylinder. So the cylinder is set into forced vibration in a direction across its path—just as Rayleigh found is the case with a wire that gives rise to an aeolian tone. Moreover from the work of Kármán and Rubach it is possible to calculate how large the C in (14) should be, and the value turns out to be fairly close to that found from Strouhal's experimental work. The theory just presented is that now generally accepted as explaining aeolian tones.[241]

[241] For further material concerning aeolian tones, and references to fur-

118. Maintained Metal Reeds.—Metal reeds are employed in certain stops on the organ, and in such instruments as the harmonium, American reed organ, melodeon, concertina, accordion, and mouth harmonica. The harmonium is an English instrument, frequently larger than the American reed organ, and differing from the latter in that in the harmonium the bellows produces a pressure greater than atmospheric and so pushes the air through the reeds, whereas in the American reed organ the bellows pumps the air out from a reservoir and so sucks it through the reeds. The concertina was invented by Sir Charles Wheatstone (1802-1875) and was patented in 1829. It was similar to an accordion, but had a range of four octaves and had the distinction of having fourteen notes to the octave: $d\sharp$ and $e\flat$ were separate notes, and $g\sharp$ and $a\flat$ were separate notes.

Metal reeds are of two types. Some of them are *free reeds,* like those described on p. 148, and others are *striking reeds.* In the former (Fig. 36) the tongue swings into the slot and out of it with a small amount of clearance. In the latter the tongue is too large to enter the slot, but closes it by rolling down over it.

How does the stream of wind through a reed produce and maintain the vibration? Consider a free reed, and let the reed be horizontal, as represented in Fig. 36, and the wind through it streaming downward. Fig. 104 is a section of the reed near the left end of Fig. 36. T is the tongue of the reed, and S the slot through which it plays. The path of the wind through the reed is indicated by the arrows. It will be seen that near the edges of the tongue the wind flows faster just below the tongue than just above it. Consequently (Art. 66) the pressure just below the

ther papers, see E. G. Richardson, *Sound* (1927), pp. 139-154; or ed. 2, (1935), pp. 141-155.

Certain strange sounds heard in the Yellowstone may be of aeolian origin. See Science, **22**, 244 (1893); **63**, 586 (1926); **64**, 119, 451 (1926); **71**, 97 (1930).

tongue is less than that above it.   If the air had no inertia
the difference in pressure would depend simply on the position of the tongue, and the tongue would soon assume a
position of equilibrium in which it would remain instead of
vibrating.   But because of the inertia of the air the stream
does not adjust itself instantaneously to the position of the

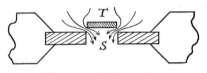

FIG. 104.—Tranverse Section of a Free Reed.

tongue.   The result is that the resultant downward force on
the tongue is greater when the tongue is moving downward
than when it is moving upward.   That is, there is a net force
in phase with the velocity of the tongue, and consequently
(Art. 71) maintenance is possible.[242]

Question 279.   In the paragraph that precedes this question it
is stated that near the edges of the tongue the wind flows faster just
below the tongue than just above it.   How do you see that this
statement is correct?

Question 280.   It is also stated that if the air had no inertia the
tongue would not vibrate.   How do you see that this is true?

Question 281.   If the wind that blows the reed is supplied at
too high a pressure or too low a pressure the reed does not speak.
Why?

Question 282.   What is the explanation of the maintenance in
the case of a striking reed?

Question 283.   Boys often whistle by placing a blade of grass
between the thumbs of the two hands and blowing through the chink
that contains the stretched grass blade.   How is the vibration of the
blade maintained?

If we make use of a set of Helmholtz resonators to listen
to the steady sound from a free reed we find that the fun-

[242] Arthur Taber Jones, Rev. Sci. Instr., **5**, 192 (1934).

damental is accompanied by a considerable series of harmonic overtones. If we mount a tiny mirror on the tongue of the reed and then examine the motion of the tongue itself, we find that it is practically simple harmonic. How are these facts to be reconciled? If we pluck a reed instead of blowing it the sound is faint. The solution of our difficulty lies in the fact that the sound from a blown reed does not come primarily from the vibration of the reed itself, but rather from the interruptions it causes in the blowing wind. The reed cuts the wind off rather suddenly, then permits it to start somewhat gradually, again cuts it off suddenly, and so on. These periodic changes in the blowing stream are the cause of the sound, and since the changes are far from simple harmonic the compressions and rarefactions to which they give rise in the surrounding air are also far from simple harmonic. The sound is a complex one in spite of the simple motion of the tongue.

Question 284. The production of sound by a reed is often compared with that by a siren. In what way is the production of sound similar?

In a reed organ each tone is produced by a reed which is not connected to any pipe or other resonator, and the differences of quality that can be obtained are not great. In one or more sets of reeds the tips of the tongues may be curled a little so as to make the cut-off of the wind less abrupt, and the tone from the reed less piercing in character. Variations in loudness can be brought about by opening or closing a shutter which is inside the case of the organ and is operated by the player's knee. The pitches of the reeds depend somewhat on the blowing pressure, and the dependence is such that two notes which have overtones that beat at a certain rate when blown softly may beat at a different rate when the blowing pressure is increased.

When reeds are used in pipe organs each reed is coupled to a resonator, and the shape and size of the resonator have an important effect on the quality of the sound. Some of the resonators used are cylindrical tubes, some are conical, some are short cones surmounted by cylinders, some have other shapes, some are open at the top, and some are nearly or quite closed at the top. The vibration of the air in the resonator is strongly damped, and the pitch from the coupled system is not far from the natural pitch of the reed.[243] The tuning is effected by moving a wire that presses against the tongue of the reed near its root, so effectively making the reed a little longer or a little shorter. The changes of pressure in the resonator are greatest close to the reed, so that the reed is to be regarded as being approximately at a node of the standing waves in the resonant tube—just as the exciting cork in a Kundt tube is approximately at a node of the standing waves in the contained air.

Question 285. In the above paragraph it is stated that the shape of the resonator is of importance, whereas in Art. 54 the shape of the resonator is said to make little difference. How is this inconsistency to be explained?

Question 286. If the tuning wire on a reed pipe is moved downward, so as to leave less of the tongue free to vibrate, is the pitch of the pipe raised or lowered? Why?

Question 287. Suppose that the resonator of a reed pipe is a cylindrical tube which is wide open at the upper end and that the reed is at a node of the standing waves in the tube. What is approximately the relation between the length of the pipe and the wave length of the fundamental note that it gives?

[243] An interesting study of the reed-resonator system is to be found in a paper by Hans Vogel, Ann. der Physik, **62**, 247 (1920). This work was done at Jena, where Vogel was studying under Max Wien. Vibration curves for a striking reed coupled to an organ pipe have also been obtained by Léon Auger, Comptes Rendus, **195**, 516 (1932).

119. Instruments with Non-Metallic Reeds.—The reeds in such instruments as the clarinet, basset horn, oboe, English horn, bassoon, and saxophone are made from a real reed that grows on the shore of the Mediterranean. If the mouthpieces of such instruments are examined it will be seen that the clarinet, basset horn, and saxophone have single reeds, and the oboe, English horn, and bassoon have double reeds. The single reed lies over an opening in a mouth piece which is so shaped as to fit readily between the player's lips. Under the pressure of his breath the operation of the reed is similar to that of a striking reed in an organ pipe. The double reed consists of two narrower reeds that are curved from side to side so that their ends have somewhat the shape of a person's slightly opened lips. The two reeds are held between the player's lips, and under the pressure of his breath they alternately close up toward each other and then spring open again.

These reeds, like those in the reed pipes of an organ, give rise to changes in air pressure, so that the air column in the instrument has a node at the position occupied by the reed. If the instrument has a cylindrical bore, i.e. a tube with a uniform bore, we might therefore expect that the tones from it would contain only the odd harmonics (Art. 60). And if the instrument has a conical tube, in which the bore increases uniformly, we should expect that the instrument might give the entire harmonic series (Art. 63). The clarinet has a tube which is nearly cylindrical, but flares somewhat at the bottom, and the tube of the oboe is nearly conical. Figs. 105 and 106 are vibration curves obtained from a clarinet and an oboe, and Fig. 107 gives sound spectra for a clarinet and an oboe. In spite of the cylindrical bore of the clarinet it will be seen that the eighth and tenth harmonics are prominent. By taking into account the fact that the effective length of the reed becomes less as it rolls down to close the opening it has been possible to

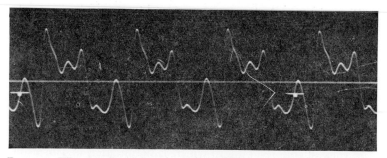

FIG. 105.—Vibration Curve from a Clarinet [Photograph kindly supplied by Professor Miller [244]].

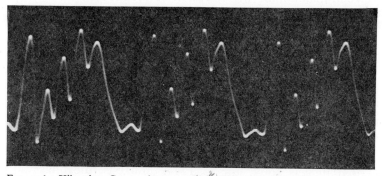

FIG. 106.—Vibration Curves from an Oboe [Photograph kindly supplied by Professor Miller [244]].

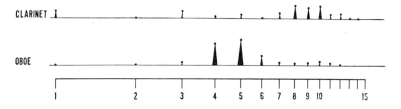

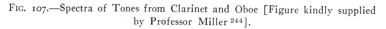

FIG. 107.—Spectra of Tones from Clarinet and Oboe [Figure kindly supplied by Professor Miller [244]].

[244] Figs. 105, 106, 107, 109, 110, 125, 126, and 127 are to be found in *The Science of Musical Sounds* by Dayton Clarence Miller, Macmillan (1916), pp. 200-204, 221-227.

build up for the clarinet a mathematical treatment that leads to strong eighth and tenth harmonics.[245]

The explanation of the production of sound by the reed instruments that we are considering is decidedly complicated. The following statements about it are not at all complete. The reeds in these instruments are light and are easily forced to vibrate with frequencies quite different from those natural to them. The reed and the air in the resonating tube form a coupled system which is maintained in vibration by the wind from the player's mouth. This wind does its share in maintaining the vibration of the reed, the vibration of the reed varies the rate at which the wind enters the resonating tube and so maintains the vibration of the air in this tube, and the varying pressure associated with this vibration in the tube reacts on the reed and forces it to assume a frequency not far from a natural frequency of the air in the tube. When the pressure in the tube becomes large it tends to open the reed and so to permit more wind to enter. Thus the wind from the player's mouth enters the resonating tube most rapidly at a time when the pressure in that tube is above the average. That is, the phase of wind supply is favorable for maintaining the vibration of the air in the tube.

120. Brass Instruments.—Among the brass instruments of music there is of course the whole family of horns—the bugle, trumpet, trombone, cornet, French horn, bass tuba, and so on. All of these instruments use cupped mouth pieces against which the lips of the player are pressed. It is possible to get a fair imitation of a bugle by using a simple piece of glass tubing. If the diameter of the tubing is about the same as that of the mouth piece for one of the brass instruments it is entirely possible for a performer to place his lips against it and play it. It is also possible to roll up a piece of heavy paper and blow it as if it were a horn.

[245] Panchanon Das, Indian Journ. Physics, 6, 225 (1931).

In many horns the resonating cavity is neither cylindrical
nor conical, but increases "exponentially." To see what this
means consider Fig. 108. Let the straight line AB be
divided into any convenient number of equal parts Aa, ab,
bc, etc. Suppose that the "coefficient of flare" is $\frac{5}{4}$. Then
the radius at a is made $\frac{5}{4}$ of that at A, the radius at b

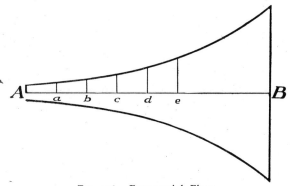

FIG. 108.—Exponential Flare.

$\frac{5}{4}$ that at a, the radius at c $\frac{5}{4}$ that at b, and so on. As the
waves pass through an exponential horn their curvature
gradually changes, so that the spreading out from the mouth
into the air beyond the horn does not involve so abrupt a
change in shape as it would if the tube were conical. That
is, a flaring horn sends out the sound more efficiently.

Question 288. Instead of actually multiplying the radii at A,
a, b, - - - in Fig. 108 by $\frac{5}{4}$ there is a convenient graphical method
of obtaining the desired radii. In
this method we begin by drawing a
right triangle OCD, and then
drawing OE so that DC is $\frac{5}{4}$ of
EC. It is then possible to draw
other lines in such a way that the

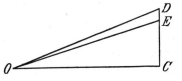

desired radii for Fig. 108 are obtained without calculation. How
are the other lines to be drawn? If you do not succeed in devising
a simple construction for obtaining the desired radii you will find it

described by E. G. Richardson in his book *The Acoustics of Orchestral Instruments and the Organ* (1929), p. 76.

The vibration in a horn is generated by the player's lips. The parts of the lips within the mouthpiece constitute the reeds, and the player can actually feel them vibrate. The forced vibration of these reeds is somewhat different from that of the reeds in the clarinet, oboe, and similar instruments. The lips of the player are soft and heavy and their natural pitch is low.

The explanation of the production of the sound is similar to that sketched in the last paragraph of Art. 119, except that in the present case an increase of pressure in the resonating cavity tends to close the opening between the reeds instead of to open it. In spite of this fact the theory of forced vibration shows that the varying pressure in the resonating cavity does its part toward maintaining the vibration of the reeds, and forces the frequency to be not far from a natural frequency of the resonating cavity. Thus the wind from the player's mouth enters the resonating cavity most rapidly at a time when the pressure in that cavity is above the average, and so maintains the vibration.

The various horns differ considerably in quality. Fig. 109 is a vibration curve for one of them, and Fig. 110 is an average from a number of horn spectra. A comparison of Figs. 105, 106, and 109 shows that the vibration curves for clarinet, oboe, and horn differ considerably in appearance.

121. **Instruments with "Air Reeds."**—When we turn to the production of musical sounds by a sheet of wind that takes the place of a reed we find a wide variety of instruments. Some are as primitive as panpipes and simple whistles, and from these have developed different kinds of flutes and the typical pipes of the organ. Possibly we might also include among these instruments the bird-call, and also the human mouth when employed in whistling.

The bird-call is a very simple instrument made of two thin plates of tin or other metal. Each plate is pierced by a hole, and the plates are fastened near to each other and

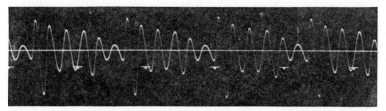

FIG. 109.—Vibration Curve from a French Horn [Photograph kindly supplied by Professor Miller [244]].

so that the holes are in line with each other. Blowing through the holes gives rise to a high pitched note much

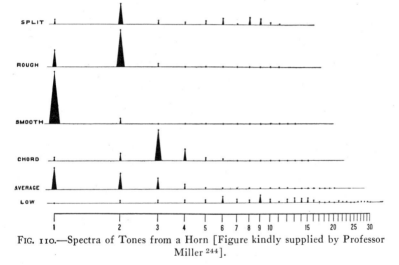

FIG. 110.—Spectra of Tones from a Horn [Figure kindly supplied by Professor Miller [244]].

like that of a bird. The pitch is easily varied by changing the blowing pressure.

One form of panpipe was made of reeds from the edge of a lake or river.[246] Some of these reeds are hollow, and

[246] See Mrs. Browning's poem *A Musical Instrument.*

the tube thus formed was plugged at one end or cut off near a knot, so that what was left was a pipe closed at one end and open at the other. By blowing across the open end a tone could be produced in the same way that it can by blowing across the mouth of a bottle or the end of a test tube. Several reeds of different lengths fastened together formed a panpipe.

Organ pipes are often divided into two classes. "Reed pipes" we have mentioned in Art. 118. We turn now to the "flue pipes"—which are also sometimes called "flute pipes" or "mouth pipes" or "lip pipes" or "labial pipes." Large flue pipes are usually made of wood or zinc, and small ones of tin or an alloy of tin and lead. Fig. 111 is a section of a wooden pipe. The mouth of the pipe is the region M between the *lower lip A* and the *upper lip B*. The wind comes up through the *foot F*, passes through the *flue* or *windway W*, between the *languet* or *languid L* and the lower lip, and then passes across the mouth and either strikes the upper lip or passes very close to it. This stream of wind is sometimes spoken of as an "air lamella" or "air reed" or "aerial reed" or "aeroplastic reed." It is this air reed and the upper lip which generate the sound, in a way that we shall consider later, and to these is coupled the resonating *body* of the pipe above the languet.

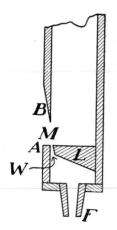

FIG. 111.—Section of a Wooden Flue Pipe.

122. Qualities of Organ Pipes.—Organ pipes may be built and "voiced" to have qualities that differ greatly. The most important factor in determining the quality of a pipe is its *scale*, a term which indicates the diameter or cross-sectional area of the pipe. The scale affects the quality in two ways. If two pipes have the same length, but one is slender and the other wide, the natural frequencies of the slender one are the more nearly harmonic. When the pipe is speaking steadily the vibration in it is periodic, and the overtones are therefore forced to be harmonic. In a wide pipe the higher overtones are accordingly forced farther from their natural frequencies than they are in a narrow pipe. For this reason the higher overtones from a wide pipe are fainter than those from a narrow pipe. It follows that the quality of a narrow pipe is more "stringy" than that of a wide pipe.

Another reason for the difference in quality is to be found in the intensities of the normal modes themselves. This is clearly brought out by the work of Anderson and Ostensen. [247] In the case of a pipe with an open end they found that the highest natural pitch which has any appreciable intensity is one in which the distance from the open end to the nodal surface nearest it is approximately equal to the diameter of the pipe. Modes with higher pitches would have nodal surfaces nearer to the open end, and it is difficult for a nodal surface to form under such circumstances. Consequently the higher modes are fainter on a wide pipe than on a narrow one. This is doubtless another reason for the more brilliant character of the narrower pipes.

Question 289. A wooden "open diapason" pipe measures 4 cm. x 4 cm. inside, and a metal "gamba" is 2.2 cm. in inner diameter. The fundamental pitch of both pipes is g_3 of 387 cycles/sec. If the speed of sound is 345 meters/sec. how many harmonic partials are to be expected from each pipe?

We have seen that a narrow tube which is closed at one end has normal modes that are practically harmonic, but lacking the components with even numbers. So we shall expect the harmonics with even numbers to be fainter in a

[247] Ref. in footnote 106 on p. 162.

closed organ pipe than in an open one. This proves to be correct, and the quality of closed pipes is softer and less brilliant than that of open pipes.

Reed pipes have a long retinue of higher partials, and therefore a pungent quality. A reed cuts off the wind rather abruptly, and any sudden change that gives rise to a sharp bend in the pressure curve is likely to involve high components. Moreover, a part at least of the body of a reed pipe is often conical, and so, in spite of the node near the reed, the series of natural overtones may be similar to that of an open pipe.

Another factor that affects the quality to some extent is the pressure of the wind. At a high pressure the wind issues from the windway more rapidly, and so forms a somewhat stiffer aerial reed. The aerial reed swings back and forth across the upper lip, and so throws its wind alternately inside of the pipe and out of it. One result of the stiffening produced by the greater wind pressure is a slight rise in pitch. Another is a more sudden crossing of the upper lip, and a consequent increase in the importance of the higher partials. So an increase in wind pressure may make the quality more brilliant.

Whether a pipe is round or rectangular in cross section has hardly any effect on the quality. So pipes are built with whatever shape of cross section is most convenient. When of metal they are usually round, and when of wood they are not far from square.

The material of the walls has little effect on pitch or quality so long as the walls are hard and smooth and are fairly rigid. But if the walls are thin or flexible the material does become important. In the case of pipes which are very short Savart [248] found that when the walls are made of parchment the pipe is flatter than when the walls are stiff,

[248] Félix Savart, Ann. de chim. et de phys., 30, 64 (1825). Savart describes this experiment very briefly, on p. 74.

and that moistening these parchment walls makes the pipe still flatter. Liskovius [249] found further that if the parchment walls are tightened or stiffened the pitch rises. Schafhäutl [250] made organ pipes and trumpets of different materials and with walls of different thickness, and found some decided differences in quality as well as in pitch. Miller [251] has made a pipe with walls of thin zinc. With this pipe "one can produce the remarkable effect of choking the pipe till it actually squeals. When the pipe is blown in the ordinary manner, its sound has the usual tone quality. If the pipe is firmly grasped in both hands just above the mouth, it speaks a mixture of three clearly distinguished inharmonic partial tones, the ratios of which are approximately $1 : 2.06 : 2.66$. The resulting unmusical sound is so unexpected that it is almost startling, the tone quality having changed from that of a flute to that of a tin horn." [252]

Miller was led to the above study by his interest in the flute, on which he is an accomplished artist. "When visiting the establishment of an eminent London flute maker, in 1900, he was shown several flutes which were tested. One instrument seemed of such unusual excellence that the remark was made that it was certainly of the finest quality of any that had ever been tried. After the instrument had been returned to its case, the writer [D. C. Miller] enquired whether it would be possible, at some time in the visit to

[249] Karl Friedr. Sal. Liskovius, Pogg. An. **57**, 497 (1842).

[250] Carl von Schafhäutl, Allgemeine Musikalische Zeitung, **14**, 593, 609, 625 (1879).

[251] Dayton Clarence Miller, Science, **29**, 161 (1909); or *The Science of Musical Sounds,* Macmillan (1916), p. 180. Miller is Professor of Physics at the Case School of Applied Science. He received the $1000 prize awarded for an important paper read before the American Association for the Advancement of Science in 1925. He has been President of the American Physical Society and President of the Acoustical Society of America.

[252] Perhaps the sound from the pipe was not entirely steady. Otherwise it would seem as if the components would be forced to be harmonic. At certain blowing pressures an ordinary organ pipe may give an unsteady sound, and we recall the unsteady effect in the wolf note on a cello.

London, for him to see one of the few gold flutes which had been made, and which were celebrated for quality. The reply was startlingly unexpected, for the maker said, with evident satisfaction, that the flute just played was of gold! . . . The flute had been examined in dim artificial light, the color thus escaping notice. . . . That the partials from the gold flute are actually fuller than from other, is proved by the photographic comparisons of wave forms. . . . Mere massiveness of the walls does not fulfill the desired condition, . . . the walls must be thin, soft and flexible, and be made relatively massive by increasing the density of the material." [253]

123. Maintenance of Flue Pipes. Early Explanations. —How does the wind set up and maintain the vibration of the air in a flue pipe? This question has interested a large number of investigators, and in the course of their studies they have discovered many interesting facts—some of them quite unexpected. We shall consider the gist of several suggested explanations of the maintenance, present some of the facts that have been discovered, and then summarize briefly the present state of the problem.

More than a century ago the brothers Weber [254] suggested that the first puff of wind from the windway starts a wave which travels up and down in the body of the pipe. Each time that the wave comes back to the mouth it acts on the wind that is coming from the windway, so that compressions and rarefactions [this seems to be the meaning] are set up in this blowing wind, and these in turn maintain the vibration of the air in the body of the pipe. That is, the brothers Weber probably meant to suggest that the sound is maintained by an alternating compression and rarefaction in the air sheet, either before it leaves the wind-

[253] D. C. Miller, reference to Science in footnote 251.
[254] Ernst Heinrich Weber and Wilhelm Eduard Weber, Allgemeine Musikalische Zeitung, 28, 235 (1826) ; or *Wilhelm Weber's Werke*, vol. 1 (1892), p. 166.

way or immediately afterward. Helmholtz, in the first three editions of his *Tonempfindungen*,[255] suggested that the wind striking the upper lip sets up a noise, that this noise disturbs the air in the body of the pipe, and that the air in the body responds with a musical tone. When Strouhal made his study of aeolian tones he suggested that the wind striking the upper lip sets up an aeolian tone, which is then reinforced by the air in the body of the pipe.

Question 290. In the aeolian harp the strings are set into vibration by the wind that passes over them. Some writers have thought that the upper lip of an organ pipe is similarly set into vibration by the blowing wind. The upper lip is held in place so firmly that it seems doubtful whether it could vibrate sufficiently to maintain a vibration of the air in the body of the pipe. How could you test experimentally whether the upper lip does vibrate?

124. Explanations by Smith and Helmholtz.—Before Strouhal's work on aeolian tones Smith [256] had been able to show that the sheet of air from the windway in an organ pipe bends like a reed, flowing alternately toward the inner and outer sides of the upper lip, and the vibration of this reed seemed to him to be an important factor in the maintenance of a flue pipe. He says, "It has been customary with me for several years, when occasion invited it, to demonstrate to my musical friends the physical action existing in the sounding organ-pipe, to show them (taking up a chance wood-shaving lying on the floor of the workshop or a strip of tissue paper) that, heterodox though the teaching be, the stream of air at the mouth of the organ-pipe constitutes a free-reed—visibly before them the film-like wood-shaving is drawn into the motion of the air, and the beautiful curve of the reed's swing displays itself beyond dispute." This streaming air reed drags with it a part of the air from each

---

[255] The preface to the first edition of the *Tonempfindungen* is dated 1862, to the third edition 1870, and to the fourth 1877.

[256] Herman Smith, Nature, **8**, 25 (1873); **10**, 161 and 481 (1874).

side of it, and so produces some diminution of pressure. Since the space from which the air at the sides can be drawn is more restricted on the inner side of the reed than on the outer side it seemed to Smith that the decrease of pressure on the inner side would be the greater, and that the reed would therefore be bent inward. The decrease of pressure would travel up the pipe as a pulse of rarefaction, and the inward bending of the reed would permit the outer air to rush in between the top of the reed and the bottom of the upper lip, so that in its turn a pulse of compression would travel up the pipe. Now that a vibration of the air in the pipe had been set up, that vibration would keep the reed bending back and forth, and so the vibration in the pipe would be maintained.[257]

A somewhat similar explanation appears to have occurred to several persons at about this time. It was suggested independently by Sonreck,[258] Schneebeli[259] wrote of it as rather generally known, and in the fourth edition of the *Tonempfindungen* Helmholtz adopted an explanation which does not differ widely from it, but is more clear and more precise. This explanation is essentially as follows.[260]

The sheet of air that comes from the windway is unstable and easily deflected. If there were above it no upper lip or pipe body it would travel only a short distance before it would break up into a turbulent stream of vortices. When the sheet strikes the upper lip, or passes close to it, it starts a slight disturbance of the air in the body of the pipe. That disturbance gives rise to a small vibratory motion of the air up and down in the pipe. The air at the mouth

---

[257] Smith gives an entertaining and somewhat fanciful account of this process, but his description is rather long to quote. It may be found on p. 162 of the second reference in footnote 256.

[258] F. W. Sonreck, Pogg. An., **158**, 129 (1876); **159**, 666 (1876). Sonreck was an organ builder in Cologne.

[259] Heinrich Schneebeli, Pogg. An., **153**, 301 (1874).

[260] Hermann von Helmholtz, *Sensations of Tone,* 4th Eng. ed., pp. 92, 390, 394.

swings slightly into the pipe and out of it, carrying with it the sheet of air from the windway. When the air sheet is deflected inward it adds to the pressure inside of the mouth, and when it is deflected outward it decreases the pressure inside. Now the last part of the inward surge of the air near the mouth, and the first part of the outward surge occur when the pressure in the pipe is above the average; and the last part of the outward surge and the first part of the inward surge occur when the pressure is below the average. So the sheet from the windway blows into the pipe and increases the pressure when the pressure is above the average, and it blows out of the pipe and decreases the pressure when the pressure is below the average. In Art. 84 on p. 227 we have seen that this is precisely the relationship needed in order to maintain the vibration. In a general way it would seem that this explanation cannot be far from correct.

125. **Air Currents in the Pipe.**—In one of Smith's articles there is a description of another effect: "Place within the pipe at the back of the mouth some fine filaments of cotton, or fluff or down; advance them from the interior to the inner edge of the windway, and you will see them shot with energy not upward into the pipe, but outward full in your face." [261] With this effect in mind we turn to a study by Van Tricht.[262] Van Tricht followed up experiments made by Ch. Lootens, "un homme assez étranger aux théories physiques, mais observateur habile et perspicace, avide de connaître et désireux depuis longtemps de *voir* ce qui se passait dans les tuyaux d'orgue." [263]

A number of experimenters have introduced smoke into the blowing wind in order to see where the wind goes. In

[261] p. 163 in ref. in footnote 256.

[262] Victor Van Tricht, Journ. de Physique, 6, 53 (1877).

[263] "A man who has little knowledge of physical theories, but is a keen and accurate observer. He has long been eager to know and desirous to *see* what goes on in organ pipes."

this way Lootens and Van Tricht found that part of the wind goes up past the outer side of the upper lip, and part of it follows a looped path that curves over to the back of the pipe and then comes out through the bottom of the mouth. If the "derived current" that comes horizontally from the mouth crosses the "principal current" that flows upward from the windway, it seemed to Van Tricht that each of these currents must be periodically interrupted in order to let the other pass. Thus the derived current would act like the plate of a siren, and the principal current would break through it periodically and so give rise to the musical tone.

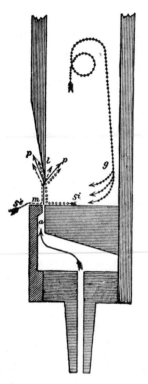

An interesting series of somewhat related experiments was carried out by Hensen.[264] By moving a lighted taper to various points in several organ pipes Hensen found a general streaming like that shown in Fig. 112. Hensen's "outer secondary stream," se, may easily be observed by bringing a lighted candle near the mouth of a pipe that is speaking. We shall not stop to take up Hensen's explanation for the maintenance of a flue pipe, but we shall turn briefly to other experimental work that Hensen did in this connection.

FIG. 112.—Streaming of Air in a Flue Pipe (Hensen).

Tyndall's assistant Mr. Cottrell had found that "by causing flame to rub against flame, various musical sounds

[264] Victor Hensen, Ann. der Physik, 2, 719 (1900); 4, 41 (1901); 16, 838 (1905); 21, 781 (1906).

can be obtained—some resembling those of a trumpet, others those of a lark. By the friction of unignited gas-jets, similar though less intense effects are produced." [265] Hensen may have discovered these tones independently. At any rate, he examined them and developed an explanation for them. In some of Hensen's experiments a stream of air was blown against the side of a flame, and under proper conditions there resulted a more or less musical sound of fair intensity. He found that he could also get a tone in this way when the gas was not burning. One of the streams he called an *ortho-lamella,* and the other a *transverse-lamella.* The ortho-lamella might, for instance, be a vertical gas flame, and the transverse-lamella a stream of air blown horizontally against it.

The tone that arises when a stream of air strikes a flame is to be explained, according to Hensen, by a struggle between the ortho-lamella and the transverse-lamella. His idea was that the ortho-lamella holds back the transverse-lamella, deflects it and causes the material in it to pile up until the pressure becomes sufficient for the transverse-lamella to force the ortho-lamella to bend considerably. This bending allows the transverse-lamella to proceed on its course with less opposition, and now it is the transverse-lamella that obstructs the flow of the ortho-lamella. So there is a hemming of the flow and a compression of material, first in one lamella and then in the other. When the ortho-lamella is a flame, and the transverse-lamella a stream of air which breaks clear through the ortho-lamella, there is no production of sound. For a tone to arise it is necessary that the transverse-lamella press against the ortho-lamella, but without cutting clear through it.

Does the blowing wind as it passes through the mouth of an organ pipe take the part of an ortho-lamella, and does

[265] John Tyndall, *Sound,* Appleton, ed. 3 (1876), p. 283.

Hensen's "inner secondary stream," *si,* or perhaps the alternating flow of air in and out of the mouth, take the part of a transverse-lamella? The question whether the vibration in the body of a flue pipe is maintained in some such way as this was examined by Friedrich.[266] He thought he found that the formation of a transverse-lamella is an essential factor in the production of the sound. For if a small obstacle is placed inside of the mouth where it prevents the transverse-lamella from acting on the ortho-lamella, the pipe refuses to speak.[267]

He also found that the changing pressure inside of the mouth gives rise to a varying pressure in the blowing wind, and that this variation can be detected backward for several meters in the tube that brings the wind to the pipe. But he found that this variation of pressure in the blowing stream is a secondary effect, and not a sufficient means for maintaining the vibration in the body of the pipe. So the explanation of the maintenance that was suggested by the brothers Weber and mentioned at the beginning of Art. 123 is not supported.

In addition Friedrich found that inside the body of the pipe there is a system of vortices, like those shown in Fig. 113, and for a time it seemed that these vortices might be of importance in the production of the sound. The vortices could be seen by using a pipe with glass sides, and introducing smoke into the blowing

FIG. 113.—Vortices in a Flue Pipe [Friedrich].

266 W. Friedrich, Ann. der Physik, 7, 97 (1901). This work was done at Rostock, where Friedrich was studying under Wachsmuth.
267 See, however, the paragraph before the last in Art. 126.

stream. If vortices were essential in the production of the sound it would follow that anything which prevented them from forming would make it impossible for the pipe to speak. The vortices can be prevented from forming by means of a thin board, just wide enough to reach from one glass side of the pipe to the other, and lowered into the pipe until its bottom is only a few centimeters above the languet. Friedrich found that such a board makes little difference in the speech of the pipe. So the formation of these vortices is also a secondary effect that is not of importance in the maintenance of the pipe.

126. Motion of the Air Reed.—The next group of studies to which we turn has dealt in more detail with the motion and structure of the sheet of wind. We turn first to one matter in a prize essay written by Van Schaik.[268] In the course of his study Van Schaik introduced talcum powder into the blowing stream, and then observed it stroboscopically (Art. 83). Fig. 114 shows two of his diagrams. It is clear that the air sheet does vibrate into the pipe and out again, somewhat after the manner of a reed.

Perhaps matters would be simplified if the body of the pipe were removed. That is, suppose that the experimenter studies the sounds produced when a thin sheet of wind strikes an edge. Such a study was carried out by Weerth.[269] In-

---

[268] W. C. L. Van Schaik, Ueber die Tonerregung in Labialpfeifen, Van Hengel, Rotterdam (1891); or Archives Néerlandaises, 25, 281 (1892). The Bataafsch Genootschap der Proefondervindelijke Wijsbegeerte (Netherland Society of Experimental Philosophy) set problems for prize essays. Problem 180 in the program for 1888 read, in French translation, "La naissance des tons par les tuyaux d'orgues labiaux n'est pas suffisamment déclarée. Les recherches expérimentales de *Sonreck* ne concordent pas avec celles de *Lootens* et de *Van Tricht*. C'est pourquoi l'on demande: De nouvelles recherches expérimentales, qui peuvent suffisamment éclaircir la naissance des tons dans les tuyaux d'orgues labiaux." It was on the basis of this problem that Van Schaik's study was made, and his essay was judged worthy of a gold medal.

[269] Moritz Weerth, Ann. der Physik, 11, 1086 (1903). Like the work of Friedrich, this was a doctor's dissertation, and the work was done at Rostock under Wachsmuth.

stead of the upper lip of a pipe he used a simple wedge, placed with its sharp edge a short distance above a slit that corresponded to the windway of a pipe. When the wind strikes such an edge it often produces a fairly clear musical tone. Under most circumstances a gradual increase in blowing pressure is accompanied by a gradual rise in pitch, but there are certain pressures at which a small increase in pres-

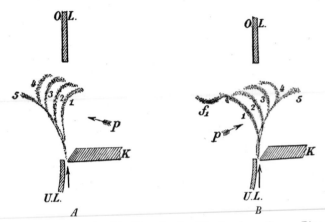

FIG. 114.—Motion of the Air Sheet in the Mouth of an Organ Pipe [Van Schaik]. *O.L.* and *U.L.* represent respectively the upper and lower lips of the pipe, and *K* the languet. Each diagram shows several positions of the air sheet, and the numbers give the order in which the positions were seen. In *A* the sheet was moving outward, and in *B* it was moving inward.

sure is accompanied by a sudden jump in pitch. Under most circumstances a gradual increase in the distance of the edge from the slit is accompanied by a gradual drop in pitch, but there are certain distances at which there is a sudden jump in pitch.

Weerth introduced smoke into the blowing wind, and then observed stroboscopically. When the apparatus gave no sound the sheet of wind glided smoothly up the sides of the wedge. When a sound was produced it could be seen that the sheet was bending back and forth for a short distance below the wedge, and that the air in the sheet flowed first to one side of the wedge and then to the other.

Weerth's explanation of the sound from an edge involved a failure of the sheet to divide quite equally at the edge. If more of it blows on one side than on the other there is on one side an increase of pressure that swings the sheet over toward the other side. This leads to an increased pressure on that other side, and so the sheet is kept swinging back and forth.

Question 291. If Weerth's explanation of the vibration of the blowing sheet is correct what is it that produces the sound?

Question 292. If Weerth's hypothesis is correct how should you expect the loudness of the sound to depend on the position of the observer with reference to the wedge? (Weerth gives no indication that he examined this question.)

Question 293. If Weerth's hypothesis is correct do you see any simple explanation of the effect produced by changing the blowing pressure? the distance to the wedge? Do you see any simple explanation of the jumps in pitch?

The work of Friedrich and Weerth was followed up by Wachsmuth.[270] With regard to Friedrich's work he found that in all probability the transverse-lamella does not function as Friedrich supposed it did. If a small wooden obstacle is placed inside of the mouth so as to screen the ortho-lamella from the transverse-lamella the ortho-lamella is deflected inward, and the air sheet (i.e. the ortho-lamella) no longer passes close enough to the upper lip to give rise

[270] Richard Wachsmuth, Physikal. Zeitschr., 4, 743 (1903); Ann. der Physik, 14, 469 (1904). The first of these references is a summary of a paper read by Wachsmuth at a meeting of German scientific and medical men. It also contains an account of the discussion that followed Wachsmuth's paper. The explanation that Wachsmuth then offered for the formation of edge tones was not satisfactory, and was deleted when the complete paper appeared in the Annalen der Physik. At the time this work was done Wachsmuth was Assistant Professor of Physics in the University at Rostock. Since 1914 he has been at the university at Frankfurt am Main. Wachsmuth edited the fifth and sixth editions of Helmholtz's *Tonempfindungen.*

to a tone. It is for this reason that the pipe refuses to speak. But if the upper lip is moved a short distance inward the sheet again strikes it and the pipe speaks as well as it did before the obstacle was inserted. The vibration of the air in an organ pipe is probably not maintained by any

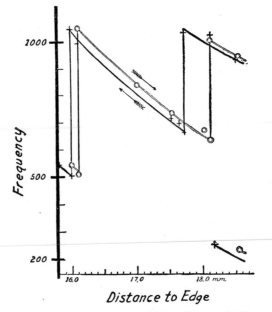

Fig. 115.—Relation Between Frequency of Edge Tone and Distance to Edge [Wachsmuth]. The curve indicated by the circles was obtained when the distance was increasing; that indicated by the crosses when it was decreasing.

such interplay between ortho-lamella and transverse-lamella as was described on p. 333.

When Wachsmuth used simply a thin sheet of wind at constant pressure blowing on the sharp corner of a wedge he found that the pitch depends on the distance to the edge in the manner shown in Fig. 115. If a resonator is brought near to the wedge while the wind is blowing on it and giving rise to a tone, and if the natural frequency of the resonator does not differ too widely from that of the edge tone, Wachsmuth found that the edge tone adjusts its frequency to that of the resonator. If the resonator has the form shown in Fig. 116, and is brought to the slit and wedge in the position shown, we have practically an organ pipe. Each

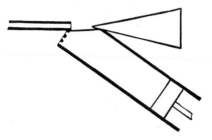

FIG. 116.—Organ Pipe Formed from Slit, Wedge, and Resonator [Wachsmuth].

flue pipe in an organ may be regarded as a coupled system: A resonator—the body of the pipe—is coupled to a slit and edge.

Question 294.   In Fig. 115 there are jumps in pitch in the neighborhood of 16 mm. and 18 mm.   In each case what is approximately the musical interval that is involved?

Question 295.   The part of the resonator shown by the three dots in Fig. 116 may be open or closed.   Wachsmuth found that the pitch was nearly the same in one case as in the other.   Why?

127. Vortices near Mouth.—Wachsmuth also succeeded in obtaining photographs that showed something as to how the sheet of wind moves. This he finally accomplished by adding ether vapor to the blowing wind, and then taking instantaneous pictures by means of bright electric sparks. The ether vapor bends the path of the light rays sufficiently to make the path of the wind visible, but it was no easy task to obtain the pictures. Fig. 117 shows some of the results. In all of these cases sound was being produced. It will be seen that the stream bends and then breaks into turbulent

motion. In *a* and *c* some of the vortices in the turbulent motion are seen clearly.

With a simple slit and wedge Wachsmuth found that when no tone is heard no vortices are seen, that tone and vortices accompany each other, and that at jumps in pitch there is a sudden change in rate of vortex formation. More-

FIG. 117.—Forms Assumed by Blowing Wind [Wachsmuth].
a, Edge Tone. Distance to edge, 16 mm. Pressure, 5 mm. water.
b, Organ Pipe. Wind pressure normal.
c, Organ Pipe. Wind pressure lower. The pictures in this series follow each other from left to right.

over, calculation showed that the frequency of the tone was, within experimental error, the same as the frequency with which the vortices were formed. The vortices appeared to be an essential element in the production of an edge tone.

Some beautiful drawings of the vortices and sheet of wind at the mouth of a large pipe have been made by Carrière,[271] and Fig. 118 is copied from one of his papers. In *a* and *d*, where the pipe was speaking its fundamental, the sheet between the windway and the upper lip appears to be vibrating as a whole—somewhat like a metal reed that is clamped at its lower end. In *b*, where the pipe is giving the octave, the middle of the sheet appears to be farthest to the left when the top of it—excluding the vortices—is farthest

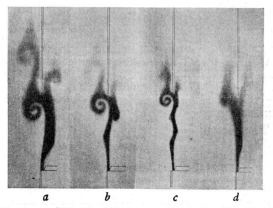

FIG. 118.—Vortices and Blowing Wind at the Mouth of a Flue Pipe [Carrière]. The blowing pressure for *a* was normal, for *b* it was lower, for *c* lower still, and for *d* it was the lowest.

to the right. Under the reduced pressure the sheet rises from the windway somewhat more slowly than in *a*, and since it is wafted back and forth sideways twice as rapidly the shape it assumes is not surprising. In *c* the sheet is bent into a larger number of segments. Here the pipe is speaking a still higher pitch, and the air as it rises is wafted back and forth more then once before it reaches the upper lip.

The investigations that have been summarized in the last few articles are only a fraction selected out of the literature on the subject. The general feeling today seems to be

[271] Z. Carrière, Journ. de Physique, **6**, 52 (1925); **7**, 7 (1926). Abbé Carrière is a professor at the Institut Catholique at Toulouse.

that the vortices are important, if not essential, in the production of edge tones, and that in a flue pipe the edge tone
produced at the upper lip is steadied, and its pitch to some
extent determined, by the resonance of the pipe body. It
is possible, as Carrière suggests, that the importance of the
vortices may be overemphasized. At any rate, it is probably safe to say that a complete account of the maintenance
of flue pipes must include the swaying back and forth of the
air sheet under the action of the vibrating air in the body of
the pipe, and the consequent streaming of that sheet, first to
one side of the upper lip and then to the other. The explanation of the maintenance of flue pipes may prove to be
one of several cases where the ideas of Helmholtz were
for a time supposed to be inadequate or mistaken, but were
later found to be essentially correct.

128. The Organ.—We have already spoken of the considerable variety in the qualities of tone that may be obtained from organ pipes of different shapes and different
types. A set of pipes having as nearly as possible the same
quality, and running from as low a pitch as desired to as
high a pitch as desired, is called a *stop*. The number of stops
in an organ may run from half a dozen to a hundred or
more—or even, in very large organs, to several hundreds.

A large part of the mechanism of the organ is to enable
the organist to play on any chosen stop or group of stops,
and to play at the same time different melodies or successions
of chords on different stops or groups of stops. For this
purpose the stops are collected into what is practically a
number of separate organs, each with its own keyboard.
The number of organs runs from three to five, or even more.
One of them is played with the feet, and is known as the
pedal organ. The keyboards for the other organs are played
with the hands and are known as *manuals*.

At least one of the organs, called the *swell organ,* is inclosed in a box, and a considerable part of one side of the

box consists of a set of shutters somewhat like a venetian blind. The position of the shutters can be adjusted by means of a pedal, and thus the loudness of the sound from the swell organ can be controlled. In modern instruments it is also customary to inclose a large part of the other organs in swell boxes. In general the loudness of the music from an organ is controlled by the number and loudness of the stops that are in use, and by the position of the shutters.

Many stops are of "8-ft" pitch. This means that on these stops the c digital near the middle of a manual plays c_3. That is, the pitches from such a stop are those which a person who is familiar with the piano would expect them to be. The designation "8-ft" is adopted because the longest pipe in the stop—if it is an open pipe, and if the organ does not have an unusual keyboard—is about eight feet long. In a 16-ft stop the notes are an octave lower than those in an 8-ft stop, in a 4-ft stop they are an octave higher, and so on.

The stops for any of the organs are not permanently connected to the keyboard, but are connected and disconnected at pleasure by means of knobs or small levers at the sides of the keyboard or in some other convenient location. The word "stop" is often applied to one of these knobs as well as to the set of pipes that it controls. And since in many organs the act of connecting a set of pipes to the keyboard is accomplished by drawing a knob toward the performer, this act is spoken of as "drawing the stop."

Various devices assist the organist in changing quickly from one combination of stops to another. Means are also provided by which he can "couple" one keyboard to another. For instance, if he employs a "swell to great" coupler, and plays on the manual of the "great" organ, he makes use of all stops that are drawn on the great organ and also of all stops that are drawn on the swell organ.

The means of admitting wind to the desired pipes was

at one time purely mechanical, and since a part of the mechanism consisted of "trackers"—thin strips of wood that exert a pull—this type of action is known either as a *mechanical action* or as a *tracker action*. In a tracker organ the force needed to press the digitals increases with the number of stops that are being used, and on a large organ with many stops drawn the playing requires a considerable amount of strength. With modern types of action no more force is needed to play the full organ than to play a single stop, and the manufacture of tracker organs has practically ceased.

The playing of organs has become much less laborious since *pneumatic actions* have come into use. In these actions

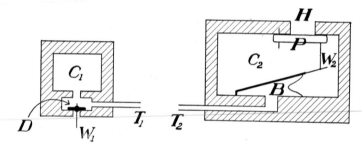

FIG. 119.—Part of the Pneumatic Mechanism for an Organ.

a force is exerted by an air-operated *pneumatic valve* or by the opening or closing of a small bellows called a *pneumatic motor* or a *pneumatic lever*.

Fig. 119 shows how these devices work. When the organ is in use the chests C_1 and C_2 are kept supplied with "wind," that is, with air under pressure. The disk D in the diagram at the left can be allowed to drop into the position shown, or can be pushed upward by the wire W_1 until it closes the opening above it. When the disk D is in the position shown the pressure from C_1 is transmitted to whatever device is connected to the tube T_1. When the disk is pushed up the connection between C_1 and T_1 is broken, air escapes from T_1 through the lower hole around the wire, and the pressure in the device connected to T_1 drops to that of the outside atmosphere.

In the other diagram in Fig. 119 B is a small bellows, attached by means of a wire W_2 to a "pallet" P, which is a sheepskin-covered block of wood. The left end of the pallet is pivoted so that the right end can swing up into the position shown or can be drawn downward while the left end hardly moves. There may also be a spring (not shown in the figure) which tends to keep the pallet in the position shown. By means of the tube T_2 the pressure inside of the bellows may be made the same as that in the chest C_2, or may be allowed to drop to that of the atmosphere outside. T_2 may, for instance, be connected to the tube T_1 in the left-hand diagram, and the pressure in C_2 may be equal to that in C_1. If the air pressure in the space above the hole H is less than that in the chest C_2 the pressure tends to keep the pallet closed. But if the pressure in the bellows B is reduced the wind in C_2 makes the bellows collapse and pull down the pallet. This occurs because the area which B exposes to the pressure in C_2 is sufficiently greater than that exposed by P. The opening of the pallet permits wind from C_2 to rush out through the hole H.

As a very simple illustration of a pneumatic action suppose that the pressing of a digital raises the wire W_1, that the tubes T_1 and T_2 are joined to each other, and that an organ pipe is above the hole H. Then whenever the digital is pressed the pressure in the tubes drops, the bellows collapses, the pallet opens, and the pipe speaks. The digital is to be thought of as extending off to the left at the bottom of the diagram, with its back end under the wire W_1.

There may be a whole row of pairs of chests like those in the figure, one pair for each digital on the keyboard, and the whole row extending in a direction perpendicular to the page. Then the partitions between the various chests

C_1 are not needed, and the partitions between the chests C_2 are not needed. We do away with these partitions, and the resulting chest C_2, containing as many bellows and pallets as there are digitals on the keyboard, is what is usually called a *wind chest*.

With the arrangement just suggested each digital would play one pipe, and as many keyboards would be needed as there are stops in the organ. The playing will be simplified if another long wind chest C_3 (not shown in the diagram) is placed just to the right of C_2, the tube T_2 is extended so as to serve the bellows in both chests, and if there is one set of pipes above C_2 and another set above C_3. Then if both chests contain wind the pressing of a digital causes two pipes to speak—one pipe on each chest—whereas if only one chest contains wind only one pipe speaks. By means of a fourth chest, containing only one bellows and pallet, and placed out at the end of C_2, it is possible to have the drawing of a stop fill C_2 with wind. Similar arrangements may be made so that the drawing of another stop fills C_3 with wind. Several wind chests may be set one behind the other (that is, one to the right of another in Fig. 119) and connected to draw-stop knobs, thus making it possible to play from one keyboard on whatever combination of these stops is desired.

With any such arrangement as has just been described the *console,* which contains the various keyboards and other devices for controlling the organ, must be fixed in position and must be close to the organ. It is often desired to have the console movable and to have it at some distance from the organ. These possibilities are realized in *electro-pneumatic actions,* which are now almost universal in new organs.

In this type of action the pressing of a digital starts an electric current that flows in a wire in a flexible cable, so that the console may be at a distance from the organ and may be moved from one location in an auditorium to another.

The electric current energizes a small magnet, beneath
which is a tiny iron disk that takes the place of the disk D
in Fig. 119. This iron disk moves through so short a distance that the air in the tube leading from it does not flow
fast enough to cause a satisfactory operation of the bellows
in a wind chest. It can however operate an air-controlled
relay, and Fig. 120 shows one type of electro-pneumatic action. M is the magnet and D_1 is the iron disk. When the
digital is pressed the disk D_1 jumps up and covers an opening
between the poles of the magnet, so that the wind pressure

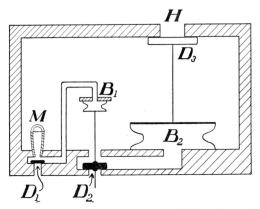

Fig. 120.—Part of an Electro-Pneumatic Action in an Organ.

in the chest no longer reaches the inside of the relay bellows
B_1. The upper side of B_1 is fixed in position, so that the
collapse of B_1 raises the disk D_2 and makes the larger bellows B_2 collapse. The lower side of B_2 is fixed in position,
and the collapsing of B_2 pulls down the large disk valve D_3
and allows wind to flow upward through the hole H.

The action just described is considerably simpler than
that to be found in an actual organ. Nothing has been said
about means for coupling one keyboard to another, about
combination pistons, by means of which the organist may,
by a mere push of his thumb, throw on with one movement

some chosen combination of stops, or about the various other details of the mechanism.[272]

129. Music from Bells.—Bells have been employed during the past several centuries for purposes which are more or less musical, and perhaps our long association with them, and the story and legend that have grown up around them may help to explain why the ringing of a distant bell or peal of bells seems to reach something elemental within us.

There are several ways in which a set of bells may be used, and the method of use determines the type of mounting. Some bells are mounted to swing, and others are mounted "dead," so that they cannot swing. Technically a bell does not *ring* unless she is swung, and a bell that is mounted dead cannot be rung. The ringing is usually accomplished by pulling on a rope that passes over a large wheel attached rigidly to the "yoke" that carries the bell, so that the bell swings when the wheel turns.

When there are, say, three bells the simplest type of play is to have one man for each bell, and each man keep ringing his bell. The smallest bell swings most quickly, and the largest most slowly. So the strokes from the different bells do not all come with the same frequency, and there is a changing pattern in the order in which they are heard.

130. Change Ringing.—A considerable development from this type of play is found in the English custom of "change ringing." This type of play has enjoyed great popularity. It is said that the eighteenth century "was the golden age of bell ringing; then above all England deserved the name of the Land of Bells. Ringers all over the country organized themselves into societies with strict codes of rules. Ringing became one of the most popular forms of sport. . . . The country squire, the professional man, the tradesman in the town and the craftsman in the village, all

[272] For a fuller treatment of the mechanism of the organ see William H. Barnes, *The Contemporary American Organ* (1933).

found admirable exercise and amusement in bell ring-ing." [273]

When changes are rung the bells are not simply allowed to swing in their natural periods, but the strokes are given at times determined by the ringers. To accomplish this each bell is so mounted that when she is swung to a point just beyond the position where she is upside down a stop arrests her motion. She stays "set" in this position until she is "pulled off" by the ringer.

A *change* consists of the series of notes obtained by ring-ing each bell once. In different changes the bells are rung in different orders. To describe the different changes it is customary to number the bells, beginning with the smallest or "treble," and ending with the largest or "tenor." With two bells there are only two changes: The bells may be rung in the order 1, 2 or in the order 2, 1. When a third bell is added there are six changes; for any one of the three bells may be rung first, and when any bell has been chosen to be first there are two changes on the other bells. Similarly with four bells there are $4 \times 3 \times 2 \times 1 = 24$ changes, and with five there are 120 changes.

Names have been given to various orders in which changes are rung on various numbers of bells. "Singles" means changes on four bells, "doubles" on five, "minor" on six, "treble" on seven, and so on with other names. "Bob," "Grandsire," "Stedman," and other names indicate the "method" or order in which the changes occur.

There are more than half a dozen cases in which ring-ing has gone on steadily for ten hours or more. A record length of time for continuous ringing was reached on April 22, 1922, when 21,363 changes of Stedman Caters were rung on nine bells at Appleton, in Berkshire, England, in 12 hours and 25 minutes.

[273] Henry Beauchamp Walters, *Church Bells of England,* Frowde, now Oxford University Press (1912), p. 84.

Question 296. How many changes are there on eight bells? on twelve? If all the changes on eight bells were rung at the rate of three strokes a second, how long a time would be required? How long if all the changes were rung on twelve bells?

131. Chimes and Carillons.—An entirely different type of bell music is provided by a *chime*. A chime often consists of from eight to a dozen bells, most of them hung dead and played by hammers that strike on the inner side of the soundbow. These hammers are often manipulated from a keyboard by means of an action which resembles an enlargement of that in a tracker organ. A chime is suited for simple melodies, where only one note is played at a time. On account of the small number of bells the melodies that can be played may not range much beyond an octave, and must not digress into distant keys. A chime is sometimes arranged for automatic play, either of tunes or in connection with a clock. In the latter case automatic play is usually provided for the figures that are sometimes heard on the quarter hours and for the phrases that precede the striking of the hour.

The largest number of bells in a single instrument for music is found in the *carillon*. The number may be as small as twenty-three, in a good sized carillon it is often about forty or fifty, and in the carillons at Lake Wales, Florida, and the Riverside Church in New York City it rises respectively to seventy-one and seventy-two. The bells are hung dead, and they are played from a clavier (Fig. 121) that looks somewhat like that of an organ.

The bells of a carillon are tuned to the equally tempered scale, and with the large number of bells it becomes possible to play almost any melody on the large bells and a rapidly flowing accompaniment on the smaller ones. Belgium and Holland have long been the home of carillons, but they are

FIG. 121.—The Keyboard of a Carillon [From an article by William Wooding
Starmer, in "The Organ" (1927)].

now spreading rapidly in Great Britain and in North America.[274]

Instruments that consist of bells are not as well suited for the playing of chords as are instruments that use strings or pipes. This is partly because of the relative strengths of the component tones and partly because of the relative frequencies of the tones. The component tones from bells are often rather far from being harmonic. For instance, the first eight normal modes of the bell on which the hours are struck in the chime at Smith College have frequencies in the ratio 1.00, 1.51, 2.02, 2.93, 3.43, 4.33, 4.60, 4.63. Fortunately a number of the components are not brought out strongly when a bell is struck on the sound bow. On the bell just mentioned the first six components that come out strongly from the soundbow have frequencies in the ratio 1.00, 1.51, 2.02, 3.43, 5.17, 7.14. Even these are highly inharmonic, and it is surprising that the bell has the good quality that it has.

132. The Strike Note.—One curious fact about the pitch of a bell is that the pitch which the ear assigns is often not the pitch of any normal mode of the bell. Studies of the reason for this remarkable situation [275] have shown that the "strike note," which is heard as the pitch of the bell, is close to an octave below the fifth of the component partial tones. For instance, in the bell just mentioned, the strike note has a frequency about 1.71 times that of the "hum note" or first partial. No partial tone of the bell has this frequency. When a bell is struck on her soundbow it is found that the fifth partial is at first the most prominent, and it seems prob-

[274] On carillons and other matters connected with bells see John Robert Nichols, *Bells Thro' the Ages* (1928), and William Gorham Rice, *Carillon Music and Singing Towers of the Old World and the New* (1930).

[275] See the references in footnotes 123 and 126 on pp. 181 and 186, the papers cited by Jones and Alderman in the reference in footnote 129 on p. 195, an article by Erwin Meyer and Johannes Klaes, of the Heinrich Hertz Institut in Berlin, Naturwis., 21, 697 (1933), and an article by A. T. Jones, Journ. Acoust. Soc., 8, 199 (1937).

able that in many bells this fifth partial determines the pitch
of the strike note, the strike note from these bells being
just an octave below the fifth partial.

The partial which has been known as the seventh is also
at first a prominent one, and the work of Meyer and Klaes
shows that this "seventh" partial is in some way important
in the production of the strike note. The difference tone
from the fifth and "seventh" partials has a pitch not far
from that of the strike note, and it may be that it is this
difference tone which causes the pitch of the fifth partial to
be judged an octave lower than its frequency would suggest.

Some founders are now tuning several of the lower partial tones on their bells, and when this is done the relative
frequencies of the first five partials are made close to 1.00,
2.00, 2.40, 3.00, 4.00. With these frequency ratios it will
be seen that the second partial is an octave below the fifth,
and is likely to coincide with the strike note.

Question 297. The third partial of a bell is often very prominent, especially shortly after the bell has been struck. On the bell
referred to in the last few paragraphs what is approximately the musical interval between the strike note and the third partial? What is
this interval on a bell which has had its first five partials tuned?

CHAPTER ELEVEN

SPEECH AND SONG

133. Introduction.—Studies of the human voice have interested a vast number of investigators, and there were various early attempts to build apparatus that would imitate human speech.[276] Some of these contrivances were simply frauds, but others were real attempts to produce speaking machines.

The Abbé Mical [277] made out of brass two colossal heads that were said to be capable of pronouncing entire sentences. He showed the heads to the French *Académie des Sciences* in 1783, but when he did not receive from the government the reward that he expected he is said to have destroyed the heads, and little information as to precisely what was in them has been preserved.

At about the same time C. G. Kratzenstein and Wolfgang von Kempelen were interested in the attempt to imitate the human voice, and both of them wrote descriptions of apparatus which they built. Up to that time the reeds that had been used in musical instruments were striking reeds. Kratzenstein was the inventor of the free reed, and by attaching free reeds to pipes of curious and complicated shapes he was able to imitate several vowels.

Question 298. A story was once written about an arctic expedition on which the men encountered a bitterly severe cold spell. The cold was so intense that the men had difficulty in understanding each other, and finally were unable to hear at all. Their words were frozen before there was time for them to be heard. When the cold became less intense the frozen speech began to thaw out, and words

---

[276] On several of these machines see Appendix One.

[277] Robert Willis (see footnote 286 on p. 363 in this book) quotes this statement from Rivarol, *Traité des Machines Imitatives*, p. 160. See also the *Scientific Papers of Sir Charles Wheatstone* (1879), p. 365.

and sentences spoken days or weeks earlier were heard at last. We smile at this story, but what is the matter with it? With modern means of obtaining extremely low temperatures why can we not hope to be able to freeze speech and send the frozen message to a friend who will then thaw it out and hear the voice speaking to him?

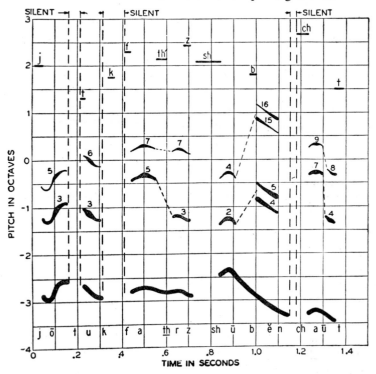

FIG. 122.—Melody Curve for the Sentence "Joe took father's shoe bench out." [278]

Not only is the human voice a musical instrument, but it is capable of an extremely wide variety of effects. In ordinary speech there is a more or less constant play up and down over different pitches, as is seen from the pitches of both fundamental and overtones in Fig. 122. The interruptions in the flow of speech are not always at the ends of

[278] Figs. 122 and 123 are copied from the article referred to in footnote 279.

words. In Fig. 122, for instance, the fundamental component of the word "shoe" flows into that of "bench" without
interruption. "Speech consists of a series of comparatively
steady states of vibration joined together in time, either by
silences or transitions from one steady state to another. Each
one of these steady states is characterized by a pitch and a
tone quality, and the sequence is essentially a melody."[279]

Changes of pitch are especially evident during song. But
in addition to the evident changes of pitch from one note of
a melody to another there may be other changes of surprising extent that pass unnoticed. During the pulsations of a
vibrato there is not only a periodic change in intensity but
also in frequency of vibration.[280] The pulsations of the
vibrato often occur at the rate of some six and a half to
seven in a second, and with each pulsation there is a rise and
fall in vibration frequency. The range of these changes is
often as much as half a step, and at times it becomes as great
as three half steps. Nevertheless in spite of this considerable variation the changes in frequency may pass entirely unnoticed.

In addition to changes in loudness and frequency it has
been found that during each pulsation of a vibrato there is
also a change in quality.[281]

It is well known that the separate sounds which make up
our speech and our song are often divided into consonants
and vowels and such "semi-vowels" as *l, m, n,* and *r.* The
intelligibility of what we say depends largely on the consonants, as may be verified by reading aloud to some one and
replacing all the vowel sounds by a single one, say by the

[279] Harvey Fletcher, Journ. Acoust. Soc., **3**, p. 3 of Supplement (Oct., 1931).

[280] Milton Metfessel, Sci. Monthly, **28**, 217 (1929).
   Carl Emil Seashore and Joseph Tiffin, Science, **72**, 480 (1930).
   Joseph Tiffin, Psych. Monographs, No. 187, p. 153 (1931).

[281] Wilmer T. Bartholomew, of the Department of Research, Peabody Conservatory of Music, Journ. Acoust. Soc., **6**, 25 (1934).

vowel sound in the word *cup*. A person who hears a passage read in this way finds little difficulty in understanding a large part of it.

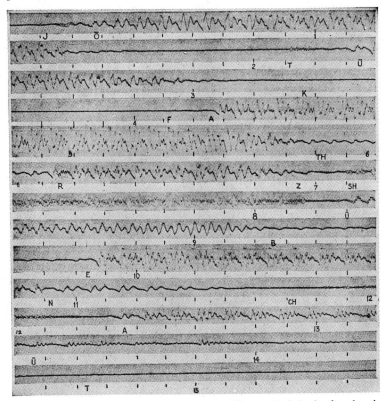

FIG. 123.—Vibration Curve for the Sentence "Joe took father's shoe bench out" [From Fletcher [278]]. The short vertical marks are 0.01 sec. apart, and the numbers give tenths of a second.

Nevertheless a considerable part of the speech energy is carried by the vowels. Years before the energy was measured it was observed that when persons are talking at a distance at which their speech is largely unintelligible a considerable part of what is heard consists of vowels. When it became possible to obtain satisfactory vibration curves for speech the curves showed clearly that a large part of the energy really is in the vowels. Notice for instance the curve in Fig. 123.

A large proportion of the sounds that we speak are produced in the larynx by the vocal cords, and then modified by the cavities above the larynx. Some of the sounds however, like those of the letters *f* and *s,* are produced in the mouth, after the breath has left the vocal cords; and a few sounds, like the *v* in *very* and the *zh* sound in *azure,* are produced by a combination of both means.

Sound may be produced by the vocal cords when the breath is drawn in or when it is expelled, but it is only the latter that is used in ordinary speech and song. The amount of breath used in singing has been examined by Stanley and Sheldon.[282] They find, contrary to what might have been expected, that a well-trained singer uses more breath when singing softly than when singing loudly, and that he uses the least breath when singing with moderate intensity. They also find that the amount of breath used does not differ greatly at different pitches, but is somewhat less near the middle of the singer's range than for his high notes and his low notes.

Question 299. Stanley and Sheldon found that for very soft singing the amount of air expelled in one second may be 400 cc. Assume the lips closed, and all of the air escaping through the nose. From an approximate measurement of the size of your nostrils how fast would this mean that the stream of air was coming from the nose?

Question 300. When the singing was at moderate intensity Stanley and Sheldon found that the air might be exhaled as slowly as 35 cc in a second. If the opening between the lips had an area of 10 cm² how fast was the air coming through this opening?

Question 301. How do the answers found for Questions 299 and 300 compare with the speed of sound?

[282] Douglas Stanley and H. H. Sheldon, Sci. Am., 131, 381 (1924).

134. The Organs of Speech.—It is well known that during speech or song the lungs force the breath upward through the trachea and the larynx into the cavities of the mouth and nose. The trachea is nearly an inch in diameter, and in the larynx, popularly known as the "Adam's apple," are the so-called "vocal cords." [283] These "cords" are triangularly shaped masses of flesh which project from the sides of the larynx as indicated in Fig. 124. At the front they touch, and they can be moved so that at the back they may be close together or some distance apart. During speech or song the cords are brought toward each other and stretched rather tightly. The space left between them is called the *glottis*, and its width depends on the sound that is produced. The width is often a few tenths of a millimeter.

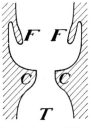

FIG. 124.—The Vocal Cords. *T* is the trachea, and *CC* the vocal cords. Above the vocal cords are the "false vocal cords" *FF*.

When the vocal cords are brought close together, and a breath of sufficient strength passes through the glottis, the cords are set into vibration. From the structure of these cords it is clear that the frequencies of their normal modes of vibration must be very different from those of stretched strings. The vocal cords probably act much more like the lips of a person who is blowing a horn. The pressure below the vocal cords increases until it forces them abruptly apart. The puff of air that escapes relieves the pressure, and the tension in the cords bring them toward each other again. That is, the flow of air through the glottis increases rapidly and then dies away more gradually; it is far from being simple harmonic. The varying flow of air, and the varying pressure that accompanies the varying flow, set up variations of pres-

[283] The name "vocal cords" appears to have been given to these structures by Antoine Ferrein (1693-1769), French physician and anatomist, who compared them to the strings of a violin.

sure in the neighboring cavities. The sounds of speech and song arise in part from the varying pressure produced at the glottis, and in part from the varying pressures thus set up in the neighboring cavities.

One cavity is that of the trachea and lungs. From the lower end of the trachea there are branches to the two lungs, and these branches divide and subdivide until the passages are very minute. Moreover the walls of these minute passages are soft. It would seem that any sound which starts down the trachea would be almost entirely absorbed, and that there could be very little real resonance from the lungs.

A simple demonstration of what would seem to be an analogous case is easily carried out with an ordinary flask. If a side of the empty flask is tapped with a knuckle while the neck of the flask is held near the experimenter's ear, the natural pitch of the flask cavity is readily heard. If a little soapy water is now introduced, and the flask well shaken until it is filled with foam, no definite tone is obtained on tapping it. There is nothing more than a dull thud. Of course the situation here is different from that which obtains in the lungs. Nevertheless, whatever the term "chest resonance" may mean it would seem that sounds which pass down through the trachea can scarcely be reinforced or returned to aid appreciably in increasing any sound given out by the vocal cords.[284]

[284] Max Giesswein [Passow-Schaefer, Beiträge zur Anat. Physiol. Pathol. u. Ther., 22, 94 (1925)] has examined the resonance of the trachea and lungs taken from a cadaver. He was not able to secure any satisfactory resonance, either by blowing across the top of the trachea or by bringing tuning forks near it. Instead of concluding that very little resonance occurs in the trachea and lungs he thought that the failure to obtain resonance might be because a large part of the smaller bronchi had sunk together or filled up with fluid or bubbles that he could not entirely remove. He also held tuning forks before the opening in the throat of patients whose tracheas had had to be opened, but without obtaining any resonance.

It is true that a vibration of the vocal cords can set neighboring parts of the body into vibration. It is even possible when certain tones are sung to

Above the vocal cords there is an irregularly shaped cavity which includes the region immediately above the vocal cords, and also the cavities in the mouth and nose. Fairly well separated from this cavity are certain others, like the sphenoidal sinuses and the frontal sinuses, which are sometimes regarded as having a bearing on the qualities of vocal sounds. The path from the mouth to the nasal cavity can be closed or opened. A part of the surface that incloses the mouth cavity is fairly hard and unyielding, and part of it is rather soft. The softer and more yielding the surfaces the greater is the extent to which they absorb sounds that reach them.

Although a large amount of detail has been omitted from the above description, enough has probably been included to show that the vocal apparatus is sufficiently complicated to provide the possibility of producing many different kinds of sounds.

Question 302. It has sometimes been thought that the vocal cords may vibrate like stretched strings, with a node half way from the front to the back of each cord. If such a mode of vibration does occur should you expect the vibration of the cords to have a frequency approximately twice that of the fundamental mode, or to deviate rather widely from the double frequency?

Question 303. If the frequency of the vocal cords in the case suggested in Question 302 were precisely twice that in the fundamental mode the sound produced would very probably be considerably more than an octave above the fundamental pitch of the cords. Why?

Question 304. Helmholtz says [285] that "with the assistance of resonators it is possible to recognize very high partials, up to the six-

feel a vibration by placing the back of a hand against a point just back of a shoulder blade. But whether this is a real case of resonance, and whether the vibration is transmitted by the air in the trachea and lungs, are open to question.

See Clarence T. Simon and Franklin Keller, Quarterly Journ. Speech Educ., **13**, 432 (1927).

[285] Hermann von Helmholtz, *Sensations of Tone,* Longmans Green and Company, 4th Eng. ed., p. 103.

teenth, when one of the brighter vowels is sung by a powerful bass voice at a low pitch." These partial tones are harmonic. Why is there so large a number of partial tones, and why are they harmonic?

Question 305. It was suggested above that the pressure beneath the vocal cords increases until it forces them abruptly apart, that the passing of the puff of air relieves the pressure, and that the tension of the cords then brings them close together again. While these statements are doubtless approximately correct, they do not provide an explanation of the maintenance. What is lacking? If you have difficulty in answering this question look back at Art. 118.

135. Vowel Sounds. Two Types of Theories.—How do the sounds of the various vowels differ from each other? Do they differ in the same way in which the qualities of musical instruments differ, or is there some additional factor which differentiates one vowel from another?

A vibration of the air in the cavities above the vocal cords may be excited in either of two more or less distinct ways, and these two possibilities have given rise to two types of theories as to the nature of vowel sounds. These theories have been called "fixed pitch" theories and "relative pitch" theories. On a fixed pitch theory each vowel is supposed to be characterized by one or more rather restricted regions of pitch, which are independent of the fundamental tone of the vowel. On a relative pitch theory each vowel is supposed to be characterized by a particular series of overtones, the frequencies of which stand in a certain definite relation to the fundamental.

If a fixed pitch theory is correct the overtones that characterize a given vowel are natural pitches of the cavities, and may be elicited by different fundamental pitches. If that is the case it is even possible that the overtones in the complex sound may not be harmonic, and that an analysis into harmonic components may lead to conclusions that really have no significance.

If a relative pitch theory is correct all the components go

up and down along with the fundamental, and if the components are harmonic a Fourier analysis will give information about the intensities of real components.

When we are speaking there is a continual change from one sound to another, and it has long been recognized that the distinctness of any vowel depends in large measure on the contrast between it and other sounds that precede it or follow it. In connected speech there is usually no difficulty in recognizing different vowels, but if any chosen vowel is sung steadily for some time the lack of contrast soon makes the vowel less easy to recognize. In fact it seems to be true that a vowel is characterized, in part, by a quality which changes while the vowel is being spoken. This is one of the difficulties that the investigator must face.

136. Investigation by Willis.—The first really important study as to the nature of vowels was made by Willis.[286] He began by repeating some of Kempelen's experiments,[287] and then passed on to others of his own. Willis employed a free reed which was usually near the closed end of a tube. The other end of the tube was open. By using reeds of different pitches and tubes of different lengths Willis was able not only to imitate various vowels but also to learn something about their real nature. He found that the pitch which the ear assigned to the sound from the combination of reed and tube was the pitch of the reed, and that a given vowel was characterized by certain lengths of tube.

If the natural pitch of the reed is considerably flatter than that of the tube, each puff of air that escapes from the reed gives rise to a rapidly damped vibration of the air in

---

[286] Robert Willis, a fellow of Caius College at Cambridge, England, Camb. Phil. Trans., 3, 231 (1830). Rayleigh speaks of this paper as a "remarkable memoir." Willis read part of it to the Cambridge Philosophical Society in November of 1828 and the remainder in March of 1829.

[287] Kempelen's talking machine, to which there is a brief reference in Art. 133, was devised about 1788. His book, telling about his study of vowel sounds and describing his machine, was published in Vienna in 1791.

the tube, and the frequency or this tube vibration depends on the length of the tube and not on the frequency of the reed. The frequency of the puffs from the reed is the frequency that the ear recognizes as characterizing the pitch of the sound, and the vowel quality is characterized by the frequency of the damped vibration in the tube. When the vowels are produced naturally instead of artificially the vocal cords take the place of the reed, and the cavity above the vocal cords takes the place of the tube. Willis's experiments seemed to show that each vowel is characterized by a certain more or less definite pitch. Such a characteristic pitch came later to be called a *formant*.

137. **Investigation by Miller.**—In an important study by D. C. Miller [288] the vowels were sung steadily, vibration curves were obtained, and the curves were analyzed into their harmonic components. Figs. 125, 126, and 127 show some of his results. Fig. 125 shows analyses of the vowel *ah*. It will be seen that when the *ah* was intoned on $d\sharp_2$ the partial that was strongest was the sixth, when on $f\sharp_2$ the strongest was the fifth, and when on $a\sharp_2$ the strongest was the fourth. Taken all together the analyses in the figure show that when the fundamental pitch was any tone in the octave from c_2 to c_3 the strongest partial was one that had a frequency not far from 1000 cycles/sec. These results suggest that when we hear the vowel *ah* there is a strong resonance in the neighborhood of 1000 cycles/sec. This is also approximately the frequency that Willis found as characteristic of the vowel in the word *far*.[289]

The results obtained by Willis and by Miller indicate that each steady vowel is characterized by one or two more or less definite regions of pitch. If that is the case it would

---

[288] Dayton Clarence Miller, *The Science of Musical Sounds,* Macmillan (1916), Lecture 7.

[289] In the table which Willis gives on his p. 243 the db'' is obviously a misprint for db'''.

seem that it should be possible to change the vowels in a phonograph record by running the instrument at a rate different from that usually employed. If the vowels depend on relative frequency and not on absolute frequency the change in speed of the disk should not change the vowels. This test has been carried out by a number of experi-

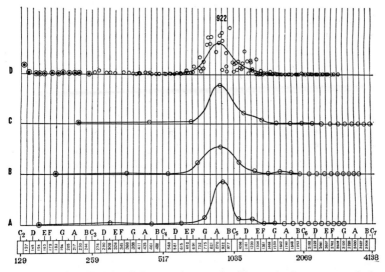

FIG. 125.—Distribution of Energy Among the Harmonic Components of the Vowel in "far" [Photograph kindly supplied by Professor Miller [244]]. The circles with black centers represent the pitches that were sung, and the plain circles show the energies of the various partial tones. Curves *A, B,* and *C* represent analyses with different fundamentals. Curve *D* is a composite, showing the results of twelve different analyses.

menters.[290] The vowels are changed. That is, the findings agree with those to be expected on a fixed pitch theory.

Question 306. If the vowels in Fig. 126 are pronounced one after another, beginning at the top of the figure, what changes are made in the positions of the tongue and the lips? Does the charac-

[290] See, for instance, Dayton Clarence Miller, *The Science of Musical Sounds* (1916), p. 232.

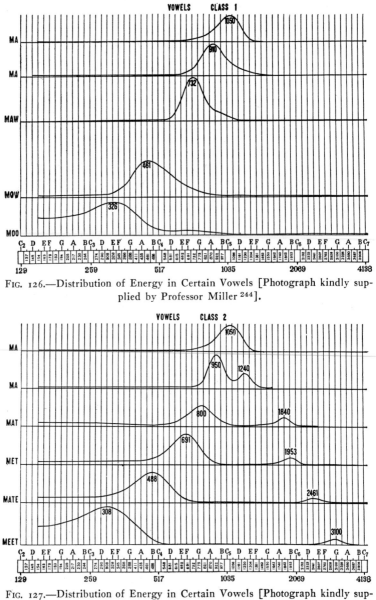

FIG. 126.—Distribution of Energy in Certain Vowels [Photograph kindly supplied by Professor Miller [244]].

FIG. 127.—Distribution of Energy in Certain Vowels [Photograph kindly supplied by Professor Miller [244]].

teristic frequency for these vowels change in the way that you should expect from the changes in the positions of tongue and lips?

Question 307.   If the vowels in Fig. 127 are pronounced one after another, beginning at the top of the figure, what changes are made in the positions of the tongue and lips?   In the cases of these vowels do you see any reason for the two regions of resonance?

138. Coupled Cavities.—More recent studies have shown two characteristic frequency regions for each vowel, including those in Fig. 126.   But in the cases of the vowels in Fig. 126 the energy in the upper regions is smaller than it is for the vowels in Fig. 127.   From Fig. 128 it will be seen that the mouth and pharynx may be regarded as two cavities, coupled through the opening toward the back or highest part of the tongue.   As this opening is made larger the coupling becomes closer, and the

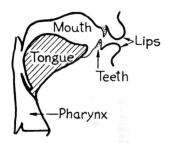

Fig. 128. — Diagram of the Mouth-Pharynx Cavity [Irving B. Crandall, in Bell System Techn. Journ. (1927)].

two cavities become more like a single cavity.   As the opening is made smaller the coupling becomes looser, and the cavities are more nearly independent.

A model based on the idea of the double resonator has been prepared by Crandall [291] and is shown in Fig. 129. When the model is blown gently with a slow current of air through the small hole at the back of the smaller cavity it gives a good whispered *ah.*   When it is connected to an artificial larynx [292] the voiced *ah* that is produced is recognizable, but it is not as good as the whispered *ah.*

[291] Irving B. Crandall, of the Bell Telephone Laboratories, Bell System Tech. Journ., **6**, 100 (1927); or Reprint B-233 from the Bell Telephone Laboratories.

[292] This artificial larynx has been devised through the cooperation of Dr. J. E. Mackenty of New York City and engineers of the Bell Telephone Laboratories.   It is of great assistance to persons whose vocal cords have been removed.   See R. R. Riesz, Journ. Acoust. Soc., **1**, 273 (1930).

When certain speech sounds are produced it is found that closing the nose either changes the quality of the sound or stops it entirely. We have been treating the cavity above the vocal cords as consisting of two simpler cavities which are coupled to each other. In cases where the closing of the nose changes the quality or stops the sound it is clear that the nasal cavity must be of importance, and that the

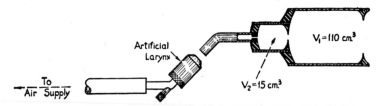

FIG. 129.—Double Resonator Model for *ah* [Irving B. Crandall, in Bell System Tech. Journ. (1927)]. V_1 and V_2 give the volumes of the two parts of the cavity.

complete cavity is to be regarded as consisting of at least three parts instead of two.

Question 308. Which speech sounds do you find are affected (*a*) to a marked extent, (*b*) to some extent, by holding your nose so that the nostrils are closed?

139. Comparison of the Two Types of Theories.—It now appears that the points of view in the two types of theories are not as different as was at one time supposed. If the puffs from the glottis are sufficiently sudden each puff may start a vibration in each of the various normal modes of the cavity. In this case there is no reason to expect the partial tones set up to fall into a harmonic series. Indeed they may deviate from such a series very widely, and a harmonic analysis of the vibration curve may have little real significance.[293]

[293] This point of view has been emphasized for many years by Edward Wheeler Scripture. See, for instance, an interesting article by him in Journ. Acoust. Soc. 5, 148 (1933).

On the other hand when a vowel is sung steadily, without change of pitch or loudness or quality, the puffs from the glottis are periodic, the whole motion must soon settle down to one which is periodic, and the component partial tones are forced into a harmonic series. In such a case a Fourier analysis into harmonic components does give partial tones that really exist.

In addition to the older attempts to build machines that would talk, and in addition to devices like the phonograph and the radio, which give back to us what is put into them, pieces of apparatus have been devised to test the possibility of producing speech sounds by combining fairly simple sounds of the proper pitches and loudnesses. For this purpose use has been made of tuning forks, of organ pipes, and more recently of sounds which are produced electrically.

One of these electrical studies was carried out by Kucharski [294] on a number of French vowels. He finds that certain general regions of pitch are not sufficient to characterize a vowel accurately. For each vowel he finds a definite ratio between the frequencies of the two important components, and he finds that the ratio of the intensities of these components must not exceed certain limits. If these conditions are satisfied he finds that each of the two important components may lie anywhere inside a range of something like an octave—in some cases more than an octave—without loss of the quality of the given vowel. If Kucharski's findings are substantiated by other experimenters it would seem that a complete theory of vowel quality must include factors from both the fixed pitch theory and the relative pitch theory.

Question 309. If you sing *ah* steadily, and alternately bring your hand up so as nearly to cover your mouth and then take it away,

[294] P. Kucharski, Comptes Rendus, **195**, 979 (1932).

what change in vowel do you notice? How is this change to be explained?

Question 310. It is well known that it is difficult for a singer —especially a soprano—to enunciate certain vowels clearly on her high notes. How is this to be explained?

Question 311. A parrot can speak various words in spite of the fact that his vocal cavities must be much smaller than those of a human being. How is this to be explained?

CHAPTER TWELVE

TECHNICAL APPLICATIONS

140. Introduction.—The past few decades have witnessed remarkable developments in a number of technical applications of the growing understanding of sound. A considerable part of this development has occurred in connection with the types of vacuum tubes that are used in radio sets. The invention and perfecting of these tubes has made possible the amplifying of extremely minute electric currents, so that we can now magnify sounds in a way that was quite impossible not many years ago. The beating of a human heart may now be made audible throughout a large auditorium. Such extremely faint sounds as those involved in the rearrangement of the small parts of a piece of iron when it is magnetized, and certain actions of termites in a piece of wood, can now be actually heard. Vacuum tubes with their associated circuits now provide convenient and steady sound sources, and the ranges of frequency that can be obtained in this way go far beyond those which can be heard. Moreover the energy involved in the vibrations set up in these electric circuits can be measured without difficulty, so that the means now available for determining the intensities of sounds are vastly better than those which were known a few decades ago.

High frequency, "ultrasonic" or "supersonic," vibrations are also produced by maintaining and amplifying the vibrations of certain crystals and of bars of certain magnetic substances. The frequency of the vibrations thus obtained runs up to several million cycles per second, and may be

kept extraordinarily steady. Some of the effects produced
are very striking. Marked pressure and heating are obtained, and also decided physiological changes. The micro-
scopic organisms that swarm in stagnant water are soon
killed by these inaudible rays. Frogs, tadpoles, and small
fishes likewise succumb to them, blood corpuscles are destroyed, and a device has been developed for the continuous
sterilization of milk by ultrasonic waves.

Considerable attention is now being paid to the elimina-
tion of unnecessary noises; vibrations set up in the earth are
employed in studying the upper layers of the earth's crust;
echoes are used for measuring ocean depths. Among the
better known technical applications of sound are those connected with the victrola, talking motion pictures, and fog
signals. In addition there is rapidly developing a branch of
engineering that deals with the acoustics of auditoriums. It
is to a few of these matters that the present chapter is
devoted.

141. The Reduction of Noise.—A large amount of noise
is not only annoying but it may have a definite effect on
health and efficiency. A person accustomed to quiet sur-
roundings finds it difficult to sleep in an outside room in a
busy part of New York City. The hearing of men engaged
in certain occupations becomes gradually impaired by the
noise to which they are constantly exposed. A study of the
work done by persons at typewriters has shown [295] that noise
increases the metabolism and increases the time required for
a given piece of work. In a certain factory experienced
workers were assembling temperature regulators, and the
work was being done close to a boiler shop where there was
a great deal of noise. The assembling was moved to a quiet
location, with the result that the workers assembled 110
regulators in the same time in which they had formerly as-

[295] Donald Anderson Laird, Journ. Indust. Hygiene, 9, 431 (1927); or
City Noise, Noise Abatement Commission, City of New York (1930), p. 296.

sembled 80, and the number of imperfections in assembly dropped at the same time from 60 to 7.[296] In another factory it was suspected that poor production was due to noise from an electric fan. When the fan was stopped the production rose twelve per cent in spite of the poorer ventilation.[296]

A study of the annoyance produced by different sounds [297] shows that loud sounds are more annoying than faint ones —as was to be expected—and that above some 500 cycles/sec. the annoyance depends on the pitch as well as on the loudness. Below 500 cycles/sec. the annoyance depends almost entirely on the loudness, but in the next four octaves the annoyance increases as the pitch goes up. "Those pitches which man himself makes in speech are the least annoying to him. . . . The low annoyance values of the more common speech sounds may represent a biological adaptation."

The first extensive survey of the noise in a large city was begun in 1925 by Free.[298] One of the results is that noises are "astonishingly local. A certain street corner is found, for example, to be extremely noisy. The noise there is practically continuous. Nevertheless, a spot even a half block away may be unusually quiet; far quieter than the average of the city. Scores of these noise contrasts between points which are geographically close together have been located. . . . One instance of this sort is important practically. It is the difference between the front rooms and the back rooms of a city house. If you live on a noisy street the rooms which face this street will be noisy. . . . The back rooms of the same house, facing on a court or other inner space, will be almost inaccessible to the street noise."

Other surveys have been made in several large cities, and in 1929-30 a second survey of noise in the City of New York

[296] Shirley W. Wynne, Journ. Acoust. Soc., 2, 14 (1930).
[297] Donald Anderson Laird and Kenneth Coye, Journ. Acoust. Soc., 1, 158 (1929).
[298] Edward Elway Free, Forum, 75, xxi (Feb. 1926); 79, 382 (1928).

was carried out under the auspices of a Noise Abatement Commission appointed by the city Commissioner of Health.[299] The Noise Abatement Commission prepared a questionnaire which was printed in all the metropolitan newspapers, and as a result more than 11,000 complaints of various noises were received. About two thirds of the complaints were of noises connected with transportation—trucks, horns, brakes, elevated and subway trains, street cars, and so on.

In order to find out something about the loudness of these noises a truck was equipped with noise measuring equipment, and more than 10,000 observations were made at 138 different locations. The noise measuring devices were of two types. In one the noise was picked up by a telephone transmitter, and the varying electric current thus set up was amplified and carried to an instrument with a dial on which the intensity of the sound could be read. In the other type of instrument special phonograph records were used. The vibration of the needle in the groove of the record gave rise to a varying electric current, and this current was amplified and led to a telephone receiver at the observer's ear. The observer heard both the noise to be measured and the sound from the record at the same time, and the intensity of the sound from the record was varied until it was just masked by the noise. Results for one locality are shown in Fig. 130, and a few others have already been included in Table Three on p. 245.

Question 312. From the most noise in the test shown in Fig. 130 to the least noise the intensity dropped by approximately what fraction?

Question 313. In the same test by approximately what fraction did the intensity vary in the course of twenty minutes?

[299] A report of this survey has been published under the title *City Noise.* See footnote 295.

Question 314. In the studies made by the New York Noise Abatement Commission the phonograph records gave a warbling tone instead of a steady one. The tone ran up and down over a range of an octave or more, and made this rise and fall of pitch about six times in a second. The intensity of the warbling tone could be changed until it was just masked by the noise. What advantage do you see in using a warbling tone instead of one that does not change in pitch?

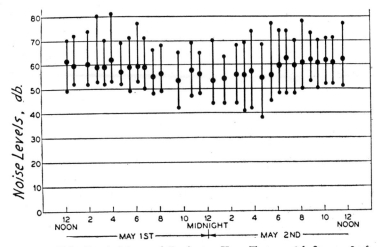

FIG. 130.—Noise Levels Measured During 24-Hour Test on 48th Street, 185 ft. West of Eighth Avenue, New York City [Rogers H. Galt, Journ. Acoust. Soc. 2, 49 (1930)]. The points plotted show maximum, average, and minimum noise levels during each 20-minute test period.

In addition to measurements at various locations outdoors and indoors, a few observations were made in the New York Zoological Gardens. "The level of the lion's roar, often used by writers to express the ultimate in terrific sounds, was found to be 87 decibels. Sounds emitted by a Siberian tiger measured only 79.5 decibels, and by a Bengal tiger, 75.5 decibels. . . . Although a roaring lion would be audible in our streets at a distance of twenty or thirty feet, there are many places where a tiger from Siberia or Benga. could roar or snarl indefinitely without attracting the auditory attention of passersby." [300]

Of the noises regarding which the Noise Abatement Commission received complaints it was recognized that some could not be greatly reduced without the carrying out of certain technical studies, but it was stated that about half of the noises could easily be prevented. The prevention would not be primarily a matter of new laws, but rather of a small number of laws and the arousing of public opinion.

142. Sound Ranging.[301]—During the World War the positions of many guns that could not be seen were determined by the method of "sound ranging." In this method the sound from a gun was picked up at a number of stations, and from the differing times of arrival it was possible to calculate the position of the gun.

If there were no wind, and the temperature were everywhere the same, the sound from the gun would spread out steadily in all directions, and would reach equal distances in equal times. Thus in Fig. 131 if the gun is at G, and if A_1, A_2, and A_3 are all at the same distance from G, the sound arrives at these three points at the same time. Conversely, if the sound arrives at the three points at the same time, it is known that the gun must be at the center of the circle on which the points lie. Since there is only one circle that passes through three given points, the location found for the gun is perfectly definite.

In most cases the gun does not happen to be at the center of the circle through the three points, and the sound does not reach all the points at the same time. If the gun is

---

[300] The values given in this quotation and in Fig. 130 are not on the same basis as those in the table on p. 245. Since the time when the Noise Abatement Commission did its work a new zero for intensity level has been adopted. 7 db are to be added to the values in Fig. 130 and to those given in the above quotation.

[301] For a more complete treatment of the subject of sound ranging see Augustus Trowbridge, Journ. Franklin Inst., **189**, 133 (1920).

at G' we see that the sound reaches A_1 before it reaches A_2, and A_2 before it reaches A_3. Let $A_1B_2B_3$ and A_2C be arcs of circles which have G' at their center. Then the difference between the times of arrival at A_1 and A_2 is the time in which sound travels the distance B_2A_2, and the difference be-tween the times of arrival at A_1 and A_3 is the time in which sound travels the distance B_3A_3. If we observe the differences in the times of arrival, and know how fast sound travels, it is easy to calculate the distances B_2A_2 and B_3A_3. Knowing these dis-tances we can draw around A_2 a circle with radius A_2B_2, and around A_3 a circle with radius

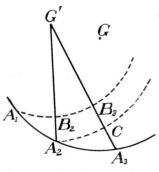

FIG. 131.—Spreading of Sound from a Gun.

A_3B_3. We then locate G' as the center of the circle that passes through A_1 and is tangent to the two circles just drawn.

Question 315. Can you devise a graphical method of drawing a circle which passes through a given point and is tangent to two given circles?

Question 316. If you are not able to devise a construction to answer Question 315 in general, can you devise one which is approxi-mately correct when the distances between the points A_1, A_2, and A_3 in Fig. 131 are small compared with the distance to G'?

Question 317. In actual practice there were usually six stations instead of three. What advantages are there in the larger number?

Question 318. What causes are likely to lead to inaccuracies in the above method of determining the position of a distant gun?

One of the sources of inaccuracy in sound ranging lies in the difficulty of determining the times of arrival of the sound at the different listening stations. A considerable part of this difficulty is overcome by having the times of arrival recorded automatically. At each station there is an instrument that picks up the sound and converts the energy into that of an electric current. The several stations are electrically connected to some one station at which a photographic film is carried on a rotating drum. A number of fine points of light, one for each station, are focussed on the film, and when a current comes from any station the corresponding trace on the film is displaced. If an observer knows how fast the film was moving, and if he reads on the film the positions at which the displacements of the traces occur, it is a simple matter for him to calculate the difference in the times of arrival of the sound.

Question 319. The diagram is supposed to represent a sound ranging record. If the heavy vertical lines are one second apart how much later did the sound arrive at A_2 and A_3 than at A_1?

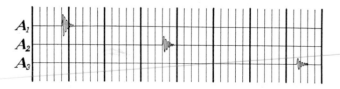

Question 320. If A_1, A_2, and A_3 were on a straight line, and $A_1A_2 = 1$ mile and $A_2A_3 = 1$ mile, what was approximately the position of the gun? What objection is there to having the listening stations in a straight line?

143. Prospecting for Oil.[302]—Some one has said that the best way to find out what is under the ground is to bore

[302] For an excellent treatment of the refraction method see Alexander Oliver Rankine, Professor of Physics in the Imperial College of Science and Technology, South Kensington, Nature, 123, 684 and 718 (1929).

For a description of the reflection method, with reproductions of several seismograms, see Eugene McDermott, of the Geophysical Service, Inc., Physics, 3, 39 (1932).

For a comparison of the two methods see C. A. Heiland, of the Colorado School of Mines, Gerlands Beiträge zur Geophysik, Ergänzungshefte für angewandte Geophysik, 3, 282 (1933).

See also L. L. Nettleton, of the Gulf Research and Development Corporation, Am. Physics Teacher, 3, 110 (1935).

a hole in it. But the cost of boring a hole to any considerable depth is not small. The drilling of a hole to find out
whether oil is present often requires the expenditure of tens
of thousands of dollars, and the cost has been known to run
up into the neighborhood of $200,000. Much less expen-
sive methods of investigation have an obvious advantage,
and within the past few decades a number of physical methods have been developed for studying the structure of the
upper layers of the earth's crust and for searching for min-
erals and for oil.

Some of these methods make use of electric currents or
of magnetic attraction, some make use of gravitational attraction, and some employ compressional waves set up by
explosions. These compressional waves are essentially
waves of sound, and the methods that make use of them are
the only ones that we shall take the space to consider. The
methods which employ these waves are known as *seismic*
methods, and the instruments used to pick up the waves are
seismographs, similar to those used for recording earthquakes.

A seismograph consists of a massive weight so suspended
that when some motion of the support occurs the weight does
not immediately follow. The support moves when the earth
moves, and the record made by the seismograph is a record
of the failure of the weight to follow the motion of the
support. A piece of paper moves steadily through the seismograph, and on the paper the instrument draws a trace.
A relative movement between the massive weight and its
support shows as a disturbance in this trace. These instruments have been developed to a point where they are very
sensitive.

Oil is found in strata like sands and sandstones that are
more or less porous. There is often water beneath the oil,
and the water has pushed the oil upward until it has been
stopped by a layer of rock that is not so porous. The meth-

ods in which we are at present interested make no attempt to locate the oil itself; they seek certain geological structures with which oil is commonly associated. Although there are several such structures the only one that we shall consider is known as a "salt dome." Such a dome, "of which there are numerous examples in Texas, is a sort of underground plateau of rock salt, sometimes with a relatively thin covering of anhydrite, called cap-rock, the whole being below an overburden of sands and clays. The superficial area of the roughly circular top of the dome may be several square miles, and its depth may vary from a few hundred to several thousand feet. Oil may be located sometimes at the top of the dome, and sometimes at various levels down its flanks. The earth's surface above and around the dome is usually very flat, and there is little in the way of reliable geological indications to determine their positions." [303]

In the rocks above the salt the speed of compressional waves may be in the neighborhood of two kilometers per second, but in the salt itself the waves may travel more than five kilometers per second. It is this difference in speed that makes possible the seismic methods of prospecting. These methods consist in determining the time taken by the waves in traveling down to the structure in question and returning to the surface. If that time can be determined, and if the speed at which the waves travel is known, it is possible to calculate the distance down to the salt dome. If no waves come back there is no salt dome in the neighborhood.

The simplest case would be one in which the top of the salt dome is level and extends for several miles, and the rocks above it are uniform and have a level surface. Fig. 132 represents such a case. If a charge of dynamite is exploded at E compressional waves travel outward in all directions. In the rocks there are both compressional waves and flexural waves, but the compressional waves travel the faster

[303] A. O. Rankine, p. 685 in the reference in footnote 302.

and are the only ones that concern us at present. In the layer of rock between AB and CD these waves travel faster than in the air above AB, and in the salt below CD they travel faster still.

When the waves reach the salt they are partly reflected and partly refracted. The reflected waves come up to the surface and may be picked up by seismographs. We shall see that a part of the energy carried by the refracted waves may also return to the surface and be picked up. Conse-

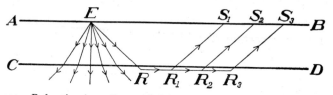

FIG. 132.—Refraction by a Layer of Salt. AB is the surface of the ground, CD the upper surface of the salt, E the point where the explosion occurs.

quently two types of seismic methods are distinguished—"reflection methods" and "refraction methods." Reflection methods were tried as early as 1913, but the difficulties involved were not successfully overcome until about 1928. In the meantime refraction methods had been considerably developed and largely employed. After the reflection methods were successfully developed they largely superseded the refraction methods.

One difficulty encountered in the early experiments with reflection methods is connected with the fact that in these methods the seismographs are located not far from the point where the charge is exploded. The disturbance which comes directly through the ground reaches the instruments before that which comes after reflection from the salt, and if the seismographs are sensitive enough to pick up the reflected waves they are likely to be damaged by the direct waves.

To understand the refraction methods look again at Fig. 132, where the paths followed by various parts of the refracted waves are shown. When the waves reach the salt their speed of travel changes, and the paths that the waves follow are consequently bent as indicated on the lines that spread downward from E. Waves which leave E in a certain direction ER travel through the salt horizontally, and it would seem that they would never get back to the surface AB. As a matter of fact, however, diffraction is always occurring, so that part of the disturbance does travel back toward the surface. It travels in the directions indicated by the lines R_1S_1, R_2S_2, R_3S_3, and may be picked up by seismographs at S_1, S_2, S_3.

Up to a certain distance the disturbance which reaches the seismographs along the straight path ES arrives before the disturbance that travels on the longer path that goes down to the salt. But since the disturbance travels faster in the salt there is some distance beyond which the disturbance that takes the longer path down to the salt and up again is the first to arrive. With a sufficient number of seismographs at different distances it is possible to determine the distance at which both disturbances arrive at the same time. And if the speed of compressional waves in the salt and their speed in the overlying rock are known, it is then possible to calculate the depth at which the top of the salt lies.

In the above discussion it has been assumed that the top of the salt dome is level. Obviously this assumption is not always correct, and the actual methods employed must allow for that fact. Moreover we have dealt with an explosion at a single point. If charges are exploded at a number of points it becomes possible to make calculations from which the salt dome may be mapped. Knowing the location of the dome, and knowing the parts of the dome where oil is most likely to be found, it becomes possible to drill with much more probability of striking oil than if the seismic study had not been made.

Question 321. In refraction methods of prospecting for oil the seismographs may be at a distance of some miles from the point where the explosion occurs, whereas in reflection methods some of them may be as close as a hundred feet. Does this fact suggest to you any advantage which the reflection methods possess?

Question 322. When refraction methods are employed it is customary to make a plot showing how the time of arrival of the first disturbance depends on the distance from the point of explosion. This curve consists of two parts—one on which the direct disturbance is the first to arrive, and one on which the disturbance that has reached the salt is the first to arrive. For the simple case shown in Fig. 132 what would be the shape of the curve? From this curve how should you determine the distance at which the two disturbances arrive at the same time?

Question 323. Suppose that the top of the salt in Fig. 132 is horizontal from C to D and then slopes downward to the right. How will this affect the shape of the curve mentioned in Question 322?

144. Fog Signals.[304]—It is hardly necessary to point out the need for adequate fog signals. During ten years in the neighborhood of 1870 273 vessels were wrecked in fog or thick weather along the coast of Great Britain. Between 1820 and 1903 there were 558 wrecks off Newfoundland— many of them probably caused by fog. From the Gulf Stream to the Polar Current the temperature of the water may drop twenty Fahrenheit degrees in a distance of only a few boat lengths, and it is not surprising that fog should often be formed in the neighborhood of these two currents.

Fog signals of some kind have been in use for many years. Bells, whistles, guns, sirens, and other types of in-

[304] For interesting material on fog signals see the following articles.

Joseph Henry, several papers, all but one printed in the reports of the U.S. Lighthouse Board for 1873, 1874, 1875, and 1877. Collected in the Annual Report of the Smithsonian Institution for 1878, pp. 455-559, and in the *Scientific Writings of Joseph Henry,* vol. 1 (1886), pp. 364-510.

John Tyndall, Phil. Trans., **164,** 183 (1874); or *Sound,* Appleton, ed. 3 (1876), chap. 7.

Louis Vessot King, Journ. Franklin Inst., **183,** 259 (1917); or more fully in Phil. Trans., **A218,** 211 (1919).

strument have been tried. Some of these have been provided with horns of considerable size to prevent the sound from spreading landward and upward, and to direct it out horizontally to sea where it is needed.

It was soon learned that the distance to which a fog signal could be heard is very capricious. A report in 1871 says, "There are six steam fog-whistles on the coast of Maine; these have been frequently heard at a distance of twenty miles, and as frequently cannot be heard at the distance of two miles, and this with no perceptible difference in the state of the atmosphere." Another curious effect that has often been observed, and that may have serious consequences, is a belt in which the signal cannot be heard, although it is audible at greater distances. This belt may begin no more than a quarter of a mile from the fog-horn, and may extend for a mile or a mile and a half before the signal is heard again.

A careful study of the irregular change in loudness with distance was carried out in 1913 by King [304] in the neighborhood of Father Point, Quebec. Father Point is about 175 miles northeast of the city of Quebec, and is on the south side of the St. Lawrence River at a point where the river is more than twenty-five miles wide.

The fog-horn at Father Point is a Northey "diaphone." [305] This instrument operates on the same principle as a siren. A hollow piston ABC (Fig. 133) is moved back and forth by the rod DA. The piston fits inside of a cylinder, and the space EF around the cylinder is inclosed and contains air at a pressure of about 25 pounds per square inch. Running around the piston-wall and around the surrounding cylinder are circular slots, and each time that the slots in the piston register with those in the cylinder a strong

---

[305] The name "diaphone" was given by Robert Hope-Jones to an organ stop which he invented in 1894. Northey's diaphone is a modification of that of Hope-Jones.

puff of air escapes. The piston is run at such a rate that there are about 180 puffs in a second, and to the right of the cylinder is a conical horn, which is of such size that the air in the combined piston and horn has a natural frequency of about 180 cycles/sec.

Question 324. If the air in a complete cone, open at the large end, has a fundamental frequency of 180 cycles/sec., how long is the cone? (See Art. 63.)

To measure the sound from the diaphone King employed a Webster "phonometer." [306] In the form used by King this

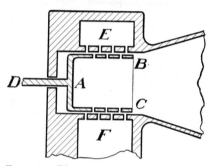

FIG. 133.—Diagram of Northey Diaphone.

instrument is a cylindrical air resonator in which a part of the rear wall consists of a flexible diaphragm. By adjusting the length of the cylinder the instrument can be tuned to pick up a sound to which it is exposed. The changing pressure of the air in the resonator causes the diaphragm to vibrate, the vibration of the diaphragm deflects a beam of light, and the double amplitude of the beam is read by an eyepiece. The more intense the sound the greater is the amplitude of the spot of light.

[306] Devised by Arthur Gordon Webster (1863-1923), a brilliant and distinguished scholar, for more than thirty years Professor of Physics at Clark University. Webster took an active part in the formation of the American Physical Society, was prominent in the discussion of papers read before it, and was its third president.

One set of King's results is shown in Fig. 134. It will be seen that the intensity of the sound varied considerably, and that the localities of greatest intensity on the outward trip were often different from those on the return trip.

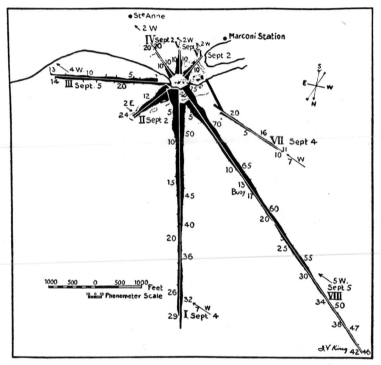

FIG. 134.—Intensity of Sound from Fog Signal at Father Point [King]. The phonometer readings are indicated by the thickness of the black trace. Observations plotted on one side of the line were taken on the journey away from Father Point, and those plotted on the other side were taken on the return trip. The numbers refer to observations of the position of the boat.

These differences were believed to depend in large measure on the wind.

The silent belts had also been explained by the action of wind. We have seen (Art. 42) that a sound is likely to be heard for a shorter distance against a wind than with it.

If the wind near the ground were blowing in one direction, and the wind higher up were blowing in the opposite direction, it would be possible to explain the existence of a silent belt followed by a region in which the sound could again be heard.

Question 325. If the explanation just suggested is correct what must be the directions of the winds?

145. Aerial Echoes.—A remarkable effect, not so serious as belts of silence, is an "aerial echo" that has often been observed to come back to points near a fog horn. This echo may arrive some seconds after the signal is given, it may come under all conditions of weather, and it may last for a time considerably longer than the original signal—gradually dying away instead of ending abruptly. This echo is not easy to explain. Henry was at first inclined to think that it might be produced by reflection from the fronts of the ocean waves that were rolling in. Later he found that the echo could be heard when the water was calm—which of course was evidence that the echo was not due to reflection from waves.

An entirely different explanation occurred to Tyndall, and occurred to him at a time when he was trying to account for the short distance to which fog signals could sometimes be heard. He recalled that when Humboldt was near the Falls of the Orinoco "he found the noise of the falls far louder by night than by day, though in that region the night is far noisier than the day. The plain between him and the falls consisted of spaces of grass and rock intermingled. In the heat of the day he found the temperature of the rock to be considerably higher than that of the grass. Over every heated rock, he concluded, rose a column of air rarefied by the heat; its place being supplied by the descent of heavier air. He ascribed the deadening of the sound to the reflections which it endured at the limiting surfaces of the rarer and denser air. . . . But with what on July 3, not with the variously-heated plain of Antures, but with a calm sea as a basis for the atmosphere, could so destroy its homogeneity as to enable it to quench in so short a distance so vast a body of sound? . . . As I stood upon the deck of the Irene pondering the question, I became conscious of the exceeding power of the sun beating against my back and heating the objects near me. Beams of equal power were falling on the sea, and must have produced copious evaporation. That the vapor generated should so rise and mingle with the air as to form an absolutely homogeneous medium, was in the highest degree improbable. It would be sure, I thought, to rise in invisible streams, breaking through the superincumbent air now at one point, now at another, thus rendering the air *flocculent* with wreaths and striae, charged in different degrees with the buoyant vapor. At the limiting surfaces of these spaces, though invisible, we should have the conditions necessary to the production of partial echoes and the consequent waste of sound." It was to these "invisible acoustic clouds" that Tyndall attributed the aerial echoes.

Henry attempted to test Tyndall's hypothesis by having the axis of a fog-horn on Block Island turned from a horizontal to a vertical direction. When the horn was horizontal the echo came from the point toward which the horn pointed. "The trumpet in its vertical position was sounded at intervals for two days, but in no instance was an echo heard from the zenith, but one was in every case produced from the entire horizon. The echo appeared to be somewhat louder from the land portion of the circle of the horizon than from that of the water. On slowly restoring the trumpet to its former direction, the echo gradually increased on the side of the water until the horizontal position was reached, when the echo as usual appeared to proceed from an azimuth of about twenty degrees of the horizon, the mid-

acoustic receiver, may be imitated by attaching to a small hollow rubber ball a tube which leads through stethoscope binaurals to the ears of the observer. When the ball is held under water a very gentle tapping on the vessel that contains the water, or even at some distance on the table on which the vessel rests, is distinctly audible.

Question 332. Should you expect the type of hydrophone just described to be more sensitive when the diameter of the ball is one inch or two inches?

The direction from which an underwater sound approaches can be determined with considerable accuracy by certain devices which practically amplify the directional effect that we get by having two ears instead of one. Suppose that two acoustic hydrophones, L and R, are mounted as shown in Fig. 135, and that a pulse of sound is approaching from the direction of S_1. The sound reaches L and R at the same time, and it is heard as coming from S_1—in a direction perpendicular to LR.

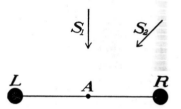

FIG. 135.—Direction Finding with Acoustic Hydrophones. L and R are hydrophones—L connected to the left ear of the observer, and R to his right ear. The connecting tubes from the hydrophones to the ears are of the same length. LR is an arm which can rotate about an axis perpendicular to the page at A. The arrows S_1 and S_2 show the directions of approach of two sounds.

If the sound comes from the direction of S_2 it reaches R before L, and it is heard as coming from a point to the right of S_1. If LR is now turned about A until the sound reaches L and R at the same time, it is again heard as coming in a direction perpendicular to LR—that is, from the direction of S_2.

The instrument just described is an awkward one to use in determining the direction from which underwater sounds

approach. But instead of turning the instrument it is possible to get the same effect by changing the time taken by
the sounds from L and R to reach the observer's ears.
In Fig. 135 if the sound from R comes to the ear through
a longer tube than that from L the effect is the same as if
the arm were swung so as to be more nearly perpendicular
to the path of the sound from S_2. Since it is much easier to
change the lengths of the sound paths than to turn the apparatus or the boat, means for changing the length of the
sound paths provide a considerable increase in ease of
manipulation.

A further improvement is effected by using a larger number of properly spaced hydrophones. In this way there is
an increased accuracy in determining the direction from
which the sound comes, and there is also an increased selec-
tivity—that is, the instrument becomes less sensitive to
sounds from other directions.[310]

Hydrophones of several types were devised during the
World War to aid in detecting submarines. The sounds
made by the submarines were picked up, and the direction
from which the sound came was determined. After the war
it was thought that similar equipment might be of value
to a ship during fog or thick weather. She could pick up
various underwater sounds and so determine her position.

In order to test such a possibility the U. S. S. Von
Steuben was equipped with an electric hydrophone, and observations were taken during a trip from Hoboken to Brest.
"The *Von Steuben* proceeded at one third speed while leaving New York harbor. During this period neighboring tugboats and ferries were readily located by determining the
direction of their propeller sounds. Arrangements had been
made to have the lightships along the approach to New
York harbor sound their submarine bells and the signals

---

[310] For a fuller treatment of receivers for underwater sounds see Harvey
Cornelius Hayes, Am. Philos. Soc. Proc., **59**, 1 (1920).

from all these lightships . . . were picked up in turn by the hydrophone and the vessels located before they could be seen. Several times signals from two or three of the lightships could be heard and located at the same time." [311]

The next day the observers were surprised and disappointed to find that the sounds from the propeller of the Von Steuben herself were not heard when the depth of the water was much more than 500 fathoms. It was known that when sound waves traveling in air meet the surface of water they are reflected in much the same manner as when they fall upon a rigid wall, but that when sound waves traveling in water are reflected from the upper surface of the water the reflection is more like that at an open end of a tube (Art. 36). Sound waves in air are reflected from water without change of phase, but when sound waves in water are reflected from air there is a change of phase. A compression in water is reflected from air as a rarefaction, and a rarefaction in water is reflected from air as a compression. The propeller sounds from the Von Steuben spread through the water in all directions. Some of the sound reached the surface of the water near the sides of the boat amidships and was reflected with change of phase. Some of this reflected sound reached the hydrophone near the bow of the boat along with the sound that had come through the water without reflection. The length of the path followed by the reflected sound was so nearly the same as that of the sound which came without reflection that the two interfered with each other. The observers concluded that the sounds they had picked up in the shallower water had not come directly from the tugboats or ferries or submarine bells, but had arrived after reflection from the sea-bottom.

This idea led to a means of determining the ocean depth. The sound employed may be that produced by the propellers of a ship or by a submarine bell or other signal which she

[311] Harvey C. Hayes, Am. Philos. Soc. Proc., **59,** 373 (1920).

carries. If the sound from the propellers is used the source
of sound is necessarily at the stern. If a hydrophone is
mounted near the bow, and if the bottom is horizontal, it is
a simple matter to determine the depth from the angle at
which the reflected sound reaches the hydrophone.

Question 333. In order to calculate the depth under the conditions just mentioned what must the observer know in addition to
the direction from which the sound comes?

Question 334. When the sea bottom is not horizontal the above
method fails. But the depth can be found by using two submarine
bells and two hydrophones.[312] Where would it be well to locate the
bells and the hydrophones, and how might the depth be found?

Question 335. If the intensity of the sound and the sensitiveness of the hydrophones are sufficiently increased it becomes possible
to pick up the returning sound from considerably greater depths.
Nevertheless the above method does not give accurate soundings except at moderate depths. Why?

148. Acoustic Sounding. By Time until Echo Arrives.
—For depths greater than about a hundred fathoms the determination of depth from the direction at which the echo
returns ceases to be very accurate. In another method the
depth is determined from the time taken by a sound in traveling to the bottom and back again.

Question 336. A sounding is to be taken by the method suggested in the last sentence, and it is desired that the value found be
within five meters of the true value. The speed of sound in sea
water is about 1450 meters/sec. How accurately must the time be
measured?

The answer to Question 336 shows that the accuracy of
the method just mentioned depends largely on the accuracy
with which the time can be measured. Several means have
been devised for attaining considerable accuracy in this measurement, and in addition to this accuracy enabling the ob-

[312] Harvey C. Hayes, Journ. Franklin Inst., **197**, 323 (1924).

server to make his readings rapidly and easily. One type of instrument sends out a series of regularly recurring sounds that are similar to the strokes of a bell. The operator wears a special telephone headset so connected that in one ear he hears the sounds that are sent out, and in the other ear the sounds that return from the bottom. He adjusts the rate at which the outgoing signals are sent until each echo arrives at the same instant at which the next signal starts. The interval from one signal to the next is then equal to the time required for the sound to go to the bottom and back.

Question 337. How can an observer know whether an echo reaches him at the time of the next signal or of some later signal?

Question 338. Sometimes the sound from the signal echoes back and forth several times between the bottom of the ocean and the surface. Do you see any way in which these successive echoes might be helpful in determining the depth?

In another instrument there is a dial, somewhat like the face of a clock. A pointer moves steadily and rapidly around the dial, and at a certain position in each rotation it makes an electric contact. This contact sends a signal by causing an electrically operated hammer to strike a submerged diaphragm. The echo from the bottom is picked up by a microphone, and the amplified current flashes a slender neon lamp that forms part of the rotating pointer. The greater the depth the farther the pointer has turned before the lamp flashes. The pointer turns behind a translucent scale that is marked off in fathoms, and all that the observer has to do is to read the position of the flashing light.[313]

149. Height of an Airplane.—In several ways the problem of using echoes to find the height of an airplane is more

[313] For further descriptions of some of the acoustic sounding methods see:
An anonymous publication by permission of the British Admiralty, Nature, 113, 463 (1924);
A. B. Wood, *A Text Book of Sound* (1930), p. 467;
Horatio W. Lamson, Journ. Acoust. Soc., 1, 403 (1930).

complicated than that of employing echoes to find the depth of the ocean. The distance from the propeller of the airplane to its tail would not be sufficient to permit of determining the height of the plane by means of the angle at which an echo from the ground arrives, so that any direction-of-reflected-sound method for determining the height is not applicable. If we consider producing an acoustic signal and observing the time the signal takes to go to the ground and return we are at once confronted with the problem of making the signal audible through the roar from the propeller. These difficulties might lead us to believe that the problem of determining the height of an airplane by any acoustic method is hopeless. Fortunately there are acoustic methods that give promise of some success.[314]

150. The Reproduction of Speech and Music.—Each new invention rests in part on earlier work. Although the reproduction of speech and music doubtless began with Edison's invention of the phonograph in 1876, the idea of causing a body to write its vibration curve, and the idea of having it do this on a cylindrical drum, were not new. Many years earlier the vibration curve for a tuning fork had been obtained by attaching to one prong a light wire or bristle, and drawing the vibrating fork quickly along a surface coated with lampblack. Later other vibrating bodies had been caused to draw vibration curves on a rotating drum. The drum was mounted on a screw, so that as it turned it also advanced slowly parallel to its axis, thus making it possible to obtain traces much longer than those that were drawn on a flat plate.

As early as 1853 Léon Scott[315] was at work on his

---

[314] L. P. Delsasso, Journ. Acoust. Soc., 6, 1 (1934).

[315] Édouard-Léon Scott, Cosmos, 14, 314 (1859); Comptes Rendus, 53, 108 (1861). In the article in Cosmos Scott points out the almost insuperable difficulties to be anticipated in any attempt to record the extremely minute and rapid movements of the air when speech is passing through it. He continues: "Attendez. Ce problème insoluble est résolu quelque part. Il existe un in-

"artificial ear" or "phonautograph." In this instrument the sound was focused on a light membrane, the membrane actuated a flexible stylus, and the stylus in turn drew the vibration curve on a piece of blackened paper wrapped on a drum. Edison's instrument appears to have been the first by which a vibration curve could be used for audible reproduction. He called his instrument a "phonograph or speaking machine." In its earliest form there was a brass drum with axis horizontal, mounted on a screw like that used by Scott and earlier inventors. Winding around the drum was a groove or screw-shaped depression, and over the drum was wrapped a sheet of tin foil. Close to the drum was mounted a short cylindrical box that was open at the top but at the bottom was closed by a light membrane carrying a sharp steel needle. The needle was immediately over the groove in the drum, and it pressed the tin foil down into the groove. The needle was prevented from moving sideways by a horizontal strip of light steel to which it was attached, but any vibration of the membrane moved it up and down. Thus a vibration of the membrane made the needle press the tin foil inward to a varying extent, so that when the drum was turned and a sound reached the membrane the up and down movement of the needle left in the tin foil a vibration curve. To reproduce the sound another similarly mounted needle was caused to move over this vibration curve. The curve in the tin foil now caused the needle to move up and down, thus causing the membrane to vibrate and reproduce the sound.

Edison made improvements in his phonograph, and other types of talking machines were invented. In some of these the vibration curve is a "hill and dale" curve like that

venteur, un artiste sublime pour lequel rien n'est impossible: c'est Dieu. Consultons-le. Considérons attentivement cette merveille entre toutes les merveilles, l'oreille humaine. Je dis que notre problème est résolu dans le phénomène de l'audition, et que les artifices employés dans la structure de l'oreille doivent nous conduire au but."

in Edison's phonograph, and in some the curve swings from side to side as it did in Scott's phonautograph.

One of the important improvements in these machines was made about 1925 when mechanical recording was replaced by electric recording. Until that time the sound had been picked up and made to cut the record by some mechanical device consisting of diaphragm and levers. The energy available for cutting the record was only that in the original sound, and the delicate balance among the various components of the sound was almost certain to be disturbed, so that the vibration curve produced was not an accurate representation of the original sound. With the development of radio tubes and associated instruments it became possible to pick up the sound by means of a microphone, which turns the sound energy into the energy of an electric current, and then to amplify this current and use it to operate the cutting instrument. The development of the necessary electric circuits made it possible in this way to make use of more energy than that in the original sound, and to cut records in which the vibration curve may represent the sound with very great fidelity.

The reproduction of the sound is also now frequently done electrically. When this is the case the needle that plays over the groove in the record no longer acts directly upon a diaphragm that gives out the sound. Instead of this mechanical action the motion of the needle excites an electric current, and this current is amplified to the desired extent and sent to a loud speaker, similar to that used for receiving radio broadcasts.

Question 339. How are musical intervals affected by running a phonograph or victrola a little faster than usual?

The sound that accompanies motion pictures has been in part made possible by these same developments of radio tubes and associated instruments and circuits. Talking pictures began their commercial development about 1928, and one way of producing the sound was to make use of a victrola record. The vibration curve on the record was picked up electrically, and the current was amplified and sent to the loudspeaker. It was necessary of course for the record to run at such a speed as to keep step with the pictures, and

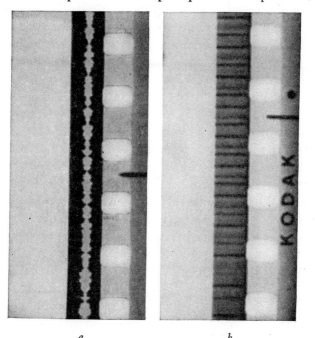

a   *b*

FIG. 136.—Two Types of Sound Record on Motion Picture Film [Kindly supplied by Warner Brothers Pictures, Inc.]. Both records are considerably enlarged. *a,* variable area; *b,* variable density.

if the film ever broke and was mended with a few frames missing—as often happens—a corresponding part of the sound record could not be cut out.

The record from which the sound is produced is now usually made near one edge of the film itself. Two different types of record are used, and illustrations of both are shown in Fig. 136. In one of these the edge of the blackened part of the sound track is the vibration curve.   In the other the varying density of the blackening on the film represents the vibration curve.   In either case there shines upon the sound track a bright light that is focused into an extremely narrow line.   This line of light is about a thousandth of an inch from top to bottom, but is wide enough to cover the whole width of the sound track.   As the film passes through this narrow beam it varies the amount of light that falls on a photoelectric cell—sometimes called an "electric eye"—and so gives rise to a varying electric current which is amplified and sent to the loudspeakers.

151. Architectural Acoustics.   The Problem.—At the beginning of the twentieth century the following words were written by Wallace Sabine.   "No one can appreciate the condition of architectural acoustics—the science of sound as applied to buildings—who has not with a pressing case in hand sought through the scattered literature for some safe guidance.   Responsibility in a large and irretrievable expenditure of money compels a careful consideration, and emphasizes the meagerness and inconsistency of the current suggestions.   Thus the most definite and often repeated statements are such as the following, that the dimensions of a room should be in the ratio 2 : 3 : 5, or according to some writers, 1 : 1 : 2, and others, 2 : 3 : 4; it is probable that the basis of these suggestions is the ratios of the harmonic intervals in music, but the connection is untraced and remote. Moreover, such advice is rather difficult to apply; should one measure the length to the back or to the front of the galleries, to the back or the front of the stage recess?   Few rooms have a flat roof, where should the height be measured?" [316]

[316] Wallace Clement Sabine (1868-1919), Am. Architect, 68, 3 (1900). Reprinted in Sabine's *Collected Papers on Acoustics,* Harvard University Press, p. 3.   For a very interesting account of Sabine's life see the biography *Wallace Clement Sabine* (1933), by William Dana Orcutt.

During the years since 1900 there has been a very great increase in our understanding of the acoustics of buildings, and Sabine himself, as we shall see, contributed in a fundamental way to this knowledge. In the paper from which the above quotation is taken Sabine stated clearly the acoustic ends at which an architect should aim: "In order that hearing may be good in any auditorium, it is necessary that the sound should be sufficiently loud; that the simultaneous components of a complex sound should maintain their proper relative intensities; and that the successive sounds in rapidly moving articulation either of speech or music, should be clear and distinct, free from each other and from extraneous noises. These three are the necessary, as they are the entirely sufficient, conditions for good hearing."

152. A Calculation by Franklin.—Before taking up Sabine's work we turn briefly to an entertaining calculation made by Benjamin Franklin, and to a study carried out by Joseph Henry. In Benjamin Franklin's Autobiography he tells [317] of hearing a Mr. Whitefield preach outdoors in Philadelphia. "He had a loud and clear voice, and articulated his words so perfectly, that he might be heard and understood at a great distance. . . . He preached one evening from the top of the Court House steps, which are in the middle of Market Street, and on the west side of Second Street, which crosses it at right angles. Both streets were filled with his hearers to a considerable distance. Being among the hindmost in Market Street, I had the curiosity to learn how far he could be heard, by retiring backwards down the street towards the river; and I found his voice distinct till I came near Front Street, when some noise in that street obscured it. Imagining then a semicircle, of which my distance should be the radius, and that it was filled with auditors, to each of whom I allowed two square feet, I com-

[317] Benjamin Franklin, *Autobiography*, chap. 8, paragraph 7. The sermon in question was probably preached about the year 1740.

puted that he might well be heard by more than thirty thousand. This reconciled me to the newspaper accounts of his having preached to twenty-five thousand people in the fields, and to the history of generals haranguing whole armies, of which I had sometimes doubted."

153. **A Study by Henry.**—Joseph Henry was for more than thirty years Secretary of the Smithsonian Institution, and before the building of the auditorium in what is now the old building—still called the Smithsonian Institution—he carried out a number of investigations in the hope of making the hall good acoustically.[318] He wished first to know at how great a distance a speaker could be heard if he were outdoors. "Many experiments have been made on this point, and I may mention those repeated in the open space in front of the Smithsonian Institution. In a circle, 100 feet in diameter, the speaker in the centre, and the hearer in succession at different points of the circumference, the voice was heard most distinctly directly in front, gradually less so on either side, until, in the rear, it was scarcely audible. The ratio of distance for distinct hearing directly in front, on the sides, and in the rear, was about as 100, 75, and 30. These numbers may serve to determine the form in which an audience should be arranged in an open field, in order that those on the periphery of the space may all have a like favorable opportunity of hearing, though it should not be recommended as the interior form of an apartment, in which a reflecting wall would be behind the speaker."

The walls and ceiling of an auditorium reflect sound and so increase the loudness of the sound and the distance at which a speaker can be heard. But a reflecting surface may

[318] Joseph Henry (1799-1878), Smithsonian Institution Report for 1856, p. 221; or *Scientific Writings of Joseph Henry*, vol. 2, p. 403.

Henry had an extraordinary capacity for work, and was a clever experimenter. He taught mathematics for four years in Albany Academy, for about fifteen years was Professor of Natural Philosophy at Princeton, and then became Secretary of the Smithsonian Institution in Washington. He is probably best known for some of his electrical discoveries.

be so far away that instead of increasing the loudness of the sound it gives rise to a disturbing echo. Henry wished to know at what distance a reflected sound began to be heard as an echo. A twelve foot square, similar to a billboard, was set up outdoors, and an experimenter stood at different distances and clapped his hands. When he stood more than some thirty feet from the reflector it was possible to hear an echo. Since the time required for a sound to travel the thirty feet to the reflector and the thirty feet back again is about a sixteenth of a second, Henry concluded that if there were no surface from which the reflected sound would reach an auditor more than a sixteenth of a second later than the direct sound there would be no trouble from echoes.

Even when there are no distinct echoes reflecting surfaces may throw the sound back and forth many times and prolong it to such an extent that one syllable is still being heard after several others have been spoken. This prolonging of the sound is known as *reverberation,* and Henry pointed out that the tendency to confusion which reverberation produces depends "first, on the size of the apartment; secondly, on the strength of the sound or the intensity of the impulse; thirdly, on the position of the reflecting surfaces; and fourthly, on the nature of the material of the reflecting surfaces." He also found that "in a room fifty feet square, in which the resonance of a single intense sound continued six seconds, when cases and other objects were placed around the wall, its continuance was reduced to two seconds."

Henry carried out a number of further experiments, the architect for the lecture room in the Smithsonian Institution varied his plans in accordance with the principles at which Henry arrived, and the acoustic properties of the room seem to have proved very satisfactory. It is no longer in use as an auditorium.

154. **Excessive Reverberation. Use of Wires.**—An excessive amount of reverberation is a defect that has been

found in many auditoriums. One notable example of a building with a long reverberation is the Baptistry at Pisa. This edifice is 100 ft. in diameter, 179 ft. high, and the walls are largely of marble, hard and smooth. A guide sings slowly the pitches *do, mi, sol,* or *do, mi, sol, do'*, and then the whole chord is heard ringing on for several seconds. A similar effect can be obtained in the discharge tunnel of the Harriman Dam near Whitingham, Vermont.[319]

In auditoriums where the reverberation is excessive it has sometimes been thought that wires stretched across the room would be set into vibration by the sound, and so would absorb a part of it and thus reduce the reverberation. "The stretching of wires is a method which has long been employed, and its disfiguring relics in many churches and court rooms proclaim a difficulty which they are powerless to relieve. Like many other traditions, it has been abandoned but slowly. . . . There are theatres and churches in Boston and New York in which four or five wires are stretched across the middle of the room; in other auditoriums miles on miles of wire have been stretched; in both it is equally without effect." [320]

Question 340. Why do not stretched wires produce the desired reduction in reverberation?

155. Sabine's Study of the Fogg Lecture Room.—The first important study of reverberation was carried out by Wallace Sabine. When the original building for the William

[319] The Harriman dam is 200 ft. high. It is built of earth, and water is not allowed to flow over it. When the water rises to too great a height the overflow passes down through a "glory hole" to a discharge tunnel which delivers it below the dam. The glory hole, shaped like the blossom of a morning glory, is 180 ft. deep, with a diameter which decreases from 160 ft. at the top to 22½ ft. at the bottom. The discharge tunnel is nearly horizontal. It is 830 ft. long and has an equivalent diameter of more than 20 ft. When there is no overflow it is possible for a visitor to enter the discharge tunnel.

[320] Wallace Clement Sabine, Arch. Quarterly of Harvard University, I, 4 (1912); or Sabine's *Collected Papers on Acoustics,* Harvard University Press, p. 132.

Hayes Fogg Art Museum [321] at Harvard was ready for use it was found that the reverberation in the lecture room was very bad. "A word spoken in an ordinary tone of voice was audible for five and a half seconds afterwards. During this time even a very deliberate speaker would have uttered the twelve or fifteen succeeding syllables. Thus the successive enunciations blended into a loud sound, through which and above which it was necessary to hear and distinguish the orderly progression of the speech. Across the room this could not be done; even near the speaker it could be done only with an effort wearisome in the extreme if long maintained." The Corporation of Harvard University asked Sabine to find out what could be done. Sabine was at this time twenty-seven years old. He had been at Harvard for a number of years, and about this time was promoted from Instructor to Assistant Professor. Throughout the rest of his life much of his work lay in the field of architectural acoustics. His high regard for accuracy, and the patient care with which he worked, are indicated by his statement that early in his study of reverberation "two months' work —over three thousand observations—had to be discarded because of failure to record the kind of clothing worn by the observer." [322]

The reverberation in the Fogg lecture room could no doubt be reduced by a sufficient amount of material that would largely absorb the sound instead of leaving it free to be reflected back and forth from wall to wall. But as to what kind of material would be best, and how much of it was needed, little was known. It seemed likely that the cushions in the near-by Sanders Theater might be good absorbers of sound, and they were brought into the lecture room, a few at a time. To test the resulting effect an organ

[321] Now Hunt Hall.
[322] Wallace Clement Sabine, Am. Architect, **68**, 76 (1900); or *Collected Papers on Acoustics*, Harvard University Press, p. 58. This paper contains a detailed treatment of the work here summarized in Arts. 155 and 156.

pipe was used. When the pipe was blown the intensity of the sound in the room increased until the sound was being absorbed as rapidly as it was being produced. When this steady state had been reached the wind was cut off, and the time was noted from that instant until the sound could no longer be heard. When the room was empty the sound continued for 5.62 sec. As the cushions were brought in it was found that the sound lasted for a shorter and shorter time. "Finally, when all the cushions from a theatre seating nearly fifteen hundred persons were placed in the room—covering the seats, the aisles, the platform, the rear wall to the ceiling —the duration of audibility of the residual sound was 1.14 seconds." The cushions were taken out and other absorbent materials were brought into the room, and in each case the duration of the residual sound was determined. The lecture room was finally rendered entirely serviceable by the use of a sufficient amount of heavy felt on certain walls.

By further studies in various rooms Sabine gradually reached the following conclusions:

"The duration of audibility of the residual sound is nearly the same in all parts of an auditorium. . . .

"The duration of audibility is nearly independent of the position of the source. . . .

"The efficiency of an absorbent in reducing the duration of the residual sound is, under ordinary circumstances, nearly independent of its position."

156. An Equation for Reverberation.—It was now desirable to formulate in as simple a way as possible the relationship between the amount of absorbing material in a room and the duration of the residual sound. For the Fogg lecture room Fig. 137 shows how one of these quantities depends on the other. The curve looks like part of a rectangular hyperbola. Now if axes are suitably drawn one end of a hyperbola approaches one of the axes, and the other end approaches the other axis. Fig. 138 shows part of a rectangular hyper-

bola. The solid part of the curve is the same as the experimental curve in Fig. 137, but in Fig. 138 the number 146

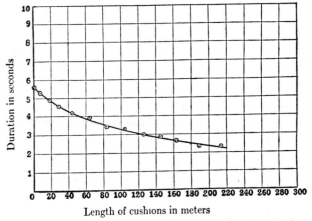

Length of cushions in meters

FIG. 137.—Relation Between Duration of Residual Sound and Amount of
Absorbing Material Added [Sabine].

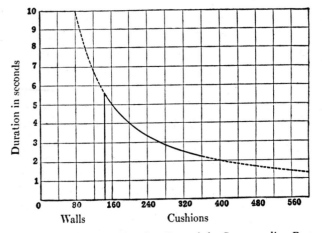

Walls   Cushions

FIG. 138.—The Same Curve, Plotted as Part of the Corresponding Rectangular
Hyperbola [Sabine].

has been added to the numbers of meters of cushions, so that
the vertical axis is farther to the left of the curve in Fig. 138

than in Fig. 137. This number has been so chosen as to make the experimental results fit most closely the equation for a rectangular hyperbola.

What is the significance of this number 146? As we go farther and farther to the left in Fig. 138 we are dealing with less and less absorbing material. The absorbing material to the right of the 146-meter line is Sanders Theater cushions. But the walls, floor, and ceiling of the Fogg lecture room must also absorb sound. This 146 represents the number of meters of Sanders Theater cushions that would absorb the same amount of sound as the walls and other boundaries of the Fogg lecture room. The numbers along the horizontal axis in Fig. 138 represent the number of meters of Sanders Theater cushions that would absorb as much sound as the boundaries of the room together with the cushions that had been brought in.

We wish to express in the simplest form the relationship shown in Fig. 138. Let a stand for the number of meters of Sanders Theater cushions that would absorb as much as everything in the room—including the walls and other boundaries—and let T stand for the duration of the residual sound. Then if the curve is a rectangular hyperbola it is known that the product aT must be the same for all points on the curve. The product turns out to be practically the same for all points, so that the curve is represented very well by a rectangular hyperbola.

When he examined the product aT for rooms of different shapes and sizes he found that the product does not differ greatly for rooms of different shapes, but that it does depend on the size of the room. He examined twelve rooms of different sizes. The smallest had a volume of 65 cubic meters, and the largest of 9300 cubic meters. As nearly as he could tell, the simplest possible relationship seemed to fit the facts—the product aT is proportional to the volume of the room.

The results thus reached may now be expressed by the very simple equation

$$aT = KV, \qquad (15)$$

where V stands for the volume of the room, and K is a quantity which we have yet to investigate. Under ordinary conditions this equation is still regarded as expressing the facts fairly well. For "dead" rooms, where the reverberation is very short, it is not so satisfactory.[323]

Unless we make restrictions of some sort the K in (15) depends on how loud the sound is before it begins to die away, and it also depends on the units that are employed. A louder sound lasts longer than a faint one. So if the a and the V in (15) are kept the same we see that the K should be larger when the initial sound is louder. Instead of putting into the equation a quantity which depends on the loudness of the sound Sabine reduced his results to what they would be if the initial intensity level were always sixty decibels above the threshold intensity. When this restriction is adopted the K depends on nothing but the units that are used.

The a in equation (15) is measured in terms of Sanders Theater cushions. The equation makes it possible to say that the time required for a drop of sixty decibels in a room of given volume is the same as if the absorption were produced by a certain number of meters of Sanders Theater cushions. This statement is awkward, Sanders Theater cushions are not everywhere available, and a running meter of these cushions is not a satisfactory unit for general use.

It occurred to Sabine that a better unit for absorption might be obtained in terms of open windows. When sound goes out through an open window, little, if any, of it ever returns. So an open window may be regarded as being very nearly a perfect absorber for sound. We might then express

---

[323] See, for instance, Carl F. Eyring, Journ. Acoust. Soc., 1, 217 (1930).

the absorption of sound in any material by saying that it absorbs half as much sound, or a third or a quarter as much,
as an open window of the same area. Sabine tested whether,
under suitable conditions, the absorption by open windows is
in direct proportion to the areas of the openings. His experiments showed that this relationship does hold fairly
accurately. That is, two square meters of open window absorb twice as much sound as one square meter, three square
meters absorb three times as much as one square meter, and
so on. He made similar tests with different areas of Sanders Theater cushions, and found that the sound absorbed
by the cushions seemed to be in direct proportion to the area
exposed. It now becomes possible to say that a given area
of a certain material absorbs as much sound as a certain
number of square meters of open window.

In actual use the a in (15) is determined by considering
the exposed area of each kind of material in the room, multiplying that area by the "absorption coefficient" for the
given material, and adding together all the products thus
obtained.

With the choices now made the K in (15) becomes a
perfectly definite number. Sabine measured the areas of absorbing material in square meters, and the volumes of rooms
in cubic meters. His experiments then led to the value 0.164
for K. If feet are used instead of meters the corresponding
value for K is 0.050.

Question 341. A certain lecture room has a volume of 3000 cu.
meters. 800 sq. meters of the wall, ceiling, and floor have an absorption coefficient of 0.05, 200 sq. meters of 0.40, and the remaining 300
sq. meters of 0.15. How long a time is required for the intensity
level to drop 60 db? How long is required when an audience occupies the last mentioned 300 sq. meters? Assume that the audience
absorbs all the sound that falls upon it.

157. Amount of Reverberation Desired.—Now that we
know how to calculate the duration of reverberation the next

questions that arise deal with the amount of reverberation
that is desirable.   It is clear that a room may easily be too
reverberant.   Do we like best a room with as little reverberation as possible?   Do we prefer a room that has some reasonable amount of reverberation?   If so, how much reverberation do we wish, and do we like the same amount of
reverberation when listening to speech as when listening to
music?

Sabine made an interesting study of the accuracy of musical taste with regard to reverberation when listening to
piano music.[324]   The tests were made in five small rooms of
the New England Conservatory of Music.   The volumes of
the rooms varied from 74 cubic meters to 210 cubic meters.
In each room there was a piano; in one room there were two.
"The rooms varied from an almost unfurnished to a reason-
ably furnished condition.   In all cases the reverberation was
too great."   The test consisted of listening to piano music
in each room, and bringing into the room Sanders Theater
cushions until the effect was judged satisfactory.   The judges
were five members of the faculty of the New England
Conservatory.

"Before beginning the experiment no explanation was
made of its nature, and no discussion was held as to the advantages and disadvantages of reverberation.   The gentle-
men present were asked to express their approval or disap-
proval of the room at each stage of the experiment, and the
final decision seemed to be reached with perfectly free
unanimity."

It proves possible to have too little reverberation.   A
certain amount is desired.   When there were too few cushions in the room, in the experiment just described, the judgments were given by such expressions as "too resonant," "too

[324] Wallace Clement Sabine, Am. Acad. Arts and Sci. Proc., **42,** 53
(1906) ; or *Collected Papers on Acoustics,* Harvard University Press, p. 71.

much echo," "harsh," and when too many cushions were in the room by "dull," "lifeless," "overloaded."

The cushions were removed from the rooms, and late the following night, when noises from street and railway traffic were sufficiently reduced, the duration of reverberation was determined experimentally in each room. The average for the five rooms was 2.43 sec. A calculation was then made to find out the duration of reverberation when the judges, the pianist, and the Sanders Theater cushions were present. With the number of cushions at which the rooms were judged best the reverberation times were the following:

Room Number	Reverberation Time
1	0.95 sec
2	1.10
3	1.10
4	1.09
5	1.16
Average	1.08

From this experiment it appears that for piano music in a small room the reverberation time should be about one second. The differences between the average and the values found in the different rooms are surprisingly small. "It is conceivable that had the rooms been alike in all respects and required the same amount of cushions to accomplish the same results, the experiment in one room might have prejudiced the experiment in the next. But the rooms being different in size and furnished so differently, an impression formed in one room as to the number of cushions necessary could only be misleading if depended on in the next. Thus the several rooms required 6, 5, 15, 10, and 5 cushions. . . . This surprising accuracy of musical taste is perhaps the explanation of the rarity with which it is entirely satisfied."

More recent studies have shown that the reverberation time in large rooms should be greater than in small ones.

For large auditoriums a reverberation time of as much as two seconds proves very acceptable. It has been thought that the most satisfactory reverberation time for music is a trifle longer than for speech, but any such difference is perhaps still open to question.

158. Reverberation and Pitch.—Another fact which Sabine discovered is that the amount of sound absorbed by a given substance depends on the pitch of the sound. He illustrates this by considering a room which has hard walls and is comparatively empty, and into which are brought elastic felt cushions and then an audience. "If the double-bass and the violin produce the same loudness in the open air, in the bare room with hard walls both would be reënforced about equally. The elastic felt brought into the room would decidedly diminish this reënforcement for both instruments. It would, however, exert a much more pronounced effect in the way of diminishing the reënforcement for the violin than for the double-bass. In fact, the balance will be so affected that it will require two violins to produce the same volume of sound as does one double-bass. The audience coming into the room will make it necessary to use three violins to a double-bass to secure the same balance as before." [325]

159. Decay of Sound not Steady.—In what we have said about reverberation it has been tacitly assumed that when an organ pipe or other source emits sound the intensity increases continuously until the steady state is reached, and that when the source ceases to give out sound the intensity decreases continuously until the sound is gone. Such a continuous increase and continuous decrease do not usually occur. During both the growth and the decay the sound pattern in the room is changing, and the locations at which interference and reinforcement occur are changing, so that at any given point the increase and decrease in intensity are

[325] Wallace Clement Sabine, Am. Acad. Arts and Sci. Proc., 42, 61 (1906); or Collected Papers on Acoustics, Harvard University Press, p. 81.

not continuous. This is one of the difficulties that has to be met in the experimental determination of reverberation times.

160. Echoes.—Another acoustic defect that has sometimes been met in auditoriums is the presence of definite and disturbing echoes. We have seen how Joseph Henry planned that no such echoes should occur in the lecture room of the Smithsonian Institution. One building in which echoes have been somewhat troublesome is the Royal Albert Hall, built in 1867-1871 in London. This building is 270 feet by 240 feet, and has a seating capacity of more than 10,000. A man who was present at the ceremonies connected with the opening of the hall wrote, "When the Prince of Wales read his address I heard every word repeated with perfect distinctness, the echo was pure and single, the two voices appeared like those of a prompter and a faithfully repeating speaker. The echo was remarkably well defined, and nearly as loud as the voice of the Prince. When the Queen replied, her words were also repeated, but far less distinctly. This was a respectful whispering echo. . . . Every note of Madame Sherrington's solo was most vexatiously mocked." [326]

Another building in which there were bad echoes is the Auditorium at the University of Illinois. "The original plans of the architect were curtailed because of insufficient money appropriated for the construction. The interior of the hall, therefore, was built absolutely plain with almost no breaking up of the large, smooth wall surfaces; and, at first, there were no furnishings except the seats and the cocoa matting in the aisles. The acoustical properties proved to be very unsatisfactory. . . . If an observer stood on the platform and clapped his hands, a veritable chaos of sound resulted. Echoes were heard from every direction and reverberations continued for a number of seconds before all was

[326] W. Mattieu Williams, Nature, 3, 469 (1871).

still again. Speakers found their utterances thrown back at them, and auditors all over the house experienced difficulty in understanding what was said. On one occasion the University band played a piece which featured a xylophone solo with accompaniment by the other instruments. It so happened that the leader heard the echo more strongly than the direct sound and beat time with it. Players near the xylophone kept time to the direct sound, while those farther away followed the echo. . . . It seemed that the Auditorium was doomed to be an acoustical horror; that speakers and singers would avoid it, and auditors would attend entertainments in it only under protest. But the apparent misfortune was in one way a benefit since it provided an opportunity to study defective acoustics under exceptionally good conditions." [327] Watson took advantage of these "exceptionally good conditions" to study the echoes in this auditorium.[328] He used three different sources, directed the sound by means of a reflector or a horn, and in this way located the surfaces from which echoes came. He was then able to place absorbing material in such locations that the auditorium was greatly improved.

A method now sometimes employed in studying the echoes that might arise in a proposed auditorium is one first used by Sabine.[329] From the architect's sketches for the auditorium plaster models are made which represent cross sections of the auditorium. A sudden sound is produced at some point in the model, say by means of an electric spark, and the pulse of sound which travels outward from the spark is observed or photographed. To make the pulse visible

---

[327] Floyd Rowe Watson, *Acoustics of Auditoriums*, Bulletin No. 73, Engineering Experiment Station, University of Illinois (1914), p. 3.

[328] Floyd Rowe Watson, Bulletin mentioned in footnote 327, or *Acoustics of Buildings*, Wiley (1923), p. 68.

[329] Wallace Clement Sabine, Am. Architect, 104, 268 (1913); or *Collected Papers on Acoustics*, Harvard University Press, p. 180.

another spark is set off at a distance from the model, and is set off after the sound from the first spark has had time to travel only a little way. The light from the second spark is bent in passing through the compression at the front of the sound pulse, and so gives an instantaneous picture of the position which the latter has reached. Fig. 139 shows two of Sabine's photographs. If the theater had been built to have the section shown in *a* the pulse coming down from the upper right indicates that there would doubtless have

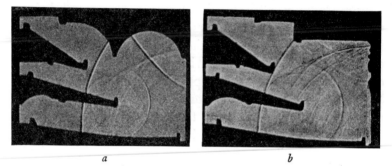

a　　　　　　　　　　　*b*

FIG. 139.—Reflection of Sound in Models of the Scollay Square Theater [Sabine]. Both photographs were taken before the theater was built. *a*, from the first sketch; *b* after a change in the design of the ceiling.

been an unpleasant echo. *b* shows that with the new shape given to the ceiling this echo is obviated.

161. Development of Architectural Acoustics.—The subject of architectural acoustics has been growing rapidly since the pioneer work so well done by Sabine. In several laboratories excellent work on architectural acoustics is now being carried out, many determinations of the sound absorption coefficients of various materials have been made, and various facts not mentioned in this book have been discovered. One of the laboratories that are doing this work was built for Sabine's researches, and in his honor it has been named the Wallace Clement Sabine Laboratory of Acoustics. This laboratory was built in 1918 by Colonel George Fabyan at

Riverbank, near Geneva, Illinois. Sabine made the preliminary plans for the laboratory, but did not live to see its work more than begun. It is now directed by a cousin, Paul Earls Sabine.

ENVOY

We have come to the end of our introduction to the subject of Sound. We have learned something about free vibration and forced vibration, about the transmission of sound from its source to the ear of the auditor and its effect upon the ear, we have given some attention to musical sounds and the instruments by which they are produced, and we have glanced at some of the technical applications of sound. Our study has been nothing more than an introduction, but it has given us some acquaintance with many curious phenomena and many interesting problems, and it has shown us something of the ways in which such problems may be attacked.

In the course of our study we have learned something about the work of many men who have contributed to our understanding of sound. If a number of persons who are familiar with the field were asked to list the half dozen men whose contributions to this understanding have been the most important the lists would of course differ. Probably most of them would include Mersenne and Sauveur, some would include Félix Savart, and it is probably safe to say that a number would include Helmholtz and Rayleigh. There are others whose names would appear on some of the lists. Although the importance of the work done by the men just mentioned has no doubt depended in part on opportunity and the state of knowledge at the times when they lived, it is hardly open to question that native ability and interest have been factors of much greater importance. Nevertheless much excellent work has been done by persons whose natural endowments were not so great, but who were blessed with an indefatigable curiosity.

As we bring to an end this introduction to the subject of Sound we can perhaps not do better than to quote words that appear at the beginning of each of the first four of the six volumes of Rayleigh's Scientific Papers:

> *"The works of the Lord are great,*
> *Sought out of all them that have pleasure therein."*

APPENDIX ONE

SOME EARLY SPEAKING MACHINES (Art. 133)

(*a*) The following paragraphs are quoted from Sir Charles Wheatstone, London and Westminster Review (Oct. 1837) ; or the *Scientific Papers of Sir Charles Wheatstone*, pp. 349 ff (1879).

"It is both amusing and instructive to recur sometimes to those crude hypotheses respecting physical phenomena which were advanced in the early dawn of science. Walchius thought it possible so to contrive a trunk or hollow pipe that it should preserve the voice entirely for certain hours or days, so that a man might send his words to a friend instead of his writing. There being always a certain space of intermission, for the passage of the voice, betwixt its going into these cavities and its coming out, he conceives that if both ends were seasonably stopped, whilst the sound was in the midst, it would continue there till it had some vent. . . . When the friend to whom it is sent shall receive and open it, the words shall come out distinctly, and in the same order in which they were spoken. . . .

"A Thomas Irson exhibited a speaking head, which excited the wonder of Charles II. and his court. It answered in several languages to questions whispered in its ear. When the astonishment was at its height, one of the pages discovered in the adjoining room a Popish priest, who answered through a pipe.

"In the last century a figure of Bacchus seated on a barrel was exhibited at Versailles. It pronounced, in a loud and intelligible voice, all the days of the week, and wished the company good day. Many persons were deceived by it, because the owner of the machine allowed them to inspect the inside of the figure and the barrel, where nothing was perceived but organ-pipes, bellows, wind-chests, wheels, cylinders, &c. But the deception did not last long. A person more inquisitive than the rest discovered a false wind-chest, in which a dwarf was concealed, who articulated the words, the sound of which was conveyed by means of a tube to the mouth of the figure.

"Professor Beckmann describes a similar pretended automaton which he saw. The figure was that of a Turk placed on a box, which was filled, as in the former case, with pipes, bellows, &c.; but the voice was communicated from a person in the adjoining room. . . .

"As a specimen of the speculations respecting the mechanism of speech which were prevalent about a century and a half ago, and which then supplied the place of observation and experiment, we may mention a small work on this subject, written by Van Helmont, the celebrated alchemist. Its translated title is, 'A short Explanation of the true natural Hebrew Alphabet, which at the same time supplies a method by which those who are born deaf can instruct themselves, not only how to understand others when they speak, but likewise how to speak themselves.' Van Helmont in this tract endeavours to establish that all the letters of the Hebrew alphabet are written in exact imitation of the position which the tongue assumes in pronouncing them. He then goes further, and proves to his own satisfaction that the letters of the alphabet ought to follow each other in the order they do, and in no other; because the tongue, whilst finishing the pronunciation of one letter, is already in the position for commencing the following. His imagination has represented the tongue in the most extravagant contortions. His work is illustrated by thirty-four plates."

(*b*) An "Invisible Girl," exhibited for some time in London, was described in Nicholson's Journal [3, 56 (1802)] as follows.

"In the middle of a large lofty room in an old house, where from the appearance of the wainscot, the position of some glass cases of natural history that occupy one side, and from other circumstances, there does. not appear to be any situation for acoustic tubes or reflectors—is fixed a wooden railing about four feet high, and five feet wide, inclosing a square space. From the four corner posts of this railing there rise painted wires, or rods, to an eminence of ten or twelve feet, (the ceiling being much loftier) and from the upper ends of these hangs, by strings resembling the lines used with curtains, a square glazed box, having a mahogany bottom nearly on a level with the top of the railing, and in the middle of this box is suspended an hemisphere (or larger portion) of tin or pewter, out of which preceed [sic] horizontally four tin trumpets at right angles to each other, and about eighteen inches long. The disk or hemisphere is covered with a portion of a quicksilvered glass globe which completes the sphere, and closes it imperfectly, so as not to prevent the inner aperture of one of the trumpets from being seen through the place of insertion. This whole apparatus is so far detached from all surrounding objects, that it can be swung about as far as the railing will allow; that is to say, the box can be swung by its four strings, and the globe and trumpets by the string that sustains them in the box. The globe may be about ten inches in diameter. . . .

"In the exhibition, the Invisible Girl is supposed or pretended to be included in the sphere, and the conversation is held by speaking into any one of the trumpets, and the reply comes out of them; that is to say, it is most clearly heard by applying the ear to one of their mouths. The voice is low, as if conveyed from a distance through a tube, but it is very distinct. The lady converses in several languages, sings, describes all that happens in the room, and displays a fund of lively wit and accomplishment, that admirably qualify her to support the character she has undertaken."

An explanation was given [Nicholson's Journal, 16, 69 (1807)] by a gentleman who had seen a similar experiment in a philosophical lecture and then visited the exhibition of the invisible girl. He was convinced that both demonstrations were carried out in practically the same way, and that the essential factor was a speaking tube. In the experiment he saw in the lecture the tube came from an adjoining room, under the floor, up through one of the legs that supported the wooden railing around the box that carried the four trumpets, and opened in front of one of the trumpets. The farther end of the tube expanded into an enlarged funnel in the adjoining room, and in this enlargement were the real girl and a piano. A small hole covered with glass enabled her to see what went on in the exhibition room.

APPENDIX TWO

A REED ORGAN TO DEMONSTRATE THE JUST SCALE (Art. 27)

This is a "baby organ" which has been in use at Smith College for a number of years. It has only two stops. One is tuned to the equally tempered scale, and the other is so tuned as to make it possible to play the just scales of *c* major,

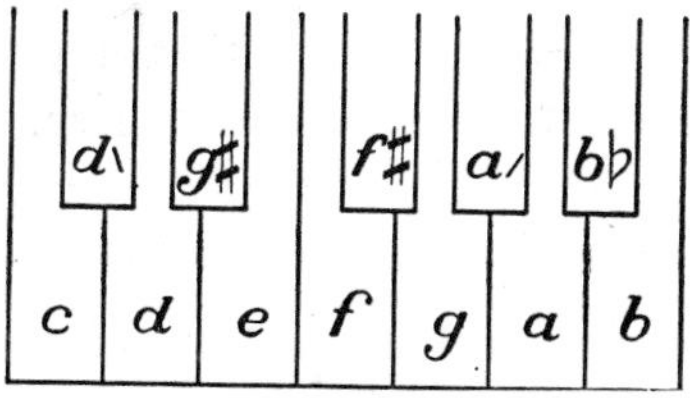

FIG. 140.—Tuning of Special Stop for Demonstration of Just Intonation. The meanings of the symbols are given on p. 65.

f major, *g* major, and *a* minor. This is accomplished by tuning the special stop as shown in Fig. 140. The white digitals give the just scale of *c* major. For *f* major *d*\ and *b*♭ are used instead of *d* and *b*; for *g* major *f*♯ and *a*╱ are used instead of *f* and *a;* and for the harmonic scale of *a* minor *d*\ and *g*♯ are used instead of *d* and *g*.

APPENDIX THREE

THE FREQUENCY OF A SIMPLE HARMONIC MOTION (Art. 52)

We desire an expression for the frequency of a simple harmonic motion in terms of the stiffness and the inertia. To obtain the expression we shall make use of a reference particle which moves uniformly around the circumference of the reference circle; we shall resolve the acceleration of this particle into two perpendicular components—one of them in the desired direction—and we shall compare a triangle of accelerations with a triangle of distances. We shall then recall the measure of stiffness and a few well known relations from elementary physics, and shall thus obtain the desired equation. The steps are carried out as follows.

In Fig. 141 the motion of the reference particle P is projected onto the line CD. The simple harmonic motion that interests us takes place along this line CD, and is in fact the motion of a particle Q which moves along CD in such a way as always to be in the same vertical line with P.

When a particle moves with uniform speed v in the circumference of a circle of radius r we know that the particle has an acceleration a_c, which is directed toward the center of the circle, and which has a magnitude given by

$$a_c = \frac{v^2}{r}. \tag{16}$$

At the right in Fig. 141 part of the diagram is drawn again, and the acceleration of P is represented by PJ. This acceleration may be regarded as the resultant of an accelera-

428

tion PK, which is perpendicular to CD, and an acceleration KJ, which is parallel to CD. The acceleration PK, perpendicular to CD, has nothing to do with the acceleration of the particle Q, for Q moves always along CD. But the acceleration KJ, which we shall call a, is the same as the acceleration with which Q moves.

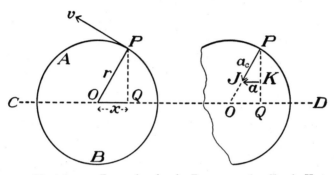

FIG. 141.—Obtaining an Expression for the Frequency of a Simple Harmonic Motion.

We see that the acceleration triangle PKJ is similar to the distance triangle PQO. Consequently

$$\frac{a}{a_c} = \frac{x}{r}. \tag{17}$$

For the a_c in (17) we may put its value from (16), and for our purposes it is also convenient to replace v by its value $2\pi rN$, where N stands for the number of times that the reference particle goes around the circle in one second—and therefore stands also for the desired frequency of the simple harmonic motion of Q. We then have

$$a = (2\pi N)^2 x. \tag{18}$$

The restoring force F that acts on the particle Q is given by

$$F = ma, \tag{19}$$

where m stands for the mass of Q; and the stiffness K is given by

$$K = \frac{F}{x}. \qquad (20)$$

From (18), (19), and (20) we eliminate a and F, and thus arrive at the equation

$$N = \frac{1}{2\pi}\sqrt{\frac{K}{m}}. \qquad (21)$$

APPENDIX FOUR

LOGARITHMS (Art. 21)

If $y = a^x$ we say that x is the logarithm of y to the base a, and we write this statement in the form $x = \log_a y$. Since $y_1 y_2 = a^{x_1} a^{x_2} = a^{x_1 + x_2}$, we see that

$$\log_a(y_1 y_2) = x_1 + x_2 = \log_a y_1 + \log_a y_2,$$

and similarly that

$$\log_a \left(\frac{y_1}{y_2} \right) = \log_a y_1 - \log_a y_2.$$

Upon these two equations rests a large part of the use of logarithms.

The base of the *common logarithms* is 10, and when writing these logarithms the symbol for the base is often omitted. Thus we have

$$\log 10 = 1, \qquad \log 1000 = 3, \qquad \log 0.001 = -3.$$

The base of the *natural logarithms*—much used in theoretical work—is the number usually represented by the letter e, approximately 2.71828. For use in music it has been suggested [330] that logarithms to the base 2 would be very convenient. With this base we have, for instance,

$$\log_2 2 = 1, \qquad \log_2 8 = 3, \qquad \log_2 32 = 5.$$

With this base the logarithm of any frequency ratio gives at once the number of octaves and fractions of an octave in the corresponding musical interval.

[330] Euler, *Tentamen Novae Theoriae Musicae* (1739), chap. vii, 4; reprinted in *Leonhardi Euleri Opera Omnia*, Series Tertia, Volumen Primum, Teubner (1926), p. 282.

A table of these logarithms has been prepared by G. H. Pohland, under the title *Binary Logarithms*, G. H. Pohland, Chicago (1931).

APPENDIX FIVE

THE CALCULATION OF CENTS (Art. 21)

Any whole number of octaves may be reduced to cents by remembering that each octave contains 1200 cents.

For fractions of an octave there is no simple method of transforming accurately from frequency ratios to cents without a table of some kind. With a five place table of logarithms results that are correct to a few hundredths of a cent may be obtained by multiplying the logarithm of the frequency ratio by 3986.3. With a four place table of logarithms results that are correct to a few tenths of a cent may be obtained by multiplying the logarithm by 4000 and then subtracting one 300th of the product.

Hornbostel [331] has prepared a table by which to find quickly the number of cents in an interval when the frequencies themselves are known. With his table there is no need of finding the quotients of the frequencies.

The table on pp. 434-435 is for the rapid transformation from frequency ratios to cents. It gives to the nearest tenth of a cent the number of cents that correspond to the frequency ratios 1.001, 1.002, 1.003, etc., throughout an octave. The value for 1.001 is in the column headed 1, the value for 1.002 in the column headed 2, and so on. Where the number of cents is 100 or more the first one or two figures are not printed except in the 0 column.

[331] E. M. von Hornbostel, Zeitschr. f. Physik, **6**, 29 (1921).

APPENDIX SIX

HISTORICAL NOTES

(a) Movement of Light Powder on a Chladni Plate (Art. 66).—On p. 299 of the paper referred to in footnote 119 Faraday says Chladni noticed that the shavings which the edge of the plate wore from the hairs of the exciting violin bow gathered on those parts of the plate where the vibration was the most violent. I have not found any such statement in any of Chladni's writings that I have seen. In the *Entdeckungen über die Theorie des Klanges* (1787) Chladni says on p. 18 that if the edge of the plate is too sharp it should be filed smooth or it will damage the hairs of the bow. On p. 31 he states that if there are very fine particles mixed with the sand that is strewn on the plate they will pile up at the points where the motion is most vigorous, and he gives three figures that show the points where they gather. In his *Akustik* (1830 edition) he mentions the effect on pp. 95 and 96, in the supplement which he called *Neue Beyträge zur Akustik* (1817) he mentions it on p. 69, and on p. 40 of his *Kurze Uebersicht der Schall- und Klanglehre* (1827) he states again that the effect occurs; but in none of these places does he say anything about the light particles being shavings from the hairs of the bow. Perhaps Faraday got his information directly from Chladni himself and not from any publication.

(b) Early Papers on Singing Flames (Art. 82).—The first person who observed a singing flame may have been Dr. Bryan Higgins. He found the effect in 1777, but it was not until about twenty-five years later that he wrote,

NUMBERS OF CENTS CORRESPONDING TO GIVEN FREQUENCY RATIOS

	0	1	2	3	4	5	6	7	8	9
1.00	0	1.7	3.5	5.2	6.9	8.7	10.4	12.1	13.8	15.5
1	17.2	18.9	20.6	22.4	24.1	25.8	27.5	29.2	30.9	32.6
2	34.3	36.0	37.7	39.4	41.1	42.7	44.4	46.1	47.8	49.5
3	51.2	52.9	54.5	56.2	57.9	59.6	61.2	62.9	64.6	66.3
4	67.9	69.6	71.2	72.9	74.5	76.2	77.9	79.5	81.2	82.8
1.05	84.5	86.1	87.8	89.4	91.0	92.7	94.3	96.0	97.6	99.3
6	100.9	02.5	04.1	05.8	07.4	09.0	10.7	12.3	13.9	15.5
7	117.1	18.8	20.4	22.0	23.6	25.2	26.8	28.4	30.0	31.6
8	133.2	34.8	36.4	38.0	39.6	41.2	42.8	44.4	46.0	47.6
9	149.2	50.8	52.4	54.0	55.5	57.1	58.7	60.3	61.8	63.4
1.10	165.0	66.6	68.1	69.7	71.3	72.8	74.4	76.0	77.6	79.1
1	180.7	82.2	83.8	85.4	86.9	88.4	90.0	91.5	93.1	94.7
2	196.2	97.8	99.3							
2	......	......	......	00.8	02.4	03.9	05.5	07.0	08.5	10.0
3	211.6	13.1	14.7	16.2	17.7	19.2	20.8	22.3	23.8	25.3
4	226.8	28.4	29.9	31.4	32.9	34.4	35.9	37.4	38.9	40.5
1.15	242.0	43.5	45.0	46.5	48.0	49.5	51.0	52.5	54.0	55.5
6	256.9	58.4	59.9	61.4	62.9	64.4	65.9	67.4	68.8	70.3
7	271.8	73.3	74.8	76.3	77.7	79.2	80.7	82.2	83.6	85.1
8	286.5	88.0	89.5	90.9	92.4	93.9	95.3	96.8	98.3	99.7
9	301.2	02.6	04.1	05.5	06.9	08.4	09.9	11.3	12.8	14.2
1.20	315.6	17.1	18.5	20.0	21.4	22.9	24.3	25.7	27.2	28.6
1	330.0	31.4	32.9	34.3	35.7	37.2	38.6	40.0	41.4	42.8
2	344.3	45.7	47.1	48.5	49.9	51.3	52.7	54.1	55.6	57.0
3	358.4	59.8	61.2	62.6	64.0	65.4	66.8	68.2	69.6	71.0
4	372.4	73.8	75.2	76.6	78.0	79.4	80.8	82.2	83.5	84.9
1.25	386.3	87.7	89.1	90.5	91.9	93.2	94.6	96.0	97.4	98.8
6	400.1	01.5	02.9	04.2	05.6	07.0	08.3	09.7	11.1	12.4
7	413.8	15.2	16.5	17.9	19.2	20.6	22.0	23.3	24.7	26.0
8	427.4	28.7	30.1	31.4	32.8	34.1	35.5	36.8	38.2	39.5
9	440.8	42.2	43.5	44.9	46.2	47.5	48.9	50.2	51.5	52.9
1.30	454.2	55.6	56.9	58.2	59.5	60.9	62.2	63.5	64.8	66.2
1	467.5	68.8	70.1	71.4	72.8	74.1	75.4	76.7	78.0	79.3
2	480.6	81.9	83.3	84.6	85.9	87.2	88.5	89.8	91.1	92.4
3	493.7	95.0	96.3	97.6	98.9	......	......	......	......	......
5	......	......	......	......	......	00.2	01.5	02.8	04.1	05.4
4	506.7	08.0	09.3	10.6	11.8	13.1	14.4	15.7	17.0	18.3
1.35	519.5	20.8	22.1	23.4	24.7	26.0	27.2	28.5	29.8	31.1
6	532.3	33.6	34.9	36.2	37.4	38.7	39.9	41.2	42.5	43.7
7	545.0	46.3	47.5	48.8	50.1	51.3	52.6	53.8	55.1	56.3
8	557.6	58.8	60.1	61.4	62.6	63.9	65.1	66.4	67.6	68.8
9	570.1	71.4	72.6	73.8	75.1	76.3	77.6	78.8	80.0	81.3
1.40	582.5	83.8	85.0	86.2	87.5	88.7	89.9	91.1	92.4	93.6
1	594.8	96.1	97.3	98.5	99.7					
6	......	......	......	......	......	01.0	02.2	03.4	04.6	05.8
2	607.1	08.3	09.5	10.7	11.9	13.1	14.4	15.6	16.8	18.0
3	619.2	20.4	21.6	22.9	24.1	25.3	26.5	27.7	28.9	30.1
4	631.3	32.5	33.7	34.9	36.1	37.3	38.5	39.7	40.9	42.1
1.45	643.3	44.5	45.7	46.9	48.0	49.2	50.4	51.6	52.8	54.0
6	655.2	56.3	57.5	58.7	59.9	61.1	62.2	63.4	64.6	65.8
7	667.0	68.1	69.3	70.5	71.7	72.8	74.0	75.2	76.4	77.6
8	687.7	79.9	81.1	82.2	83.4	84.6	85.7	86.9	88.0	89.2
9	690.4	91.5	92.7	93.9	95.0	96.2	97.3	98.5	99.6	
7	......	......	......	......	......	......	......	......	......	00.8

NUMBERS OF CENTS CORRESPONDING TO GIVEN FREQUENCY RATIOS—*Cont.*

	0	1	2	3	4	5	6	7	8	9
1.50	702.0	03.1	04.3	05.4	06.6	07.7	08.8	10.0	11.2	12.3
1	713.5	14.6	15.7	16.9	18.1	19.2	20.3	21.5	22.6	23.8
2	724.9	26.0	27.1	28.3	29.4	30.6	31.7	32.8	34.0	35.1
3	736.2	37.4	38.5	39.6	40.8	41.9	43.0	44.1	45.3	46.4
4	747.5	48.6	49.7	50.9	52.0	53.1	54.3	55.4	56.5	57.6
1.55	758.7	59.8	60.9	62.1	63.2	64.3	65.4	66.5	67.6	68.7
6	769.8	71.0	72.1	73.2	74.3	75.4	76.5	77.6	78.7	79.8
7	780.9	82.0	83.1	84.2	85.3	86.4	87.5	88.6	89.7	90.8
8	791.9	93.0	94.1	95.2	96.3	97.4	98.5	99.6	00.7	01.7
9	802.8	03.9	05.0	06.1	07.2	08.3	09.3	10.4	11.5	12.6
1.60	813.7	14.8	15.8	16.9	18.0	19.1	20.2	21.3	22.3	23.4
1	824.5	25.6	26.6	27.7	28.8	29.8	30.9	32.0	33.1	34.1
2	835.2	36.3	37.3	38.4	39.5	40.5	41.6	42.7	43.7	44.8
3	845.8	46.9	48.0	49.0	50.1	51.2	52.2	53.3	54.3	55.4
4	856.4	57.5	58.5	59.6	60.7	61.7	62.8	63.8	64.9	65.9
1.65	867.0	68.0	69.1	70.1	71.2	72.2	73.2	74.3	75.3	76.4
6	877.4	78.5	79.5	80.5	81.6	82.6	83.6	84.7	85.8	86.8
7	887.8	88.9	89.9	90.9	92.0	93.0	94.0	95.1	96.1	97.1
8	898.2	99.2	00.2	01.2	02.3	03.3	04.3	05.4	06.4	07.4
9	908.4	09.4	10.5	11.5	12.5	13.5	14.6	15.6	16.6	17.6
1.70	918.6	19.6	20.7	21.7	22.7	23.7	24.7	25.7	26.8	27.8
1	928.8	29.8	30.8	31.8	32.8	33.8	34.9	35.9	36.9	37.9
2	938.9	39.9	40.9	41.9	42.9	43.9	44.9	45.9	46.9	47.9
3	948.9	49.9	50.9	51.9	52.9	53.9	54.9	55.9	56.9	57.9
4	958.9	59.9	60.9	61.9	62.9	63.9	64.9	65.9	66.8	67.8
1.75	968.8	69.8	70.8	71.8	72.8	73.8	74.7	75.7	76.7	77.7
6	978.7	79.7	80.7	81.6	82.6	83.6	84.6	85.6	86.5	87.5
7	988.5	89.5	90.4	91.4	92.4	93.4	94.4	95.3	96.3	97.3
8	998.3	99.2	00.2	01.2	02.1	03.1	04.1	05.0	06.0	07.0
9	1008.0	08.9	09.9	10.9	11.8	12.8	13.7	14.7	15.7	16.6
1.80	1017.6	18.6	19.5	20.5	21.4	22.4	23.4	24.3	25.3	26.2
1	1027.2	28.1	29.1	30.1	31.0	32.0	32.9	33.9	34.8	35.8
2	1036.7	37.7	38.6	39.6	40.5	41.5	42.4	43.4	44.3	45.3
3	1046.2	47.2	48.1	49.0	50.0	50.9	51.9	52.8	53.8	54.7
4	1055.6	56.6	57.5	58.5	59.4	60.3	61.3	62.2	63.2	64.1
1.85	1065.0	66.0	66.9	67.8	68.8	69.7	70.6	71.6	72.5	73.4
6	1074.4	75.3	76.2	77.2	78.1	79.0	79.9	80.9	81.8	82.7
7	1083.6	84.6	85.5	86.4	87.3	88.3	89.2	90.1	91.0	92.0
8	1092.9	93.8	94.7	95.6	96.6	97.5	98.4	99.3	00.2	01.1
9	1102.1	03.0	03.9	04.8	05.7	06.6	07.6	08.5	09.4	10.3
1.90	1111.2	12.1	13.0	13.9	14.8	15.7	16.7	17.6	18.5	19.4
1	1120.3	21.2	22.1	23.0	23.9	24.8	25.7	26.6	27.5	28.4
2	1129.3	30.2	31.1	32.0	32.9	33.8	34.7	35.6	36.5	37.4
3	1138.3	39.2	40.1	41.0	41.9	42.8	43.7	44.6	45.5	46.4
4	1147.3	48.2	49.1	49.9	50.8	51.7	52.6	53.5	54.4	55.3
1.95	1156.2	57.1	57.9	58.8	59.7	60.6	61.5	62.4	63.3	64.1
6	1165.0	65.9	66.8	67.7	68.6	69.4	70.3	71.2	72.1	73.0
7	1173.8	74.7	75.6	76.5	77.3	78.2	79.1	80.0	80.9	81.7
8	1182.6	83.5	84.3	85.2	86.1	87.0	87.8	88.7	89.6	90.5
9	1191.3	92.2	93.1	93.9	94.8	95.7	96.5	97.4	98.3	99.1

for publication in Nicholson's Journal, the letter in which
he described his discovery. The letter appeared in Nicholson's Journal of Natural Philosophy, 1, 129 (1802).
In the meantime the effect may have been discovered
independently by others. J. A. DeLuc described it in his
Idées sur la Météorologie, vol. 1 (1786), p. 171, but did not
say whether he discovered it himself or learned of it from
some one else. Professor Hermbstädt of Berlin [Crell's Che-
mische Annalen, p. 355 in part 1 for 1793] says that the
Russian Count von Moussin Bouschkin [Puschkin (?)]
showed him the experiment and told him that it was described by DeLuc. Chladni [Ges. Naturforschender
Freunde zu Berlin, Neue Schriften, 1, 125 (1795)] speaks
of the singing flame as having been discovered by DeLuc.
Charles Gaspard Delarive [Journ. de Physique, 55, 165
(1802)] and Michael Faraday [Quarterly Journ. of Science
and the Arts, 5, 274 (1818)] say that Pictet described the
experiment at Geneva, and both William Nicholson (Editor
of the Journ. of Nat. Philos.) and Delarive refer to an
article on singing flames by Professor Brugnatelli, probably
Luigi Valentino Brugnatelli of Pavia. I have not found the
papers by Pictet and Brugnatelli.

(c) The Discovery of the Stroboscopic Principle (Art.
83).—The possibility of stroboscopic observation was perhaps first seen clearly by Joseph Antoine Ferdinand Plateau,
Bulletin de l'Académie royale des sciences et belles-lettres de
Bruxelles, 3, 365 (1836). In this paper Plateau tells of
using a rotating sectored disk for stroboscopic observation,
and describes it as if it were something new and were his
own invention.

The word "stroboscopic" had been used somewhat
earlier. Simon Stampfer wrote a paper *Ueber die optische
Täuschungs-Phänomene, welche durch die stroboskopischen
Scheiben (optischen Zauberscheiben) hervorgebracht wer-
den,* which was published in the Jahrbücher des kaiserlichen

königlichen polytechnischen Institutes in Wien, 18, 237 (1834). The idea of Stampfer's stroboscopic disks was suggested to him by a paper of Michael Faraday's in the Journ. Roy. Institution of Great Britain, 1, 205 (1831) and in Pogg. An., 22, 601 (1831). Faraday's paper in turn dealt in part with an interesting optical illusion described by P. M. Roget in Phil. Trans., 115, 131 (1825).

In spite of Stampfer's use of the word, the stroboscopic principle as we know it today seems not to be clearly expressed in the papers by Roget, Faraday, and Stampfer, and is probably to be attributed to Plateau.

APPENDIX SEVEN

A FEW BIBLIOGRAPHIES

The following bibliographies are simply illustrative. Similar bibliographies might be prepared for many other topics in Sound. Moreover these bibliographies are not complete, and they do not include papers mentioned in footnotes in the body of the text. They may however be suggestive for the student who wishes to do additional reading, and they at least give some indication as to the large amount of study that has been devoted to these subjects.

(a) Sensitive Flames (Art. 88)

John Tyndall, Phil. Mag., 13, 473 (1857).

Count Franz von Schaffgotsch, Pogg. An., 100, 352; 101, 471; 102, 627 (1857).

W. Fletcher Barrett, Phil. Mag., 33, 216, 287 (1867); Nature, 10, 244 (1874); 16, 12 (1877).

A. Weinhold, Pogg. An., 136, 333 (1869).

Gilberto Govi, Nuovo Cimento, 3, 328, 334 (1870).

H. Planeth, Pogg. An., 144, 639 (1872).

A. S. Herschel, Nature, 10, 233 (1874); 11, 6, 45, 88 (1874).

R. H. Ridout, Nature, 15, 119 (1876).

V. Neyreneuf, Journ. de Physique, 9, 280 (1880).

Lord Rayleigh, Nature, 23, 163 (1880); Camb. Phil. Soc. Proc., 4, 17 (1880); Phil. Mag., 13, 345 (1882); Roy. Inst. Proc., 15, 786 (1898); Nature, 58, 429 (1898).

W. Le Conte Stevens, Am. Journ. Sci., 37, 257 (1889).

E. Bouty, Comptes Rendus, 120, 1260 (1895); 122, 372 (1896).

John G. M'Kendrick, Roy. Soc. Edinb. Proc., 21, 45 (1896).

Joseph H. T. Roberts and E. Meigh, Phil. Mag., 23, 368 (1912).

Karl L. Schaefer, An. der Physik, 48, 109 (1915).

Heinrich Mache, Phys. Zeitschr., 20, 467 (1919).

E. G. Richardson, Nature, 116, 171 (1925).

A. T. Jones, Science, 63, 355 (1926).

R. C. Colwell, Rev. Sci. Inst., 1, 347 (1930).

Josef Zahradníček, Physikal. Zeitschr., 34, 182 (1933).

Z. Carrière, Revue d'Acoust., 3, 221 (1934).

(b) The Trevelyan Rocker (Art. 89)

Michael Faraday, Roy. Inst. Journ., 2, 119 (1831).

Georg Wilhelm Muncke, Pogg. An., 24, 466 (1832).

August Seebeck, Pogg. An., 51, 1 (1840).

Charles G. Page, Am. Journ. Sci., 9, 105 (1850).

John Tyndall, Phil. Trans., 144, 1 (1854); Phil. Mag., 7, 223 (1854); 8, 1 (1854); 17, 417 (1859).

Wilhelm Rollmann, Pogg. An., 105, 620 (1858).

George Gore, Phil. Mag., 15, 519 (1858); 18, 94 (1859).

James D. Forbes, Edinb. New Philosoph. Journ., 9, 266 (1859).

Carl F. J. Sondhauss, Pogg. An., 115, 71, 177 (1862).

J. Schneider, Pogg. An., 117, 622 (1862); 120, 654 (1863).

Borlinetto, Les Mondes, 23, 183 (1870).

W. H. Eccles, Phys. Soc. Lond. Proc., 23, 204 (1911).

(c) Sense of Direction (Arts. 101-102)

Paul Rostosky, Philosophische Studien, 19, 557 (1902).

Lord Rayleigh, Phil. Mag., 13, 214, 316 (1907); Roy. Soc. Proc., A83, 61 (1909).

C. S. Myers and H. A. Wilson, Roy. Soc. Proc., **A80**, 260 (1908).

Louis T. More, Phil. Mag., **18**, 308 (1909).

G. W. Stewart, Phys. Rev., **9**, 502 (1917); **15**, 425, 432 (1920).

Margery Simpson, Phys. Rev., **15**, 421 (1920).

Annibale Stefanini, Nuovo Cimento, **23**, 5 (1922).

H. Banister, Brit. Journ. Psych., **15**, 280 (1925).

F. A. Firestone, Journ. Acoust. Soc., **2**, 260 (1930).

E. Russell Wightman and F. A. Firestone, Journ. Acoust. Soc., **2**, 271 (1930).

INDEX

441